Electroluminescence
and
Related Effects

Advances in
Electronics and
Electron Physics

Edited by
L. MARTON
National Bureau of Standards, Washington, D. C.

Assistant Editor
CLAIRE MARTON

Editorial Board

SUPPLEMENT 1

Electroluminescence and Related Effects

HENRY F. IVEY

Electroluminescence

and

Related Effects

HENRY F. IVEY

*Research-Engineering Consultant, Lamp Division,
Westinghouse Electric Corporation,
Bloomfield, New Jersey*

1963

ACADEMIC PRESS   New York and London

ACADEMIC PRESS INC.
111 FIFTH AVENUE
NEW YORK 3, N. Y.

United Kingdom Edition
Published by
ACADEMIC PRESS INC. (LONDON) LTD.
17 OLD QUEEN STREET, LONDON, S.W. 1

Library of Congress Catalog Card Number 63-12814

PRINTED IN THE UNITED STATES OF AMERICA

FOREWORD

From time to time we receive contributions to "Advances in Electronics and Electron Physics" that exceed in size the average review, and it is necessary to redistribute the contributions to various volumes. The present work of Dr. Ivey, in its entirety, did not allow a simple rearrangement and was sufficiently different from the average critical review to justify a different procedure. Several publications, similar to ours, have issued supplementary volumes as the occasion arose; the Editor and the publishers felt that a similar experiment for our "Advances" was timely. It is hoped that this supplement will be well received.

L. MARTON

Université de Paris
January 1963

PREFACE

Electroluminescence involves both the optical and the electrical properties of solids and is therefore the meeting ground of semiconductor activity and of normal work in luminescence. It is hoped that a discussion of phenomena in materials as apparently different as ZnS phosphors and Ge semiconductors, side-by-side in the same volume, will prove of interest to workers in both these fields and stimulate interdisciplinary activity which will lead to a better understanding of the complicated processes in electroluminescence.

The study of electroluminescence and of other effects of electric fields on phosphors received its original impetus in France. Today it is no longer so restricted; workers in England, Holland, Germany, America, Russia, Japan, and Czechoslovakia have all made important contributions. Although this is not the case abroad, most of the work in this country has been confined to industrial or governmental laboratories. It is therefore hoped that the present volume may also stimulate activity in electroluminescence in academic institutions since it is believed that this should also contribute to faster solution of the many remaining problems in this field.

I am indebted to R. M. Zabel and J. W. McNall, respectively Manager and Assistant Manager of Engineering for the Westinghouse Lamp Division, for making available part of the time required to prepare this article. I am also grateful to E. G. F. Arnott, formerly Director of Research for the Lamp Division, for introducing and actively supporting the study of electroluminescence at Westinghouse, and who has also been very helpful in proofreading the manuscript. Any errors or misinterpretations are, however, my own responsibility. I am also deeply grateful to the late Professor G. Destriau and to his colleague Professor Mattler for their pioneering in this field and for many stimulating contacts and discussions. Much of my knowledge of phosphors in general and electroluminescence in particular has been gained from my colleagues in the Phosphor Research Section, W. A. Thornton, W. Lehmann, C. H. Haake, A. Wachtel, and P. M. Jaffe. My thanks are also due to Mrs. R. Knapik and Mrs. F. J. Kolen, who struggled in the preparation of the manuscript with almost illegible handwriting and manifold changes. Finally, acknowledgment must be made to all the workers whose efforts have provided the material for this lengthy review and to the various organizations which have permitted reproduction of figures.

HENRY F. IVEY

Bloomfield, New Jersey
February, 1963

ix

CONTENTS

I. INTRODUCTION

Electroluminescence is at an awkward stage of development for the preparation of a general review on this subject. It is now so old and so advanced that it cannot be hoped to give a comprehensive detailed treatment in a small number of pages. On the other hand, it is so new, rapidly changing, and complex that it cannot be hoped to give a complete explanation of all the observed phenomena or even that all the explanations attempted will still be valid by time the publication actually reaches the reader. Several other reviews have already appeared in various places.* Despite these facts, the continued advances in materials and techniques in this field and their important applications to illumination and to electronic information display and control appear to make worthwhile yet another review bringing together some of the more recent and widely scattered information on the subject. Specific applications of electroluminescence to light sources, digital indicators, display devices, image amplifiers, and logic control circuits will not be discussed here.

Electroluminescence, that is, the emission of light which is not due to temperature alone (incandescence) resulting from the application of an electric field to a solid†, was first observed in SiC by Lossew (15) in 1923. Light appearing at one of the electrodes in an electrolytic solution is commonly called galvanoluminescence and was known at least as early as 1898 (16). In some cases such emission is due to chemiluminescence induced electrolytically; in others it is undoubtedly electroluminescence resulting from fields produced across a poorly conducting film (perhaps formed electrolytically) on the electrode. A typical example of the latter case is Al_2O_3 (17, 18, Section IV,F).

Although the most important material today in electroluminescence is ZnS:Cu, discovered by Destriau (19) in 1936, the phenomenon has been observed in a large number of materials as shown in the list of Table I. The efficiency of light production in most cases, however is very low compared to that of ZnS; figures of $10^{-6}\%$ are sometimes observed, for example

---

* References (1–7) are reviews of electroluminescence and related effects while reference (8) is a comprehensive bibliography for the same field, containing over 1850 references. References (9–14) are recent reviews covering general topics of luminescence common to both electroluminescent and nonelectroluminescent phosphors.

† In the older literature the word electroluminescence is often used to describe the emission resulting from the passage of electric current through a gas or vapor; it has also sometimes been used for cathodoluminescence (excitation by cathode rays). In modern usage, however, it is restricted to the definition given here.

see reference (71). The low output in many cases may make detection of electroluminescence difficult. If dielectric breakdown occurs the resultant visible emission or photoluminescence of the material excited by ultraviolet radiation generated in the breakdown may confuse the observation. Thus as little as ten years ago Herwelly (80) denied the existence of true electroluminescence and ascribed the observed emission to such spurious effects. Techniques for discriminating between the two phenomena, however, have been described (1, 81–83).

TABLE I. MATERIALS IN WHICH ELECTROLUMINESCENCE HAS BEEN OBSERVED[a]

Material	Reference	Material	Reference
Group II–IV Compounds		*Other Materials*	
ZnS	19, 20	Ge	49–52
CdS	21–24	Si	49, 53–55
ZnSe	25–27, 647	C (diamond)	56–60
CdTe	28	SiC	15, 61, 62
ZnO	15, 20, 29–31	NaCl	63
BeO	32	AgCl	64
MgO	33, 34, 545	ZnF_2	65
CaS	35	CaF_2	66
SrS	36	Al_2O_3	16–18, 32, 67, 68
BaS	35, 36	Cu_2O	69
Group III–V Compounds		SnO_2	70, 471
GaP	37–41	TiO_2	71
GaN	42	$BaTiO_3$	71, 72
GaSb	43	$SrTiO_3$, $CaTiO_3$	71
GaAs	43, 649	$KNbO_3$, $PbZrO_3$	71
InP	43	$CaWO_4$	67
InSb	44, 45, 648	Zn_2SiO_4	29, 73–76
BN	46	Ice	77
AlN	47	Organic Matls.	78, 79
AlP	48		

[a] The references are not meant to be exhaustive; a complete bibliography is given in reference (8). Here papers in English have been selected where possible.

In Section II below the mechanisms which have been suggested as being important in electroluminescence are summarized. Section III discusses the observed phenomena in ZnS while electroluminescence in a large number of other materials is covered in Section IV. Finally, Section V is concerned with the effects when electric fields and external radiation (visible, ultraviolet, X-rays, cathode rays, alpha particles, etc.) are applied simultaneously to a phosphor.

II. MECHANISMS OF ELECTROLUMINESCENCE

Electroluminescence is in a sense the meeting ground of two fields of scientific activity—phosphors (9–14) and semiconductors—both in themselves quite complicated. It is not surprising, therefore, that electroluminescence is also complicated both theoretically and experimentally. Several possible mechanisms for electroluminescence excitation can be envisaged and have been discussed in detail. As shown by Table I, the phenomenon is found experimentally in a wide variety of materials and for a wide variety of conditions. It has therefore been difficult in many cases to ascertain with certainty the mechanism which is actually responsible for the observed emission. The possibility of more than one mechanism being active under different conditions must also be considered. Before discussing the proposed electroluminescent mechanisms in detail, some general comments on the effects of electric fields, and particularly very strong fields, on the electrical and optical properties of solids are in order.

A. Effects of Electric Fields on Solids

Perhaps the oldest and most striking effect of the application of high electric fields to solids, aside from the observed conduction current, is that of dielectric breakdown (84–86). Even here nature is not simple and one must distinguish, for example, between "intrinsic breakdown" and "thermal breakdown." Since heat is generated by the passage of current and since the conductivity of insulators and semiconductors increases with increasing temperature, a regenerative effect may occur and this is responsible for "thermal breakdown." Some older theories ascribed "intrinsic breakdown" to mechanical or ionic effects (85). Today it is assumed to be electronic in nature, at least in most common materials, but a number of different mechanisms have been suggested. Zener (87) at an early date suggested quantum-mechanical electron tunneling from the filled valence band to the empty conduction band as the source of the electrons responsible for dielectric breakdown. Several Russian workers (88–90) also proposed mechanisms for breakdown. Frenkel (88) focused attention on bound electrons as the source of carriers and considered lowering by the field of the potential barrier responsible for the binding as a kind of "internal Schottky effect" similar to that for lowering of the electronic work function in the thermionic or photoelectric emission of electrons from surfaces. Vol'kenstein (89) considered reduction of the energy band gap by a "solid-state Stark effect."

Von Hippel (91) also very early proposed a model for dielectric breakdown similar to that for gaseous conductors; a few electrons normally

3

present in the conduction band are assumed to be accelerated by the field and to acquire sufficient energy to cause production of additional carriers in an avalanche process. This process has also been considered in detail by Fröhlich and Seitz (*84, 92–94*). Fröhlich (*84*) calls this the "low-temperature case"; it applies when collisions between electrons are rare compared to those between electrons and the base lattice (or defect centers). For the other extreme, the "high-temperature case" where interelectron collisions are much more important than collisions between electrons and lattice vibrations, Fröhlich (*84, 95*) has developed another theory leading to an electron temperature which is greater than the lattice temperature.

These theories of dielectric breakdown, which were originally developed with insulators largely in mind, are today applied to semiconductors, although attention is often focused on p-n junctions rather than on a uniform region. "Zener diode" is now an everyday word. The "Esaki diode" also works by means of a tunneling mechanism (*96*). The subject of electron tunneling or "internal field emission" has been extensively studied by Franz (*86*) and Chynoweth (*97*) and has been extended to include tunneling from a localized level to the conduction band ("field ionization") as well as interband transitions. Dexter (*98*) has considered tunneling from one localized center to another of equal energy, while Markham (*99*) has considered a similar case of radiative tunneling between two centers of different energy. Electron tunneling from the metallic cathode into an insulator has also been shown by von Hippel and his coworkers (*100*) and by Geller (*101*) to be important in some cases. The reverse process, leading to "hole" injection must be presumed to be possible at the anode.

The formation of electron avalanches in solids has also been studied, for example, by McKay and Chynoweth (*102*) and others (*103*). Whether a given junction breaks down due to tunneling or to avalanching depends on its width and other electrical properties. The presence of "hot electrons" according to Fröhlich's high-temperature theory and the resultant non-ohmic conductivity have been demonstrated (*104*). The existence of energetic electrons in solids has also been evidenced by external electron emission under the action of an applied field (*105–110*). "High field effects" in semiconductors have been reviewed by several writers (*97, 111, 112*).

Mention was made above of the action of electric fields in liberating electrons from centers or traps, either by thermal escape over a barrier lowered by the field (*88*) or by tunneling (*86, 97*). Release of electrons in this way can be detected by conductivity measurements, yielding so called "electrically excited glow curves," apparently first studied experimentally by Böer and Kümmel (*113*) and theoretically by Haering (*114*).* If the

---

* The terminology for the "glow" effects is very muddled. Experimentally one may increase either the temperature (T) or the field strength (F) and measure either the

liberated electrons produce luminescence the result is the very ancient Gudden-Pohl effect (*115*, Section V,*A,1*). The effect of electric fields in de-exciting photoconductors has also been studied by Kallmann and Mark (*119*).

A variety of optical effects (other than luminescence) due to electric fields in solids have been discussed. The action of fields on an isolated hydrogen atom (Stark effect) was studied theoretically many years ago (*120, 121*). It is well known that many impurity and trapping centers in crystals have hydrogenic energy levels. The effects of electric fields on excitons in solids have been recently considered by several workers (*122–124*). As pointed out by Lehovec (*125*), injection of charge carriers into semiconductors may result in optical absorption from three different sources; (1) absorption due to injected carriers which become trapped, (2) absorption due to free injected minority carriers, (3) absorption due to majority carriers which compensate for the injected minority carriers (*126*). In more insulating crystals which can support high fields, the absorption edge may be shifted due to a change in energy band gap, a kind of solid-state Stark effect (*89, 127–132a*). Williams (*130*) observed a shift of 70A to longer wavelengths when 120 volts was applied to a CdS crystal. Böer and his co-workers (*129*) also earlier studied this effect in CdS, while Damaskova and Patek (*132a*) have recently observed it in ZnS. The effect of an applied electric field on the spectral sensitivity of the photovoltaic effect ("internal photoelectric effect") has also been investigated (*133*).

These and other possible actions of electric fields on solids have been reviewed elsewhere (*5, 134, 135*). Most of them have found application at some time or other in attempted explanations of the complex phenomena which occur when luminescence is produced by, or observed in the presence of, electric fields. In the following paragraphs the major mechanisms which have been advanced for electroluminescence are summarized.

B. *Injection Electroluminescence*

Perhaps the simplest type of electroluminescence mechanism which can be envisaged is that following injection of minority charge carriers, either at an electrode contact or a *p-n* junction. At such a junction in the absence of an applied voltage there is a state of dynamic equilibrium between the processes of thermal production and subsequent recombination of electron-hole pairs. Some of the recombinations occur with the emission of radiation, which contributes to the normal thermal ("black-body") radiation of the

---

luminescence (*L*) or the current (*I*). A conventional thermoluminescence curve may therefore be designated as *TL*. The Gudden-Pohl effect (*115*) corresponds to *FL*, Böer and Kümmel's (*113*) "electrically excited glow curves" to *FI*, and "conductivity glow curves" or "thermally stimulated currents" (*116–118*) to *TI* processes.

material. When a voltage is applied in the forward direction and additional carriers are injected, however, this equilibrium is upset and the rate of recombination increased. If some of these recombinations occur with the emission of radiation the result may be called injection electroluminescence* (see Fig. 1).

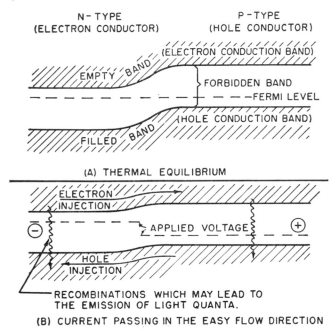

FIG. 1. Energy level diagrams for a *p-n* barrier in the absence of an applied field (A) and for current flow in the forward direction with consequent injection of minority charge carriers (B). In addition to direct radiative recombination of holes and electrons as shown, recombination may also occur via luminescence activator centers or in a radiationless manner. (From Lehovec *et al., 61*.)

Lossew not only first observed electroluminescence in rectifying crystals of silicon carbide (*15*), but later studied the inverse (blocking-layer photoelectric or photovoltaic) effect in this material (*136*). He was therefore familiar with the essentials of the explanation of the emission in SiC as involving *p-n* junctions. This explanation was first clearly stated in modern terminology by Lehovec *et al.* (*61*). Since then similar emission has been observed in a wide variety of semiconductors. It may be noted that no high electric field is required in this case; since the junction is biased in the for-

---

* The designation "recombination radiation" is often used in the literature. This seems to be too broad in scope, however, as many nonelectroluminescent emission processes involve recombination.

ward direction the junction field is actually lower when the voltage is applied than in its absence. Other types of electroluminescence may also be observed in SiC under other conditions; in his early work Lossew (15) observed what he called "Luminescence I" (reverse bias) and "Luminescence II" (forward bias). In the previous discussion a simple p-n junction was assumed. Patrick (62) has shown, however, that in SiC a p-i-n junction is probably responsible for the emission; radiative-recombination is apparently favored in a region which is not so highly doped. This is another way of saying that it is difficult to have good light emission (phosphor) characteristics and good carrier injection (semiconductor) characteristics in the same region.

Once the minority carriers are injected, a variety of recombination mechanisms are possible (137–138); some of these do not lead to luminescence and thus contribute to the low efficiency usually observed. Radiative recombination may occur either as a result of interband recombination ("intrinsic" emission) or recombination at localized impurity or activator levels ("extrinsic" or "activated" emission). The former is familiar to workers in luminescence as "edge emission"*; in semiconductors such recombination is often described as Shockley-Van Roosbroeck recombination because of the analysis of the process made by these workers (143). The recombination spectrum, $I(\nu)$, in this case is related to the absorption coefficient $\alpha(\nu)$ and to the sample geometry. If the emission must traverse a thickness d of the material, then

$$I(\nu) \simeq \nu^3 e^{-h\nu/kT} \alpha e^{-\alpha d}. \tag{1}$$

The theory for interband recombination radiation has been extended by other workers (144, 145), including direct and indirect transitions. Recombination at localized levels is the origin of the luminescence in most common phosphors; Shockley and Read (146) and Hall (147) studied this process for semiconductors and their name is often used to denote this type of recombination; the theory has been extended by Eagles (148). The kinetics of recombination at localized centers have been analyzed for the cases of phosphors and photoconductors by several workers (149–152).

If there were few competing nonradiative recombination processes then the efficiency of injection electroluminescence would be high, since in the limit one emitted photon should be obtained for each injected minority carrier. Furthermore, since the electrical energy required to inject a carrier may be much less than that of the emitted photons, the energy efficiency can theoretically even exceed 100%; in this case the additional

---

* In reality edge emission probably does not result from completely free-free transitions but from transitions between loosely bound carriers in levels just above the valence or just below the conduction band (139–142).

energy would be extracted from the surroundings as heat (*153–156*). However, it can be shown (*155, 156* and Section III,*F*) that the thermodynamic limitations on the efficiency do not permit large excesses over 100%. As yet, however, such values have not even been approached; a typical result in most materials is 10^{-6} photons/injected carrier.

C. *Acceleration-Collision Electroluminescence*

The mechanism which has been most generally accepted to explain the electroluminescence of zinc sulfide, for example, is one of acceleration of

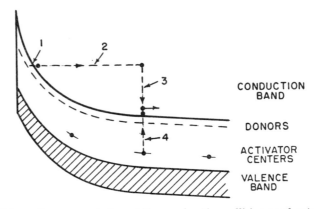

Fig. 2. Schematic representation of the acceleration-collision mechanism of electroluminescence. Electrons from traps in the localized high field region are liberated by the action of the field and/or temperature (1) or are injected from a "contact," are then accelerated by the field (2) to acquire kinetic energy above the bottom of the conduction band, and collide with activator centers whereby they lose their energy (3) and the activator center is ionized (4) or excited. Emission usually occurs later in the cycle when the alternating potential is reversing. (From Destriau and Ivey, *1*.)

electrons in the conduction band followed by collision excitation of luminescence centers. The steps in this process are described in Fig. 2. The probability of excitation in this case is (*20, 157*)

$$p \sim \exp\left(-E/elF\right), \tag{2}$$

where E is the energy required, l the mean-free-path of the electrons, and F the field strength. In addition to direct excitation of luminescence centers, electron-hole pairs may be formed by excitation of the base lattice.*

* For the simplest case of completely free carriers it can be shown on the basis of conservation of energy and momentum that the minimum energy required is 1.5 E_g, where E_g is the band gap. For a review of electron avalanches in semiconductors see reference (*111*).

Luminescence centers may then be emptied by capture of holes from the valence band. In either case the acceleration process may be repeated and an "avalanche" formed. Such an acceleration process for electroluminescence excitation was first proposed by Destriau (20); the model has been elaborated by Curie (4, 157), Piper and Williams (5, 158–160), Zalm (2, 161) and others.

It is usually assumed (2, 5, 158–161) that the field strength necessary for acceleration to energies sufficient for excitation of luminescence centers is higher than the applied fields (which are of the order of 10^5 volts/cm) and that the potential difference must therefore be localized in small regions of the crystal, giving rise to potential barriers as shown in Fig. 2 (the possible origin of these barriers is discussed in Section III,B). Curie (4, 157), however, believes that acceleration to the required energies can occur for field strengths of 10^4–10^5 volts/cm and that it takes place in the volume of the crystal rather than at barriers (although barriers may be essential in supplying the initial carriers). Goffaux (162–163) and Nagy (164) have suggested that electroluminescence excitation in ZnS may result from "hot electrons." On the basis of this theory the electron temperature T_e is related to the lattice temperature T_0 and the field strength F by

$$\frac{h\nu}{kT_0} - \frac{h\nu}{kT_e} = HF^2, \tag{3}$$

where ν is the frequency of lattice vibrations and H is a constant.* In Section III,J it will be shown, however, that there is no universal agreement that an electron acceleration mechanism is involved in ZnS at all.

The source of the initial electrons which are accelerated is obviously an important point. A small number of free conduction electrons are always present even at room temperature. In the case of sinusoidal voltages, however, free electrons would presumably be swept away before the field becomes high enough to accelerate them to useful velocities. Normal phosphors also always contain a large number of electron traps and in the presence of a high field these may supply carriers by a tunneling process or by thermal release over a lowered trap barrier. Electrons may also be injected from electrodes or other conductive regions in contact with the phosphor. It should also be noted that excitation of a luminescence center may be confined to that center (typical, for example, of Mn in ZnS) or may involve removal of an electron or ionization of the center (typical of Cu in ZnS).

* Equation (3) is obtained from the more general relation (84)

$$\exp\left[(h\nu/kT_0) - (h\nu/kT_e)\right] - 1 = DF^2 \exp\left(-\Delta V/kT_0\right).$$

D. *Other Electroluminescence Mechanisms*

It is conceivable in principle that an activator center (in ZnS, for example) could be emptied directly by the field by tunneling or field ionization and Ueta (*74*) has proposed this mechanism for some ZnS and Zn_2SiO_4 phosphors. It is also obvious that the same effect would result if Zener tunneling from the valence band was followed by capture of the resultant hole in the valence band at a luminescence center.

In either of these cases (or for field emission from an electrode) the number of transitions depends on the field strength F according to a relation*

$$j = AF^n \exp\left(-BE^{3/2}/F\right), \tag{4}$$

where E is the energy involved and n is a constant between 1 and 3 (*86, 97*). Piper and Williams (*159*) have shown that the results of Franz reduce in typical cases to

$$F_z = \frac{6 \times 10^6 \, E_g{}^2}{7 + \log_{10}\left(F_z\tau\right)}, \tag{5a}$$

and

$$F_i = \frac{10^7 \, E_g{}^{1/2} E_i{}^{3/2}}{8 + \log_{10}\left(F_i\tau\right)}, \tag{5b}$$

where F_z and F_i are the field strengths (in volts/cm) required to produce a mean transition time τ for the case of Zener (band-to-band) tunneling or field ionization of centers, respectively, and where E_g is the band gap and E_i the ionization energy of the centers (in ev). On this basis if E_g is set equal to 3.7 ev and E_i to 2.8 ev (typical for ZnS) and if τ is arbitrarily taken as 10^{-2} sec for the case of ionization of centers or 10 sec for the Zener effect (to correspond to a concentration of activator centers one-thousandth that of lattice atoms), the results are $F_z = 5.6 \times 10^6$ and $F_i = 7.0 \times 10^6$ volts/cm. These figures (which would be even higher for smaller values of τ) are above the dielectric breakdown strength for most materials.

Piper and Williams (*5, 159*) have also considered a mechanism in which the field could perturb the emitting state of a luminescence center sufficiently to allow a reasonable occupation probability of this state from the ground state, corresponding to direct excitation of the center by the field. They concluded, however, that the polarizability of the center required even for fields as high as 10^8 volts/cm is not realistic. Furthermore, even if excitation could be achieved in this way the field would have to be

---

* In Eq. (4) the constant B involves the effective mass of the electrons, which is also related to the band gap E_g in a complicated manner, but in the simplest case introduces a factor $E_g{}^{1/2}$.

removed in a time short compared with the lifetime of the excited state and the excited state would have to be sufficiently localized to prevent ionization by the high field. This then appears to be a most unlikely process indeed.

In the section on injection electroluminescence above, "recombination radiation" due to interband recombination of electrons and holes following minority carrier injection at a *p-n* junction biased in the forward direction was discussed. If such a junction is biased in the reverse direction the carriers may acquire appreciable kinetic energy from the field and form avalanches which can produce electron-hole pairs with appreciable kinetic energy. Recombination in this case may correspond to energies much greater than the band gap. Thus visible "avalanche emission" has been observed in silicon (*53, 55*) and germanium (*165*) (where normal recombination is in the infrared region). The excitation in this case may be confined to small localized spots at which "microplasmas" (*166*) are formed.

TABLE II. POSSIBLE ELECTROLUMINESCENCE MECHANISMS

Excitation	Emission
A. Minority carrier effects	1. Interband recombination
a. Injection	a. Intrinsic or "edge" emission
b. Accumulation	b. "Avalanche emission"
B. Electron tunneling	2. Recombination at impurities or
a. Interband (Zener effect)	defects (activated emission)
b. Ionization of activator centers (Franz)	3. Intraband radiation
c. Level-to-level (Dexter, Markham)	("deceleration emission")
C. Impact by accelerated carriers	
a. Ionization of lattice	
b. Excitation or ionization of activator centers	
D. High electron temperature ("hot electrons")	

Emission corresponding to an energy less than the band gap has also been observed in silicon under these conditions. This radiation has been ascribed to intraband transitions, i.e., to "deceleration radiation," a kind of "bremsstrahlung." The efficiency of such radiation would be expected to be quite low; the experimental value is about 10^{-8} photons/carrier. The theory of avalanche and deceleration emission has recently been discussed by Wolff (*167*). As mentioned previously, emission from reverse-biased SiC junctions ("Luminescence I") was first observed by Lossew (*15*) long ago.

Henisch and Marathe (*168*) have also proposed that the process of "carrier accumulation" (*169*) may be responsible for some electroluminescence which has been ascribed to carrier injection. The main distinction experimentally is that for carrier accumulation the emission should be localized at the cathode (for *n*-type material) and be confined to a region which becomes smaller as the voltage is increased, rather than appearing at the anode in a region which grows with increasing voltage as for injection. It is not known at this time to what extent this mechanism occurs in practice.

In Table II are summarized the various mechanisms which have been proposed for electroluminescence.* Since any one of the excitation processes might be followed by several of the emission processes, it is obvious that in principle a very large number of possibilities exist.

* A similar list was given by L. Patrick in an internal Westinghouse report dated Jan. 12, 1959.

III. ELECTROLUMINESCENCE IN ZINC SULFIDE AND RELATED PHOSPHORS

Zinc sulfide and related compounds form the basis for many photoluminescent and cathodoluminescent phosphors and are also the most efficient electroluminescent phosphors known to date. ZnS exists both in a low-temperature cubic (sphalerite or zincblende) and a high-temperature hexagonal (wurtzite) structure. The situation, however, is far from simple because the difference in energy of the two structures is small. ZnS, in common with SiC, exists in many polytypes (at least 10) (*170, 171*). Some data on the energy band gap for several of the Group II–VI compounds of interest are given in Table III. Aside from the "edge emission"

TABLE III. SOME PROPERTIES OF THE GROUP II–VI COMPOUNDS

Compound	Lattice structure	Band gap	
		ev	Equivalent wavelength (A)
ZnS	hexagonal	3.70	3350
ZnS	cubic	3.64	3410
ZnO	hexagonal	3.2	3880
ZnSe	cubic	2.60	4770
Cds	hexagonal	2.43	5100
ZnTe	cubic	2.15	5780
CdSe	hexagonal	1.74	7115
CdTe	cubic	1.42	8710

(*139–142*), which is normally strong only at low temperatures, ZnS in common with most (but not all) inorganic phosphors must be "activated" by suitable impurities in order to produce luminescence. Photoluminescent emission in ZnS may be activated by a variety of elements (*172*), including

Cu, Ag, Au, P, As, Sb, Sn, Pb, Mn, V,
Fe, Na, Li, Ga, In, Tl, Sc, Rare Earths.

To these should be added zinc vacancies in the lattice, which are assumed to be responsible for the "self-activated emission" (*173–176*).

The solubility of many of these activator elements (Mn is an exception) in the ZnS lattice is usually limited unless another element, called the coactivator, is introduced at the same time. The coactivator is usually a halide (Cl,Br,I) or a trivalent ion (Al, Ga, In, etc.) (see Fig. 3) and its

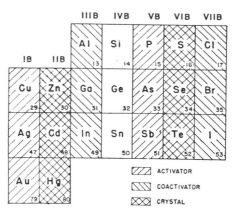

FIG. 3. Portion of the periodic chart relevant to the ZnS family of phosphors and the most common activator and coactivator impurities. (From Piper and Williams, 5.)

action is usually explained on the basis of charge compensation as introduced by Kröger (173, 177). Thus*

$$[Cu^+]_{Zn} + [M^{+++}]_{Zn} \rightarrow 2Zn^{++},$$
or
$$[Cu^+]_{Zn} + [X^-]_S \rightarrow Zn^{++} + S^{--},$$

if an ionic model† is used for ZnS. On this model Mn is divalent and can substitute directly for Zn and hence does not require charge compensation.

The effect on the solubility of the activator is not the only action of the coactivator, however.‡ When a coactivator is incorporated into the lattice an electron is transferred from it to an activator atom to affect the charge compensation. Subsequently when the phosphor is excited and electrons appear in the conduction band the coactivator centers can capture these electrons and subsequently release them under thermal action or some other form of stimulation. They thus act as electron traps or donors, in the same manner that the activators serve as hole traps or acceptors and influence many phosphor properties (thermoluminescence, phosphorescence, etc.) in addition to electroluminescence. (Other traps may, of course, be introduced by other impurities or defects.) The positions of various im-

* The symbol $[Cu^+]_{Zn}$ denotes a Cu^+ ion at a normal Zn lattice site.

† The best estimate seems to be that the ZnS lattice is about 75% ionic (14, 178); that is the actual charges are near Zn^+ and S^- rather than Zn^{++} and S^{--} (completely ionic) or Zn^{--} and S^{++} (completely covalent).

‡ The nature of the coactivator also has a slight effect on the emission, at least in self-activated ZnS. The emission peak for ZnS:Al or ZnS:Ga is at 4700A, while that for ZnS:Cl or ZnS:Br is at 4620 A (176). This has been interpreted by Prener and Weil (176) in terms of differences in distance between activator and coactivator centers on the basis of the associated-pair theory of Prener and Williams (179, 180).

TABLE IV. Ionization Energies of Imperfections in II–VI-Compounds[a]

Material	Impurity	Substitutes for	Ionization energy (ev)	
			Donors ($E_C - E_I$)	Acceptors ($E_I - E_V$)
ZnS	Cl,Br,I	S	0.25	
	Al	Zn	0.25	
	Sc	Zn	0.35	
	Ga	Zn	0.42	
	In	Zn	0.50	
	Cu	Zn		0.95
	Ag	Zn		0.55
ZnSe	Br	Se	0.21	
	Cu	Zn		0.6
	Ag	Zn		0.6
	Sb	Se		0.7, 1.3
	As	Se		0.7
CdS	Cl,Br,I	S	0.03	
	Al,Ga,In	Cd	0.03	
	Cu	Cd		(0.6), 1.0
	Ag	Cd		($\leq$1.0)
	(Cd vac.)			1.0
ZnTe	Cu	Zn		0.11 (0.34)
CdSe	Cl,Br,I	Se	0.03	
	Cu	Cd		0.64
	(Se vac.)		0.14, $\sim$0.6	
	(Cd vac.)			0.6, 1.0
CdTe	I	Te	$\sim$0.01	
	Li	Cd		0.27
	Sb	Te		0.36
	P	Te		0.38
	Na	Cd		0.29
	(Cd vac.)			0.3
ZnO	H	(Interstitial)	0.05	
	Li	(Interstitial)	0.05	
	Zn	(Interstitial)	0.05	

[a] Taken from reference (181). ($E_C - E_I$) denotes the separation from the conduction band; ($E_I - E_V$), that from the valence band.

purity levels in ZnS and other II–VI compounds, as summarized by Bube (181), are listed in Table IV. As noted above, Ga and In, among others, may also serve simultaneously as emitting or activator centers. Finally, since the melting points of the halides normally used are below the firing temperatures used in phosphor preparation, they also serve as "fluxes" or "mineralizers" in promoting crystal growth and incorporation of added elements. Just as vacant zinc lattice sites may serve as "self-activator" centers, vacant sulfur sites may act as "self-coactivator" centers (*175, 182*). Emission which has been ascribed to such sulfur vacancies has also been reported (*183, 184*). Compensation by vacancies normally requires considerably more energy than compensation by foreign atoms. The statistics governing the incorporation of such imperfections in solids have been reviewed by Kröger and Vink (*185*).

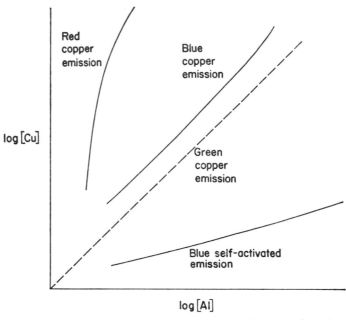

FIG. 4. Effect of activator and coactivator concentration on color of emission of ZnS:Cu,Al. (From van Gool and Cleiren, *193*.)

With an activator such as Cu in ZnS, however, the situation is far from simple. Depending upon other conditions the photoluminescent emission of ZnS:Cu is usually either blue (peak at about 4550A*) or green (peak at 5200A) or a combination of these. The green emission is favored the higher the coactivator/activator ratio. Under other conditions however (mainly high copper content and absence of halide or oxygen), a broad "red" (really orange) emission band (peak at 6500–6700A) may be obtained (*182, 186, 187*); a secondary yellow sub-band at 5800A has also been re-

* The exact position of the emission depends upon the crystal structure; the transition energies are about 0.06 ev higher for the hexagonal form than for the cubic form (see Table III).

ported (*186, 188*). In addition, there is also emission in the infrared region (*189–192*); two bands at 1.5 and 1.7μ have been observed. The occurrence of the various visible emissions as a function of activator and coactivator concentration is shown in Fig. 4 for the case of ZnS:Cu,Al (*193*). Although many models have been advanced to explain the occurrence of such a variety of emission bands arising from a single activator impurity (*177, 179, 180, 182, 186, 190, 193–202*), the question is far from settled.

Excitation energy may be transferred from one place to another in a phosphor (from one type of center to another type, or from the base lattice to a center, or in some cases from a center to another of the same type) by a number of different methods (*12*). These include:

(1) Transfer by photons. One center may be optically excited by the emission from another type of center, giving "cascade" excitation.

(2) Transfer by quantum-mechanical resonance (*203, 204*). A de-exciting transition occurs in one center simultaneously with an exciting transition in another. The probability of transfer depends on the distance between the two centers and the type of coupling between them. This process is usually referred to as "sensitization."

(3) Transfer by charged carriers. A carrier (electron or positive hole) may be transferred from one center to another, thus filling one and emptying the other.

(4) Transfer by excitons (*205*). Energy may be transferred by coupled electron-hole pairs without a net flow of charge.

A. Preparation and Chemical Properties

The number of types of electroluminescent zinc sulfide phosphors is much smaller than the number of photoluminescent or cathodoluminescent sulfides. For example, of the activators of ZnS listed earlier, only Cu and Mn are of any importance in electroluminescent materials, and not all ZnS:Cu phosphors are electroluminescent by any means. Although electroluminescent single crystals and thin films can be made, most work has been with powders, which is also the form used commercially.

Destriau's early phosphors (*20, 206*) were ZnS:Cu made without any flux (halide); high copper content was found to improve the sensitivity. Repeated firing in air (with mixing between firings) was found to improve the sensitivity (see also *82*). As a matter of fact, almost any nonelectroluminescent ZnS:Cu phosphor may be made at least weakly electroluminescent by heating a thin layer of the material in air at about 1100°C for a short time. Destriau (*20, 206*) also added ZnO directly to the ZnS before firing and found that between 50 and 90% ZnO was best.

The first commercial electroluminescent phosphors made by Homer *et al.* (*207*) were also prepared with about 5% ZnO added.* It was stated that in this case, however, the effect of ZnO was only to improve the uniformity, not the brightness; after firing the phosphors were washed in acetic acid to remove excess ZnO and decrease the conductivity.† These phosphors also contained a small amount of lead (which apparently was considered essential) and a relatively high amount of copper. It was noted that properly prepared materials were dark or grey in appearance; insufficient lead or copper resulted in materials lighter in color and poorer in electroluminescent performance. No halide or other coactivator was intentionally introduced in these phosphors; the raw ZnS used, however, had a very high chloride content. It may well be that one (if not the only) function of lead‡ in this case was to reduce the chloride content by volatilization during firing; the importance of controlling the halide content will be discussed further below.

Thorington (*211*) very early observed that many sulfide phosphor powders became electroluminescent when placed between electrodes and the container evacuated; from this and other studies he concluded that the state of the surface is important for electroluminescence excitation. Zalm *et al.* (*2, 212, 213*) also showed that it is possible to render a photoluminescent but nonelectroluminescent ZnS:Cu phosphor electroluminescent by simply depositing a small amount of copper on the surface. This may be done by direct evaporation in vacuum or by washing the phosphor in a solution of $CuSO_4$. Gold or silver may be used in a similar manner. In this case the electroluminescence is destroyed by washing the phosphor with NaCN or KCN, which are solvents for Cu_2S. The same effect can be produced by alkali sulfide on the surface (*2*); in this case washing in water destroys the electroluminescence. These observations, and many others, support the assumption that electrical inhomogeneity is necessary in an electroluminescent phosphor; this assumption was made by many early workers (*2, 20, 207, 214–216*). Homer *et al.* (*207*) pointed out that simply placing a nonelectroluminescent sulfide phosphor in contact with a metallic electrode was often sufficient to make it a least weakly electroluminescent, while Thorington (*211*) had earlier found that a mechanical mixture of two phosphor powders might be electroluminescent even when the components were not. Lehmann (*217*) also observed that many non-electroluminescent phosphors (including many nonsulfide types) become electroluminescent

* The influence of ZnO addition has also been studied by Fritzsche (*208*) and Wachtel (*209*). Schwager (*210*) has also recently studied the electroluminescence of fused mixtures of ZnS and ZnO.

† Ammonium acetate or sulfide may be used for the same purpose (*210a*).

‡ Waymouth (*188*) states that Pb also causes an absorption band in the infrared in these phosphors.

when mixed with a metallic or semiconducting powder; he called this "contact electroluminescence."*

From the above discussion it is apparent that the surface may be important in determining the electroluminescent properties of a phosphor. This, however, is not necessarily or desirably so. In the best electroluminescent phosphors the desired inhomogeneity is apparently not restricted to the surface. The conditions of preparation seem to be such that some material which is more conductive than ZnS, such as ZnO, PbS, or Cu_2S,† is present in a quantity higher than the amount which can exist in solid solution in ZnS and therefore the remainder is segregated as a separate conducting phase. These segregated regions need not be (and in the most desirable case do not seem to be) localized on the surface but are distributed through the particle at internal cracks and other faults in the crystal structure (213, 217). The effect of crystal structure and of such segregations on electroluminescence will be discussed in more detail in the following section. Of the "contact" materials listed, Cu_2S seems to be the best (2, 209, 217); most modern electroluminescent phosphors are made with oxygen carefully excluded. Since the solubility of Cu in ZnS is determined by the amount of Cl or other coactivator present, the importance of relatively high copper content and of controlled coactivator concentration, as discussed above, to produce precipitation of Cu_2S is explained (219). The presence of such second phases (although present in amounts too low for detection by X-ray diffraction) is believed to explain the dark color of most electroluminescent sulfide phosphors. Figure 5 shows the effect of copper and lead content on the reflection spectra of such phosphors (207). In this case the addition of lead presumably causes loss of chlorine and hence decreased incorporation of copper into the ZnS [Sn,As,Sb, and Bi behave in a similar manner (220)].

Many papers have been written concerning the preparation of electroluminescent ZnS:Cu phosphors (2, 25, 26, 182, 186, 199, 207, 209, 212, 214, 220–223). Although electroluminescent phosphors with the "copper red" emission can be prepared (182, 186), they are relatively low in output and have not found commercial application. The best phosphors currently available seem to be those with blue or green copper emission. Various procedures have been given for their preparation; in many cases the dif-

* Morosin and Haak (218) have charged that what Lehmann saw was really photoluminescence, which is reminiscent of the Herwelly-Destriau argument. Although photoluminescent excitation may occur in some cases, it is believed that "contact electroluminescence" is a real effect (83).

† Cu_2S is written here as "shorthand"; the exact composition is not known. It may also be noted that Froelich (214) suggested that Al_2O_3 could serve as a segregation to evoke electroluminescence; Zalm (2), however, disagrees with this view and believes Cu_2S to be responsible in ZnS:Cu,Al phosphors as well.

ferences seem to arise purely from the past experience of the worker involved and from reasons of convenience. In addition to the use of Cl as an activator, materials coactivated with Al (2, 214, 221) and with Br or I

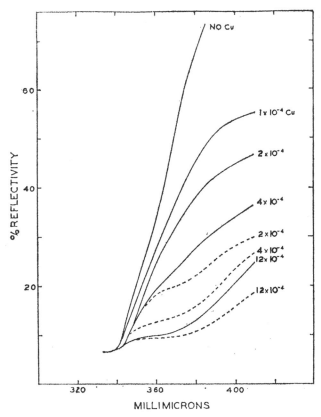

FIG. 5. Effect of concentration of copper and of lead on reflection spectra of electro-luminescent ZnS:Cu phosphors. (——)—no Pb; (- - -)—with Pb. (From Homer et al., 207.)

(25, 26) have been described. One procedure which may be employed for small laboratory samples is described below (209) (the formulation given results in a green-emitting phosphor):

(1) Slurry 10 gm luminescent-grade ZnS (free of halide) with 3.0 ml of $0.2N$ $Cu(CH_3COO)_2$ solution (corresponding to 0.6 atom % Cu) and 1.7 ml of $0.2N$ NH_4Cl solution (corresponding to 0.34 atom % Cl). Dry at 120°C and mix with 0.5 gm purified sulfur.*

* The effect of firing in an atmosphere of sulfur has also been discussed by Larach and Shrader (26).

(2) Place mix in transparent silica tube (volume about 13 ml) sealed at one end and with close-fitting cap consisting of slightly larger similar tube. Place in silica firing tube provided with inlet and output for purified nitrogen. After flushing fire at 950°C for 90 min with continuous flow of nitrogen.

(3) Crush with 0.5 gm purified sulfur and repeat step (2).

(4) Crush, wash with 10% NaCN(+ NaOH) solution, wash with H_2O until neutral, wash with alcohol, dry, and sieve.

The procedure of washing electroluminescent phosphors in sodium (or potassium) cyanide to remove excess Cu_2S from the surface (186) is now a standard technique and is important for decreasing the conductivity and improving the performance of electroluminescent lamps or cells. Other less toxic but generally less effective solvents which may be used for this purpose are thiourea [$(NH_2)_2CS$], sodium thiosulfate ("hypo," $Na_2S_2O_3$) or sodium thiocyanate (NaSCN) (224).

It is well known that the emission of ZnS:Cu photoluminescent or cathodoluminescent phosphors may be shifted to longer wavelengths by partial or complete substitution of Se for S or of Cd for Zn, with little or no effect on output. The color of electroluminescent ZnS:Cu phosphors may similarly be shifted by partial substitution of Se for S (2, 25, 26, 223). The shift thus obtained, however, is limited by the fact that ZnSe:Cu itself has its emission peak in the orange-red region (at about 6450A), rather than in the deep red, and has low output at low applied frequency due to thermal quenching. Gelling and Haanstra (647) have recently shown that the quantum emission of electroluminescent ZnSe:Cu,Al phosphors is as great for high-frequency operation as that of ZnS:Cu,Al. Since the shift obtained for substitution of Cd for Zn is greater than that for substitution of Se for S, it is tempting to try to prepare electroluminescent (Zn,Cd)S:Cu phosphors. Contrary to the case of Se substitution, however, it is found that the output decreases very rapidly (at least if the coactivator is a halide) if the Cd content exceeds about 8%, which produces only a rather small color shift (2, 209, 225-227). According to Wachtel (209) and Lehmann (226) this is connected with a change in crystal structure from cubic to hexagonal for higher Cd concentration, the cubic structure being preferred for electroluminescence; some data of Lehmann concerning this point are shown in Fig. 6. In the case of Se substitution this problem does not arise as ZnSe is also cubic (see Table III). Although Zalm (2) agrees that the cubic structure is desirable for electroluminescence (see also the next section), he attributes the poor behavior of (Zn,Cd)S phosphors to deep electron traps introduced by Cd (the influence of traps on electroluminescence is discussed in Section III,J). Lehmann has recently found that, contrary to the results of Fig. 6 for (Zn,Cd)S:Cu,Br, good electroluminescent hexagonal (Zn,Cd)S:Cu phosphors may be prepared if a coactivator other than a halide is employed. (Zn,Cd)(S,Se):Cu,Al phosphors have also been studied by Gelling and Haanstra (647).

Wachtel (228) found that it was possible to shift the copper emission band far to the red and even into the infrared region while still maintaining good output by partial substitution of HgS. The crystal structure in this case remains cubic even in the simultaneous presence of fairly large amounts

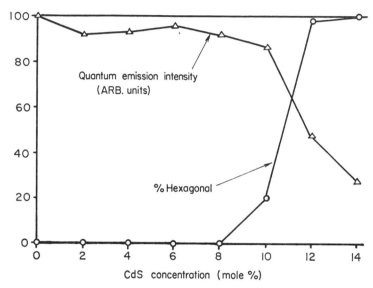

FIG. 6. The effect of Cd concentration on quantum output of electroluminescence and the crystal structure of (Zn,Cd)S:Cu,Br phosphors fired at 750°C for one hour; 1% Cu and 0.3% Br in raw mix. (From Lehmann, 226.)

of Cd, so that both (Zn,Hg)S:Cu and (Zn,Cd,Hg)S:Cu phosphors are possible. Thus (87Zn,13Hg)S:Cu and (78Zn,12Cd,10Hg)S:Cu both have their emission peak at about 7000A for excitation at 400 cps. These materials are somewhat more difficult to prepare than ZnS phosphors, however, because of the high vapor pressure of HgS at the firing temperature (900°C). As yet it has also not been possible to incorporate them into glass dielectrics because of the temperatures required to fuse the glass. Furthermore, their maintenance of output is as yet poor compared to ZnS:Cu. Jaffe (229) has also studied the results of partial substitution of Mg for Zn in ZnS:Cu, which causes the emission to shift toward shorter wavelengths. Between about 5% and 8% Mg content the crystal structure shifts to hexagonal and there is a large decrease in electroluminescent output.

Lehmann has shown that the emission of single-band (Zn,Cd,Hg)S phosphors can be represented by Gaussian curves (plotted as energy per unit wavelength interval as a function of frequency, not wavelength) with a constant width (between 50% points) of 0.36 ev; the position of the peak is determined by the phosphor composition. Figure 7 is the standard C.I.E.

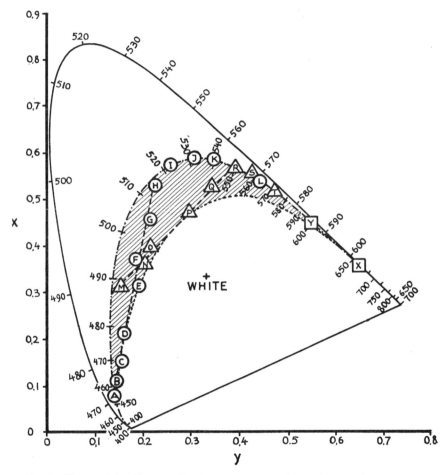

Fig. 7. Chromaticity diagram showing colors attainable with cubic (Zn,Cd,Hg)S:Cu electroluminescent phosphors (see text for discussion). Point Y represents emission of ZnS:Cu,Mn and X represents ZnSe:Cu. (Data from Lehmann, unpublished.)

chromaticity diagram on which has been plotted (dashed curve) the color coordinates calculated for such a series of hypothetical emitters with peak emission at the wavelength (in mμ) indicated on the curve. The outer solid curve represents the locus of similar monochromatic emitters. Point A corresponds to the blue emission (single-band) of ZnS:Cu (low halide) while point H corresponds to the green (single-band) emission of ZnS:Cu (high halide) phosphors as normally prepared (excited at 400 cps). Points between A and H represent experimental double-band phosphors with intermediate halide content. Points from I to L correspond to very high Cu and Cl content; the emission is apparently shifted to longer wavelength because of complex interactions at this high doping level.* Although the photoluminescent efficiency of the latter phosphors is good, their electroluminescent output decreases with increasing doping (see Fig. 8) and they are not practical materials.

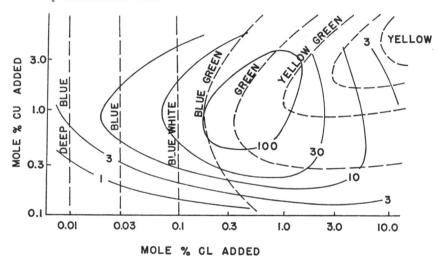

FIG. 8. Color and brightness (for 4000 cps excitation) of ZnS:Cu,Cl electroluminescent phosphors as a function of amount of Cu and Cl added before firing. The composition of the finished phosphor will differ due to losses during firing and cyanide treatment. (Data from Thornton, *337*.)

Other regions of the chromaticity curve of Fig. 7 may be reached with (Zn,Hg)S:Cu, (Zn,Hg,Cd)S:Cu, (Zn,Cd)S:Cu with low Cd content, and Zn(S,Se):Cu. The point X corresponds to ZnSe:Cu while the points M through R to T are for a series of cubic (90Zn,10Cd)S:Cu phosphors similar to the ZnS samples represented by A through H to L. The shaded area in this diagram therefore represents the range of colors attainable in practice with single phosphors. Intermediate points, such as white, may of course be attained by blending individual emitters.

The only other activator of practical use in electroluminescent phosphors other than Cu is Mn (*20, 207, 230–236*). If sufficient Mn (a few per

* A similar color shift was observed by Froelich (*214*) for ZnS:Cu,Al phosphors.

cent) is introduced into a conventional electroluminescent ZnS:Cu phosphor, the emission due to Cu is suppressed completely and instead the yellow-orange emission due to Mn appears (emission peak at 5900A, point Y in Fig. 7). ZnS:Mn made in a similar way without Cu is only very weakly electroluminescent, if at all. This result has been attributed by Froelich (230) to sensitization of Mn centers by quantum-mechanical resonance transfer of energy from Cu centers. This conclusion does not seem definite, however, since Ag, In, or Ga are equally or more effective in sensitizing photoluminescence from Mn but are ineffective in the case of electroluminescence (230). The observations that ZnS:Cu,Mn is superior to ZnS:Cu for dc excitation (see Section III,D) and that no secondary peak similar to that for ZnS:Cu is normally observed in its output waveform (see Section III,I) favor direct excitation of Mn centers or sensitization by the lattice (electron-hole pairs) (237) rather than sensitization by Cu. Furthermore, in phosphors containing ZnO it is possible to obtain electroluminescent emission from Mn without the presence of Cu (231, 233), although admittedly Cu is better in this respect than ZnO. In practice Cu in ZnS:Cu,Mn probably functions mainly to provide conducting inclusions of Cu_2S. It is generally found that, compared to emission from ZnS:Cu, the emission of such yellow ZnS:Cu,Mn phosphors increases more slowly as either the exciting voltage or frequency is increased.

With lower concentrations of Mn than normal for yellow ZnS:Cu,Mn phosphors, emission from both Cu and Mn may be seen and phosphors prepared whose emission color changes strikingly with the operating conditions (233–235). In this way Lehmann (238) has prepared a three-color phosphor with yellow Mn or green or blue Cu emission* (see Fig. 9); in the "transition regions" indicated a variety of colors may be obtained (as predicted by combination of the points A, H, and Y in Fig. 7), including white. It has not been possible to prepare an efficient single-component white electroluminescent phosphor in this way, however; better output can always be obtained from a blend of two separate components such as Y and D or E in Fig. 7. It may be noted that in this case increasing the voltage favors Mn emission over that due to Cu. Mattler and Ceva (239) have recently shown that in phosphors with both Cu and Mn emission there may be a break in the curve describing the dependence of Mn emission on applied voltage. At low voltages the Mn emission (separated by filters) may increase less rapidly with increasing voltage than the Cu emission, but at high voltages the Mn emission increases much more rapidly. Mattler suggests that at low voltage the Mn centers are primarily sensitized by Cu centers but that at high voltage they are mainly excited by other mecha-

* The effect of frequency on the blue and green emission of Cu is discussed in Section III,E.

nisms (which may still require the action of Cu_2S segregations). The behavior of $ZnS:Mn$ phosphors is very complicated and not well understood (*239a–239c*), even in the case of photoluminescence.

Both Ag and Au are good activators for photoluminescence in ZnS type phosphors (*240, 241*). Ag is also the most common activator in cathodoluminescent ZnS phosphors. As mentioned earlier, Zalm (*2*) found that deposition of Cu, Ag, or Au on the surface of nonelectroluminescent

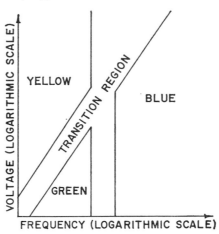

Fig. 9. Schematic representation of color changes in specially prepared $ZnS:Cu,Mn$ electroluminescent phosphor with low Mn content. (From Lehmann, unpublished.)

phosphors induces electroluminescence; in this case the emission is characteristic of the phosphor employed and $ZnS:Ag$ for example, may be used. Thorington (*211*) also was able to make $(Zn,Cd)S:Ag$ electroluminescent by vacuum treatment while Lehmann (*217*) observed contact electroluminescence from $ZnS:Ag$. Despite these facts, an efficient electroluminescent $ZnS:Ag$ or $ZnS:Au$ phosphor seems never to have been prepared.* The reasons for this are obscure, although Zalm (*2*) feels that it results from the larger energy difference between levels due to Cu and the valence band (see Table IV and Section III,*J*). It may be that gold sulfide (presumed necessary as a conducting phase) is unstable at normal phosphor firing temperatures, but then one would expect gold itself to be effective. On the other hand, there may be some morphological requirement for the conducting segregations which is not yet understood.† In any event, the problem remains.

---

* Ballentyne (*242, 243*) reports a $ZnS:Ag$ electroluminescent phosphor but no quantitative information concerning its output is given. Gobrecht *et al.* (*82, 244*) also studied some $ZnS:Ag$ phosphors but they were only poorly electroluminescent.

† Cu_2S and Cu_9S_5 both exist in cubic forms (*245*).

Ballentyne (243) has described a phosphor made by firing ZnS with 10% TlCl at 800°C in wet H_2S. No Tl (or Cu) was found spectroscopically in the final product; all the Tl was presumed to have sublimed during firing. The author states that "This phosphor was brilliantly photoluminescent and moderately electroluminescent in the green due presumably to vacancies." Since the normal ("self-activated") emission due to Zn vacancies in ZnS is blue, the support for this statement is not clear. It would seem that the possibility of copper contamination (even though not detected spectroscopically) should be considered, but the real explanation of this isolated experiment is uncertain; the lack of quantitative information concerning the brightness is unfortunate. Although many of the rare earths can serve as activators of photoluminescence in ZnS (172), electroluminescence has been obtained only with Nd, Er, and Tm by Oranovskii and Trapeznikova (246–248). In this case the presence of Cu was also necessary and it was found that the presence of Mn enhanced the emission of Er and Tm.

Weak red emission has also been observed in ZnS:Cu,Fe phosphors (249, 250). The emission peak in this case is at about 6500A, but it seems impossible to achieve high output of Fe emission without simultaneous emission from Cu (251). It should also be mentioned that Smith (252) and Narita (253) obtained electroluminescent "edge emission" (extending in the ultraviolet to 3400A) from single crystals of ZnS. Narita observed ultraviolet emission only in crystals containing Cu but no Cl and only in the "in-phase" component of the emission (see Section III,H). No such "edge electroluminescence" has ever been observed in ZnS powder phosphors.

The action of Fe in promoting red emission in ZnS was mentioned above. Fe, Co, and Ni are normally considered to be "killers" or "poisons" for luminescence in ZnS, presumably because they introduce radiationless (or infrared-radiating) transitions (194, 250, 254). Burns (255), however, claims that the introduction of a very small amount (10^{-5}–10^{-4}%) of Fe, Co, or Ni improves the performance of electroluminescent ZnS:Cu. A similar enhancement of the photoluminescence of ZnS:Au was reported by Arpiarian (256). Lehmann (257) found that additions (10^{-4}–10^{-3}%) of these elements to green-emitting ZnS:Cu depressed the output more for low-frequency excitation than for high-frequency excitation; in the latter case the effect of the "killer" may not be observed at all. In this way materials whose output increases more rapidly with increasing frequency than is normally the case can be prepared; in addition phosphors which are electroluminescent (at high frequency) but not (or only very weakly) photoluminescent can be made (258).

Goldberg (249) has studied the action of such killers more in detail. He found that Co at very small concentrations increased the output of blue-emitting ZnS:Cu, but only depressed that of green-emitting materials; this enhancement is less pronounced with Ni than with Co but occurs also with Fe and Cr. Goldberg suggests that the enhancement is due to the action of the additive in depressing the photocapacitive effect (259) in these materials (see Section III,C on electrical properties of electroluminescent phosphors); Arpiarian (256) attributes it to a change in the position of the Fermi level. Goldberg also studied the effect of Ni and Co on the light output waveform (see Section III,I). Differences in the action of Fe, Co, and Ni are also observed in the case of photoluminescent phosphors (254, 256, 260). Destriau (261) also found that Co was beneficial in increasing the enhancement of the X-ray excited luminescence of (Zn,Cd)S:Mn,Cl by an electric field, while Fe and Ni were deleterious.

In addition to electroluminescent powders some work has also been done with single crystals of ZnS (2, 158, 199, 213, 252, 253, 262–268a). In principle mechanisms should be easier to study in crystals because of the better geometry; however, this is not always true in practice. As stated by Piper and Williams (5), "The gross geometry and the crystal perfection are quite sensitive to experimental conditions; consequently, these techniques are not yet fully adequate for the control of all the electroluminescent properties . . . Methods of activating single crystals to provide homogeneous electrical and luminescent properties await the development of improved techniques." It is also possible to prepare thin electroluminescent films of ZnS only a micron or so thick (269–272); such films require comparatively low voltage for their operation and will work on either ac or dc. These films may be made either by a vapor-phase reaction method (269) involving H_2S, first used for nonelectroluminescent phosphors by Studer and Cusano (273), or by a process involving evaporation and deposition in vacuum, followed by suitable activation treatment (270–272), first used for nonelectroluminescent phosphors by Feldman and O'Hara (274). The formulations used are similar to those for electroluminescent powders. Cusano (632) has shown that application of a surface layer of Cu, which is probably converted to Cu_2S as in the experiments of Zalm, Diemer, and Klasens (2, 212, 213) with powders, may cause electroluminescence in films activated with P, As, or Sb. The efficiency in this case, however, is quite low (7×10^{-6}) as compared to Mn (3×10^{-4}), for example.

B. Structural Properties; Localization of Emission

One of the most striking and important observations concerning electroluminescence is afforded by microscopic observation of the emission of single crystals or of individual particles of a powder. Piper and Williams (158) found that each of the two light pulses emitted by ZnS single crystals for one cycle of applied alternating voltage is characteristic of one of the electrodes and originates at that electrode when it is negative for dc excitation or is becoming negative for ac excitation. It is found that although the photoluminescence of ZnS phosphor powders is uniformly distributed, the electroluminescence of the same phosphor is localized at small emitting spots (2, 212, 213, 216, 266, 275–279). For the case of ac excitation, Waymouth and Bitter (216) found that most if not all of these spots emit only on one half-cycle of the applied voltage; Bodo and Weiszburg (277) state that the emission intensities from a spot may differ by a factor of 10^3–10^4 for the two polarities. Numerous workers (2, 216, 278–280) have observed that the number of particles which emit increases with the applied voltage. Kremheller (278) has made an extensive microscopic study of the particles of a normal electroluminescent powder. He noted that not only is the emission confined to small regions, but large differences in emission from particle to particle exist; the most frequent particle brightness is about one-sixth of the maximum value observed, while about 20% of the particles do not emit at all. Obviously if all the particles emitted as well as the brightest a considerable increase in output could be achieved. If the entire volume of the particles emitted with the same intensity as the few spots observed, then an even more remarkable improvement would result.

Waymouth and Bitter (216) distinguished two types of emitting sports in powder particles. One type occurred at the point of contact between two particles and was brightest when the electric field was approximately perpendicular to the interface. The second type was observed at the end of needle-shaped particles and was brightest when the field was approximately parallel to the axis of the particle. Other workers (278, 281) have also commented on the effect of particle-particle contacts in increasing electroluminescent output in many cases (by as much as a factor of 4 according to Kremheller). Later observers (278, 279), working with what were probably better materials, have seen lines of emitting spots inside individual particles. Kremheller (278) states that these lines appear in fissures parallel to the c-plane in hexagonal crystallites or the (111)-plane in cubic crystallites. He concluded by observations in polarized light that these fissures separate contiguous crystallographic regions which are in many cases disoriented by as much as 5°.

Diemer (213) made microscopic observations of single hexagonal crystals of ZnS made electroluminescent by diffusion inward of Cu deposited on the surface and found the emission to originate from lines of closely spaced spots; these lines had the same direction as the direction of growth of the crystals. Zalm (2) observed lines of emitting spots lying in the [10$\bar{1}$0] direction in the interior of hexagonal crystals* (see Fig. 10) and found

* Despite this observation Zalm insists that the emission in electroluminescent powders is confined to the surface.

that alternate dots emitted during successive half-cycles of the applied voltage. Loebner and Freund (276) also observed phase reversals for emitting spots in ZnS crystals. In hexagonal crystals maximum emission is obtained if the field is perpendicular to the direction of the c-axis (2, 213, 247, 282, 283); Oranovskii, Panasiuk, and Feduishin (see 247) found a

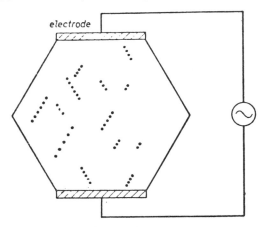

FIG. 10. Schematic representation of the emitting spots of an electroluminescent hexagonal single crystal as observed microscopically. The microscope was focused below the surface, which was perpendicular to the c-axis. The lines of dots lie in the [10$\bar{1}$0] directions. (From Zalm, 2.)

dependence of light output on $V\cos\varphi$, where V is the magnitude of the applied voltage and φ is the angle between the direction of the field and the c-plane. Lempicki et al. (283) also found large anisotropies in conductivity of such crystals paralleling those of the luminescence output. Since the variation in conductivity was much greater than that in brightness, the efficiency was found to be a maximum in the direction of lowest output, i.e., parallel to the c-axis.

Zalm (2) has used the dependence of electroluminescence brightness on crystallographic direction to explain the observed higher brightness for cubic phosphor powders compared to hexagonal. The [110] direction in cubic crystals is equivalent to the [10$\bar{1}$0| direction in hexagonal crystals and on the average the orientation of powder particles with respect to the applied field is more favorable in the cubic case. Destriau (284) also observed that the emission of ZnS microcrystals was increased if they were rotated about an axis perpendicular to an alternating electric field, thus effectively subjecting all directions in the crystals perpendicular to the axis of rotation to the field.* Various workers (234, 279, 285–287) have also

* Destriau had observed earlier (20) that electroluminescent phosphors would emit if rotated in a static field; this is obviously a way to remove polarization and to generate an alternating field in the material.

observed that application of a field to a suspension of electroluminescent particles in a liquid medium will cause alignment of the particles (and formation of "bridges" between the electrodes) and increased output. In this case there are several factors which may play a role besides changes in the angle between the field and the crystallographic directions of the particles; these include particle-to-particle contacts and effects resulting from differences in permittivity of the particles and the medium, which have an effect on the field strength inside the particles.

In the preceding paragraphs the localization of electroluminescent emission in small regions and their connection with the crystallographic properties were described. In the preceding Section the apparent necessity for excess Cu in the form of Cu_2S was also discussed. The emitting spots were observed to bear some relation to the presence of black specks (presumably Cu_2S) in single crystals and powder particles by Diemer (213) and Lehmann (279), respectively. Numerous workers (213, 217, 276, 288–291) have connected the occurrence of electroluminescence with some type of crystal disorder. Diemer (213) suggested that the copper diffused along dislocations or other imperfections. The presence of stacking faults resulting from the polytype formation in ZnS mentioned previously was also suggested fairly early as a possible cause of electroluminescence (276, 283, 288). It may also not be a coincidence that electroluminescence was first observed in SiC and ZnS, which are similar in structure and both of which are particularly prone to formation of stacking faults (288).* Short et al. (289) observed bands of emission in ZnS crystals which were parallel to bands of birefringence (due to stacking faults) perpendicular to the c-axis as observed in a polarizing microscope; similar observations have also been made by Strock (290).† The correspondence in neither case was perfect, however, as some cases of birefringence occurred without electroluminescence and vice versa. It should be emphasized that the photoluminescence in these cases was uniform. Strock concluded that "Although disorder may not be a necessary condition for electroluminescence . . . boundaries between ordered regions of ZnS can provide conditions particularly favorable for electroluminescence."

McKeag and Steward (291) prepared electroluminescent powders by first forming hexagonal ZnS by firing at 1100–1300°C and then refiring with added Cu at 700°C for long times. Although the densities of the cubic and hexagonal forms of ZnS differ by only 1% they were able by a "panning" technique to separate the resultant material into two portions, one of which was weakly electroluminescent, markedly birefringent, and mainly hexagonal in structure (with considerable stacking disorder) while the other

* Stacking disorder has also been observed in ZnSe, ZnTe, and CdTe (292).
† See also the recent paper by Baum and Darnell (290a).

was strongly electroluminescent, relatively nonbirefringent, and with more advanced transformation to the cubic structure (more stacking disorder). It is claimed that phosphors made by this disordering technique were brighter than cubic materials fired only at 700–900°C. In view of these experiments McKeag and Steward concluded that disorder favored the introduction of the excess amount of Cu (probably present as Cu_2S) needed for electroluminescence.

The transition temperature for the hexagonal-cubic transformation in ZnS is also a function of the Cu content (*242, 293, 294*); high Cu (or Ag) concentrations favor the cubic form,* probably due to formation of a separate phase of (cubic) Cu_2S. Ballentyne (*242, 243*) fired ZnS:Cu powders at a constant temperature above that normally reported for the transition (1024°C). Amounts of Cu less than 0.01 weight-% resulted in hexagonal nonelectroluminescent products; higher amounts of Cu caused the appearance of the cubic phase and crystals with more than 0.1% Cu were predominantly cubic. The phase transformation coincided with the precipitation of Cu_2S on the surface and the appearance of electroluminescence. However, in the case of ZnS:Ag Ballentyne observed the hexagonal-cubic transition and the appearance of weak electroluminescence only at 1.0% Ag, despite the fact that precipitation of Ag_2S was observed for concentrations of 0.01%. Thermoluminescence studies of these phosphors showed that at the phase transformation there was a redistribution of trapping states, the deeper levels disappearing.† It is to this effect of structure on the electron traps rather than on the segregation of a separate phase that Ballentyne attributed the appearance of electroluminescence. He also stated (*243*) that all electroluminescent phosphors he had examined by means of X-ray diffraction showed a mixture of cubic and hexagonal structure. It seems difficult to reconcile these statements with the phenomena of "contact electroluminescence" (*217*) and the induction of electroluminescence by surface treatment (*2*). In a later publication Ballentyne and Ray (*227*) admit that "The weight of evidence, therefore, appears to be in favor of an electron rich material in conjunction with one-dimensional stacking faults" rather than disorder alone. Ballentyne (*296a*) has also recently suggested yet another possibility, the formation of an impurity conduction band due to Cu.

---

* The presence of oxygen is reported to favor the hexagonal form (*294, 295*). Larach and Shrader (*26*) also state that the nature of the halogen used influences the structure, I favoring the cubic and Cl the hexagonal form. It seems more likely, however, that the effect they observed is due to variation in Cu_2S segregation resulting from incorporation of different amounts of Cu into the lattice with different halogens.

† The effect of the hexagonal structure in producing long phosphorescence compared to cubic ZnS phosphors is well known (*296*).

In the previous section it was pointed out that the electroluminescence output falls rapidly if enough CdS or MgS is introduced into ZnS to cause partial conversion to the hexagonal structure (*209, 225–227, 229*). In disagreement with Ballentyne, there is no detectable hexagonal structure for Lehmann's samples of Fig. 6 with less than 8% CdS (the detectable limit of the X-ray powder diffraction technique used was about 1%) nor would any be expected for the low firing temperature employed (750°C). On the other hand, Goldberg (*297*) reports that good electroluminescent ZnS phosphors of either cubic or hexagonal structure may be prepared, although Zalm (*2*) agrees that the cubic form is preferred as discussed above. Microscopic observation of Lehmann's phosphors (*226*) indicated that the cubic particles showed visible striations and inclusions, presumably of Cu_2S,* while the particles of the corresponding hexagonal phosphors showed few striations and few inclusions and were lighter in body color. None of these phosphor powders showed birefringence. The striations observed in these electroluminescent phosphors may indeed be the result of local disorder, but it appears that the degree of disorder required is far below that detectable by the X-ray technique employed and that which Ballentyne and McKeag and Steward considered desirable.

Thus, although it must be admitted that there is a connection between the structure of electroluminescent phosphors and their performance, the nature of this connection is not completely clear. Strock (*290*) has considered three types of stacking disorder in ZnS. In view of the lack of one-to-one correspondence between birefringence and electroluminescence, he suggests a one-atom displacement or "broken bond disorder" as being specifically and basically connected with electroluminescence. In this case Zn or S atoms are left with incomplete bonding, which should obviously affect the electrical properties at the location of the fault. Such disorders may, of course, occur along with other types. Disorders of this type may also be connected with the values of photovoltage many times higher than the energy band gap which have been observed in ZnS (*299–302*) and CdTe (*303*) (see also Section III,*J* and Fig. 38).

Goldberg (*297*) has recently observed another structural characteristic in electroluminescent phosphors which apparently has a bearing on the emission process. If such phosphors are etched in H_2O_2 and then observed in an electron microscope, triangular etch pits are observed; the number of such pits in similar nonelectroluminescent phosphors is much less. These etch pits always occur in conjunction with striations and have a fixed geometrical relation to the striation lines, pointing in the direction of the c-axis in hexagonal crystals and in [111] direction in cubic crystals. One

---

* The decoration of imperfections in ZnS with Zn or Ag has been discussed by Bontinck and Dekeyser (*298*).

suggested possibility is that these pits result from dislocations (or partial dislocations arising from the termination of a stacking fault), perhaps decorated with Cu_2S. Although Goldberg thinks that such defects are necessarily present in electroluminescent phosphors, this is not a sufficient condition as some nonluminescent crystals also show etch pits.

The observed limitation of electroluminescence emission to small regions of single crystals and differences in phase between emission from neighboring spots naturally leads to the assumption that the applied voltage is concentrated in these small regions and that this occurs because of some kind of rectifying potential barriers (213, 264, 276, 304, 305). Frankl (264) observed that in some crystals there is no change in distribution of the emitting spots when the field polarity is reversed; in some cases the distribution of spots over the crystal was almost uniform. The existence of such internal potential barriers and their connection with electroluminescence has been experimentally demonstrated in single crystals (304) although it has also been stated that microscopic barriers are not a necessary condition for electroluminescence (306).

In addition to localization of emission at natural disorders in the material, localization near the cathode electrode, ascribed to an exhaustion barrier, has also been observed in single crystals (158, 265).* The fact that the nature of the metal electrode in contact with a crystal or powder particle may have an effect on the electroluminescence behavior as observed by Piper and Williams (158) and others (307–309) also indicates some influence of a surface barrier. Alfrey and Cooke (310, 311) found that ZnS crystals were electroluminescent when potential barriers were present at the cathode but did not emit when the contacts were made ohmic by "forming." Harper (312) reports that good electroluminescence is obtained with Al or Mg electrodes on ZnS films but that no, or only poor, emission is obtained with Ag, Cu, In, Zn, Sn, Fe, or Pt electrodes. Even the latter, however, were effective if a thin insulating layer was interposed. Alfrey and Taylor (311, 313) also established the presence of Schottky barriers at the cathode of ZnS crystals by irradiating with alpha particles through one electrode and observing the effect of the polarity of an applied voltage in quenching the luminescence; no effect was observed in nonelectroluminescent crystals. The possible action of such barriers in electroluminescence excitation has been discussed in detail (2, 160).

Although potential barriers of the Schottky type may obviously be formed at electrode contacts with single crystals, what of the case of elec-

* Woods (634) observed three different types of emission in ZnS single crystals depending upon the treatment: (1) emission excited by ac only and localized in streaks, (2) dc electroluminescence throughout the bulk of the crystal, and (3) emission localized at the cathode.

troluminescent powders embedded in a dielectric? Presumably here the presence of segregations of a conducting phase like Cu_2S (as influenced by crystal disorder) is important but there is little agreement as to details. As mentioned earlier, Zalm (2) believes that the excitation in this case is confined to the surface and does not occur at internal barriers. Burns (215) and Curie (157) also suggested the presence of surface barriers of the chemical type.* Direct evidence to the contrary, however, seems to be afforded by microscopic observations (278, 279, 291), although one cannot rule out the possibility that both observations were correct but the materials different. From an analysis of the dependence of output on applied voltage for particles of different size Goldberg (316) concluded that, at least to a first approximation, the number of barriers per particle is small and independent of particle size.

There are several possible functions of Cu_2S in promoting these potential barriers. As discussed above, it may serve a secondary role in inducing local cubic-hexagonal disorder which is responsible for electroluminescence. Since Cu_2S is a p-type semiconductor (317, 318) it may produce p-n junctions. Cu_2S segregations may also play a direct role as "contacts" for the formation of physical or Mott-Schottky space charge barriers or as the source of electrons which tunnel into the ZnS (449a). They may also produce local concentration of field by geometrical effects as a result of the high conductivity of Cu_2S compared to that of ZnS as suggested by Lehmann (217) and Maeda (319, 320). Larach and Shrader (26, 321) believe that the action of the excess Cu is the formation of a potential barrier of the chemical rather than the physical type, probably by the formation of an interdiffused copper-zinc sulfide region.

Destriau (1) successively reduced the diameter of the particles of an electroluminescent powder by acid treatment and analyzed the copper content of the dissolved material. He found that the copper concentration appeared to be a maximum near the surface while the electroluminescence sensitivity (as determined by the voltage required for visible emission) first increased and then decreased as the diameter was reduced. A similar increase in output by slight acid attack or milling has also been observed by Kremheller (278), who attributed it to an optical effect on the surface whereby light which would otherwise be internally trapped and absorbed in the particles (index of refraction of ZnS = 2.3, references 322, 323) is enabled to escape.† The decline in output observed by Destriau for further

---

* In connection with the role of oxygen in early electroluminescent phosphors it may be noted that the effect of oxygen on the surface barrier of sulfide photoconductors is well known (314, 315).

† The existence of a nonluminescent "dead" layer on cathodoluminescent phosphors is also well known (324) but in this case it is not removed by etching.

etching might be taken as evidence for the importance of barriers near the surface rather than internal barriers. This conclusion, however, is far from certain. In the first place, it is now known (*316, 325*) that the particle size itself has an effect on the voltage dependence of electroluminescence (see Section III,*D*) and therefore on the "sensitivity" measured by Destriau. Furthermore, one is not dealing with ideal spherical particles and the possibility of selective etching and redeposition of copper sulfide must be considered.

Destriau's experiments have recently been repeated by Goldberg and Faria (*326*) with more attention to such details with the result that no evidence was found for a surface layer rich in copper, nor a critical role of the surface in the electroluminescence mechanism. As much as 90% of the material may be removed without appreciably affecting the electroluminescence. If field intensification does occur at the surface, removal of this surface brings new material into play which is equally effective. The fact that these results are at variance with the conclusions of Destriau, Zalm (*2*), and Larach and Shrader (*26, 321*) may be due to differences between the older phosphors and newer better ones. It should also be re-emphasized that modern electroluminescent phosphors are customarily washed in a NaCN solution or a similar solvent for Cu_2S.

The most direct and convincing evidence for the localization of electroluminescence excitation and emission to small regions of the phosphor is, of course, microscopic observation (for powders and single crystals).* Other evidence for this localization and the existence of potential barriers may also (or has been claimed to) be found in other experimental aspects [see also (*2*) and (*247*)] including the following:

(1) Differences in height of the light pulses emitted from a cell consisting of many randomly oriented particles during alternate half cycles of voltage. However, care must be taken in interpreting such effects and the conclusions are uncertain (see Section III,*I*).

(2) In cases where electrical contact exists, the effect of the electrode material and the nature of the contact on the magnitude and waveform of the output (*158, 307–312*).

(3) Measurement of electrical capacitance under ultraviolet and field excitation for conditions which lead to equal brightness. According to Zalm (*2*) the change in capacitance is much greater for the photoluminescent case, but Lehmann finds the opposite. Furthermore, since electroluminescent phosphors have nonlinear characteristics (see the next section) and because one measurement must be made with high applied voltage (to obtain electroluminescence) and the other with only low voltage (to avoid it), the

---

* No microscopic structure is visible in the electroluminescence of thin phosphor films.

interpretation of this effect is also difficult. Ince and Oatley (327) and others have also shown that electroluminescent phosphors shown dielectric dispersion at low frequencies which is not shown by nonelectroluminescent phosphors, and this has been interpreted as indicating the presence of barriers. As the electroluminescent properties of a phosphor deteriorate during aging the dielectric properties also change and approach those of nonelectroluminescent materials (see Section III,G,3).

(4) Destriau (20) applied a magnetic field of 60,000 oersteds perpendicular to the electric field in an electroluminescent phosphor and observed no effect on the output; Ince (328) later also obtained a similar result at 130,000 oersteds. If it is assumed that electron acceleration is important in electroluminescence then such a magnetic field would be expected to reduce the mean free path and hence to decrease the output, the effect being greater the higher the ratio of the magnetic and electric field strengths (1). The negative experimental results seem to indicate that the effective electric field strength in electroluminescence is many times that applied externally, i.e., that there is field localization (328). If electron acceleration is not important in the excitation process (see Section III,J) then this conclusion is invalid.

(5) From the relative intensities of emission from Mn and Eu centers in ZnS:Cu,Eu,Mn phosphors under conditions of photoluminescence or electroluminescence leading to equal (averaged) brightness, Oranovskii and Trapeznikova (246–248) concluded that about 7% of the volume of the particles is active in electroluminescence.

(6) It is generally found that high excitation intensity leads to faster phosphorescent decay than lower intensities because the deep electron traps are filled first and shallower faster-emptying traps are then utilized. Thus the decay of cathodoluminescence is normally faster than that of photoluminescence of equal intensity in the same material because of the difference in the depth of penetration of the exciting energy (329). The fact that the phosphorescence decay following electroluminescent excitation is faster, and therefore the "light sum" (the integral under a curve of output as a function of time) is smaller, than that following photoluminescence of the same brightness for the same phosphor may be taken as an indication of localization in the former case (247, 330).

(7) Zalm (2) has claimed that the thermoluminescence intensity following electroluminescence excitation at low temperatures is much less than that following ultraviolet excitation and considers this as evidence that only traps in small regions of the crystal are filled in electroluminescence. According to Thornton (331), however, thermoluminescence following field excitation is easily measurable and in some cases is almost as great as that following photoluminescence of equal brightness. Destriau (20) also

showed that although application of a field to a photoluminescent phosphor following excitation may cause a transient increase in the phosphorescence (due to emptying of traps, the Gudden-Pohl effect), subsequent thermoluminescence is essentially unaffected, indicating that the field acts only on a small fraction of the traps filled in photoluminescence. Zalm also states that the same results hold for electroluminescent phosphors.

(8) As shown by Haake (332), filling of electron traps by previous electroluminescence excitation has almost no effect on photoluminescence buildup but a large effect on electroluminescence buildup (see Section III,G,1), indicating that different regions are mainly involved in the two types of excitation.

(9) Thornton (333) has shown that the current-voltage characteristics of electroluminescent powders and films obey the normal relation for a forward-biased diode rectifier (see Sections III,D and III,J), thus establishing the existence of rectifying barriers but giving no information as to their source (p-n junctions, space charge exhaustion regions, etc.).

(10) The width of a Schottky (space-charge) potential barrier varies as $V^{1/2}$, where V is the applied voltage, according to the equation

$$d = (kV/2\pi Ne)^{1/2}, \tag{6}$$

where k is the dielectric constant and N the density of carriers. The maximum field strength therefore also varies as $V^{1/2}$. For low voltages one might therefore expect in this case a functional dependence between the electroluminescent output and $V^{1/2}$. It has been suggested that for higher values of voltage the barrier extension should be limited by the particle diameter or other geometrical factors, the field should be proportional to V, and the brightness be related to V rather than $V^{1/2}$. Such dependencies and transitions between them have been reported (247, 334, 335).* However, the interpretation of the form of the dependence of output on voltage is very complicated, particularly when the combined output from many particles is measured (336), so that this result should probably be treated with reserve (see also Section III,D).

(11) Thornton (337) has also found evidence from a study of the maintenance of output of electroluminescent phosphors during life (see Section III,G) that the size of the excitation region increases as the applied voltage is increased (as would be expected of a Schottky barrier) or as the frequency is decreased (perhaps due to the variation in a dielectric constant). Alfrey and Taylor (311, 313, 313a) reached a similar conclusion from experiments on the effect of electric fields in quenching the scintillations excited in ZnS

---

* Curie (4, 157) claims that the emission at low voltages may be seen visually to be limited to small regions which grow as the voltage is increased; more recent microscopic observations, however, do not support this view.

by alpha particles. However, it has not been possible to verify such effects by microscopic observation of the emission.

(12) Ivey (135) has shown that the experiments of Thornton (338) on the enhancement of electroluminescence by ultraviolet radiation can be explained by assuming that the emission occurs in small regions which are effectively in series with the bulk of the crystal, which acts as a photoconductor and controls the voltage across the barrier region. (Section V,D,2).

C. Electrical Properties

The electrical properties of electroluminescent ZnS phosphors are of obvious interest. The permittivity (static "dielectric constant") of pure ZnS is 10.3 (323) and the resistivity is greater than 10^{13} ohm-cm (213, 269). In the case of activated luminescent ZnS, however, affairs are much more complicated. Not only do these materials exhibit photoconductivity, but also the photodielectric or photocapacitive effect (13, 259). Actually these two effects are closely related, since they may be considered as an increase in the imaginary and real parts, respectively, of the complex dielectric constant under the action of radiation. Furthermore, in a nonhomogeneous material they are not really separable since a change in conductivity will affect the capacitance (13). The photocapacitive effect in electroluminescent phosphors has been studied by Roberts (275), Ince and Oatley (327), and Zalm (2). Electrical measurements on electroluminescent phosphors should be made in the dark as either sunlight or light from incandescent or fluorescent lamps will produce the photocapacitive effect in ZnS. Such phosphors, however, do not normally adsorb their own emission sufficiently to cause a self-induced effect.*

The electrical properties of electroluminescent phosphors have been studied by a number of workers (26, 163, 212, 275, 285, 327,340–344). Both the real (k') and the imaginary (k'') parts of the complex dielectric constant increase by appreciable factors as the applied voltage is increased or the frequency decreased (see Fig. 11). These changes are greater for large particles than for small ones (325). The apparent dielectric constant may reach values much higher than that for pure ZnS. Since the increase in k'' is greater than that of k', the loss angle δ also increases as the voltage is increased, i.e., the phosphor becomes more conductive; this is to be expected since power is being consumed in the electroluminescence excitation and other losses (the efficiency of electroluminescence is discussed in Section III,F). Because of these nonlinear effects the current produced in an electroluminescent cell by a sinusoidal voltage is not generally sinusoidal; at higher voltages it may even display a second peak in phase with the voltage.

---

* Exceptions may exist (249), however, since there is some excitation of green centers at wavelengths as long as 440 mμ (338, 339).

Such complications prevent accurate measurement of the power dissipated in the cell from being a straightforward matter (*26*).

Lehmann (*285*) has shown that the increases in k' and k'' with increasing voltage are proportional to $(L/f)^{1/2}$, where L is the electroluminescence output and f the frequency. This result may be interpreted as indicating that the output is proportional to the square of the number of carriers in the conduction band, i.e., that a bimolecular recombination law holds in

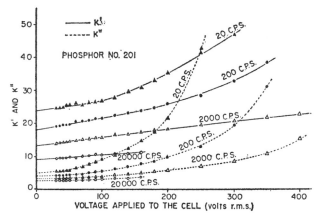

FIG. 11. Variation of the real (k') and imaginary (k'') parts of the complex dielectric constant of an electroluminescent ZnS phosphor with applied voltage and frequency. (From Lehmann, *285*.)

electroluminescence in ZnS as well as in photoluminescence. A connection between the dielectric losses and the electroluminescence output (both of which arise from the same electronic motion) has also been discussed by Morehead (*345*, *346*). Goffaux (*163*) has also interpreted the electrical properties of electroluminescent phosphors on the basis of a "hot-electron" theory.

The apparent values of dielectric constant obtained by measurements on electroluminescent phosphors should not be interpreted as having any basic physical significance. Such phosphors, as shown above, are very non-uniform electrically and hence cannot be specified by a single physically meaningful "dielectric constant" (*275*). Fairly complicated equivalent circuits have been proposed by several workers (*212*, *327*, *341–343*, *346a*). The possibility that ionic conduction plays a role in determining the electrical behavior has also been suggested (*327*, *347*).

Electroluminescent powders are employed by embedding them in a dielectric material (to avoid glow discharges and electrical breakdown). The electrical properties of both the phosphor and the dielectric are therefore of importance in determining the field strength in the phosphor. Consider a powder of dielectric constant k_1 embedded in a medium of dielectric constant k_2. The volume concentration of phosphor is c ($c = 0$ for no phosphor and $c = 1$ for no embedding material).* It can be shown (*340, 348, 349*) that the electric field strength E in the interior of the particles (assumed to be homogeneous spheres) is related to the applied field strength, V/d, by the relation

$$\frac{E}{V/d} = \frac{3k_2/k_1}{\left(1 + 2\frac{k_2}{k_1}\right) - c\left(1 - \frac{k_2}{k_1}\right)}. \tag{7}$$

This result is based on a very crude model. Not only are the particles of an actual phosphor not spherical but, as discussed above, they are far from

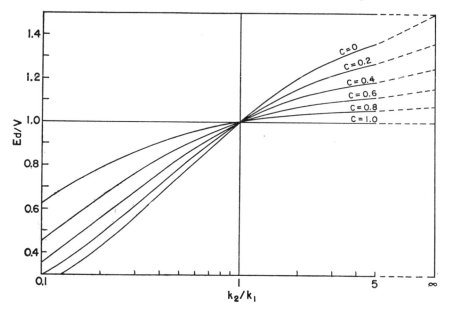

FIG. 12. Effect of the relative values of the dielectric constant of the phosphor (k_1) and of the embedding medium (k_2) on the value of field strength (E) inside the phosphor particles compared to that (V/d) applied to the mixture for various values of phosphor concentration (c) [see Eq. (7) of the text].

being homogeneous electrically and their dielectric properties are a function of applied voltage, frequency, temperature, and external illumination.

Equation (7) is rigorously restricted to values of c so low that the field in one particle is not disturbed by the presence of other particles. Several

* The maximum value of c for close-packing of equal-sized spheres is $\pi/3\sqrt{2} = 0.74$.

attempts (350–354) have been made to derive more general relations; the results, however, are very complicated and are not amenable to easy treatment. Furthermore, the improved results usually do not differ greatly from those of Eq. (7) on a numerical basis and indeed generally reduce to it as a first approximation. The applicability of Eq. (7) to electroluminescent phosphors has been demonstrated by Roberts (340). As shown in Fig. 12, the field strength in the phosphor (and hence the brightness) is always higher the higher the ratio of dielectric constants, k_2/k_1, but the benefit becomes small for high phosphor concentration or if the ratio is made very high. It should also be noted that Eq. (7) is valid for the complex dielectric constant as well as its real part. Thus the effective field strength may under some cases (355) be increased by increasing the loss factor of the embedding material (increase in k_2'') but the resultant decrease in efficiency and increased phosphor temperature do not seem to be desirable in practice.

D. *Variation of Output with Voltage*

The dependence of the electroluminescence output on the applied voltage is of obvious importance. Destriau (20) used a relation similar to Eq. (4), with three parameters (A, B, and n). Although a number of empirical or theoretical relations have been proposed (1, 20, 160), the one which is usually found to fit the results for phosphor powders over a wide range (see Fig. 13) and which is most often employed is

$$L = L_0 \exp\left[-(V_0/V)^{1/2}\right], \tag{8}$$

where L_0 and V_0 are parameters which depend on temperature and the frequency of the alternating voltage (Section III,E),* on the phosphor, and on other details of the construction of the test cell. This form was first employed by Alfrey and Taylor (262) and Zalm (280). In general the voltage dependence (value of V_0) is greater at high frequency and low temperature.† The presence of the square root of the voltage is normally explained on the basis of an electron acceleration mechanism [Eq. (2)] together with the fact that the maximum field strength in a Mott-Schottky barrier varies as $V^{1/2}$ [see Eq. (6)]. Over a limited range of voltage Eq. (8) may, of course, be approximated by a power law. At very low voltage, and therefore very low output, the brightness may vary as the 9th or 10th power of the voltage; at voltages approaching breakdown of the layer, the dependence usually approximates V^2 or an even lower power of V, in some cases less than unity.

---

* Excitation by nonsinusoidal voltages is discussed in Section III,*H*.

† Howard (650) has considered that the increase in V_0 with increasing frequency is due to lowering of the effective voltage across the barrier; the circuit considered consisted of a nonlinear capacitor (the potential barrier) in series with a nonlinear resistance (the phosphor bulk).

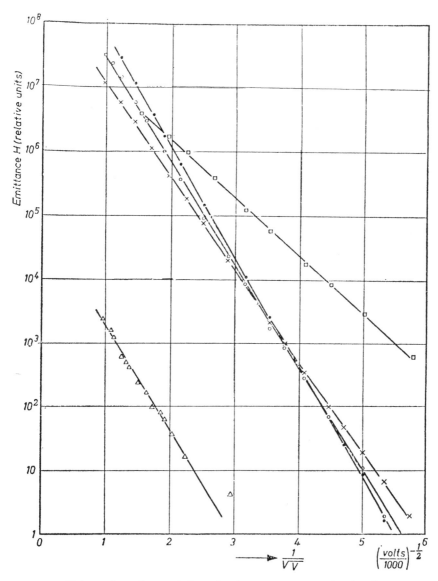

FIG. 13. Voltage dependence of electroluminescence output, showing fit to Eq. (8) of the text. ×—ZnS-Cu-Al 50 cps (green e.l.); ○—ZnS-Cu-Al 500 cps (green e.l.); ·—ZnS-Cu-Mn 1500 cps (orange e.l.); □—ZnS-Cu-Cl 250 cps (blue e.l.); △—ZnS-Li₂S-Mn d.c. (From Zalm, 2.)

Some comments concerning the relative voltage dependence of ZnS:Cu and ZnS:Cu,Mn have been made earlier in Section III,A.

Departures from Eq. (8) are often observed. Thus it has been claimed (247, 334, 335) that Eq. (8) holds at low voltages but that at high voltage the expression

$$L = a \exp\left(-b/V\right), \tag{9}$$

(Destriau's relation with $n = 0$) is better.* Zalm et al. (280) found the emission from single particles of a phosphor powder to follow the same law as that of the integrated output of many particles, i.e., Eq. (8), but with a distribution of values for V_0. Waymouth and Bitter (216) earlier reported the output of a single particle to be a linear function of the voltage above a minimum threshold value and suggested that the more complicated behavior for an assembly of particles is due to a distribution of characteristics (threshold and slope) for different particles. Lehmann (336, 357) found the emission of single particles to obey Eq. (9) and showed that summation of the output of a large number of particles with sizes distributed as usually observed in powders leads to the normally observed Eq. (8). He thus considers Eq. (9) to be the basic one for electroluminescence, while Eq. (8) results only from a statistical effect in powders.

Morehead (345) derived a theoretical expression which reduces to Eq. (8) at low frequency, high voltage, and high temperature and to

$$L = L_0 V \exp\left[-(V_0/V)^{1/2}\right] \tag{10}$$

for the opposite conditions. Fritzsche (358), on the other hand, says Eq. (8) holds for low Cu content and Eq. (10) for high Cu content, while Goldberg (249) found Eq. (8) to apply to normal phosphors and Eq. (10) to those "poisoned" by Co or Ni. A relation similar to Eq. (9),

$$L = a \exp\left[-b/(V + V_1)\right], \tag{11}$$

first proposed by Ivey (1), has been used with some success (346, 357). Morehead (346) considered the parameter V_1 to result from a statistical variation of the properties of individual particles.

The effect of particle size on the voltage dependence of electroluminescence has been studied by Lehmann (325, 336) and Goldberg (316), using samples fractionated from a parent sample. It is found that the smaller the particle diameter the higher the values of the parameters L_0 and V_0 in Eq. (8) (see Fig. 14). Thornton (359) has shown that this may be explained on the basis of the statistics of a random dispersion of particles in a dielectric of different dielectric constant, without the necessity for

---

* Neumark (356) has presented a theoretical equation which seems to predict exactly the opposite behavior.

assuming electrical or emissive differences among particles of different size. Lehmann and Thornton (see *360*) and Fritzsche (*208, 358*) have studied the effect of phosphor composition on L_0 and V_0 in Eq. (8). Lehmann (*257*) found that addition of Fe, Co, or Ni affected the value of L_0 only while Goldberg (*249*) also observed a slight effect on V_0.

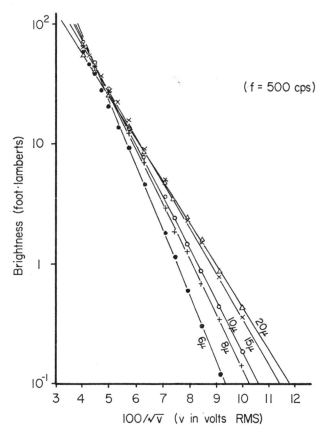

Fig. 14. Dependence of electroluminescence brightness on voltage for phosphor fractions of different mean particle diameter. (From Lehmann, *325*.)

Harper (*312*) has observed that the electroluminescence output of ZnS:Cu,Cl films, for a given applied voltage, may be increased if a thin insulating layer is interposed between the ZnS and the metal electrode. This obviously implies an improvement in the excitation process as the voltage across the film is lowered by insertion of the insulator.* As the insulator

---

* The effect of high-resistance layers on carrier injection has been discussed by Harrick (*361*).

thickness is increased from zero, the first effect is an increase in the parameter a in Eq. (9) while b remains constant. Above a critical thickness, however, (about 0.015μ SiO_2 on a 1.8μ ZnS film in one example) the value of a remains constant while b increases with increasing thickness, corresponding to reduced output. The maximum efficiency is also increased by the use of such insulating layers and occurs at higher applied voltages (see Section III,F).

The occurrence of a voltage threshold has often been mentioned in the literature and would be of obvious theoretical significance. In his earliest experiments Destriau (20) used the value of voltage required to produce an output visible to the dark-adapted eye as a measure of phosphor sensitivity and called it the "threshold." As mentioned above, Waymouth and Bitter (216) also reported a threshold voltage for the output of single phosphor particles as observed microscopically. Oranovskii, Panasuik, and Fediushin (see 248) also state that there is a well-defined voltage threshold; Piper and Williams (160) observed such a threshold and incorporated it in their theoretical treatment of electroluminescence. On the other hand, Destriau and Domergue (362) used a sensitive photomultiplier technique to show that there was no tendency to extinction at voltages as low as nine volts (brightness of 10^{-8} ft-L) and suggested that any apparent threshold is only an instrumental limitation. As shown in Fig. 15, Thornton, using thin ZnS films, later extended such measurements to 1.5 volts rms (corresponding to 2.2 peak volts and a brightness of 10^{-10} ft-L) (363) and to 2.0 volts dc (364); emission has also been observed in powder layers at 2.0 volts rms (363). In all cases the dependence of output on voltage showed no indication of a threshold, in accordance with either Eq. (8) or (9), nor was any change in emission spectrum observed. It should be noted that emission was obtained at a voltage less than the forbidden energy gap of ZnS (3.7 ev), the minimum optical excitation energy (2.8 ev), or the average energy of the emitted photons (2.1 ev).

Piper and Williams (158) observed that for low alternating voltages applied to a single crystal of ZnS, a light pulse which is out of phase with the voltage is observed for each half cycle of voltage. For higher voltages additional peaks which are in phase with the voltage appear; these increase much more rapidly as the voltage is increased than do the out-of-phase peaks. If a direct voltage is applied the light output (identified with the in-phase output for ac) is proportional to the current and increases exponentially with applied voltage. Emission may also be obtained for dc excitation of electroluminescent powders if they are placed in a conducting medium (such as tricresyl phosphate) (2) or if very little or no dielectric is used and the particles are in contact with the electrodes (212, 234, 365, 366). Thin phosphor films are also easily excited by dc (270, 364).

ZnS:Cu,Mn is much more responsive to dc excitation than is ZnS:Cu; samples of the latter which show green emission for ac excitation are usually blue for dc. Zalm (2) also found that activators in which the transitions are believed to be confined to the center are best for dc excitation.

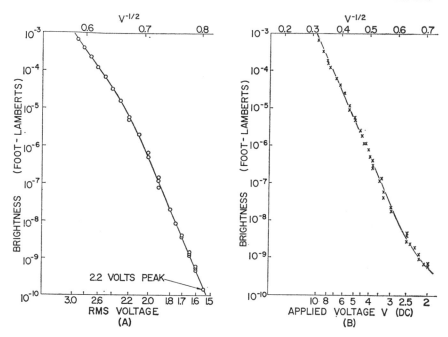

Fig. 15. Electroluminescence in thin phosphor films at low voltage. (A) ac excitation of ZnS:Cu,Cl (f = 1000 cps); (B) dc excitation of ZnS:Cu,Mn,Cl. (From Thornton, 363, 364.)

The voltage dependence of the output for dc excitation is more rapid than that of the same material for ac excitation (158, 253, 360, 366). Thornton (360) has shown that although the ac characteristic of thin films may be expressed by the usual Eq. (8)* the dc characteristic is given by

$$L = A\,[\exp\,(V/B) - 1]. \tag{12}$$

Narita (253) obtained the same result for the out-of-phase and in-phase components, respectively, of the emission of ZnS single crystals. The quantity $d^2(\log L)/d(\log V)^2$ in this case is always positive, while that for Eq. (8) is always negative. Thornton observes that the current through these films is much higher when the metal electrode is negative than for the

* Lehmann (336) and Harper (312) report that some films on ac obey Eq. (9) rather than (8), while Vlasenko and Popkov (271) give $L = \alpha \exp (V/\beta)^{1/2}$ (see also 311).

opposite polarity with the transparent (tin oxide) electrode negative. The brightness also shows a polarity dependence but to a lesser degree; the differences disappear as the film thickness is increased. The output per unit current is greatest when the metal electrode is positive while the output per unit voltage is greatest when the metal electrode is negative (367).* Vlasenko and Popkov (271) found that for excitation by low alternating voltages the output was greatest during the half-cycle when the metal was negative but that the reverse was true for very high voltages. Both Thornton and Cusano (632) have observed "forming" effects in thin films, but these changes with time are not yet understood.

Thornton has also studied the direct current-voltage characteristics of electroluminescent ZnS:Cu,Mn,Cl films and found them to obey the relation

$$I = I_0 e^{-E/kT}(e^{V/V'} - 1). \tag{13}$$

At low voltages V' is essentially constant but at high voltages it is roughly proportional to the temperature. The alternating current-voltage characteristics of ZnS:Cu powders also obey the same equation (see Fig. 16)

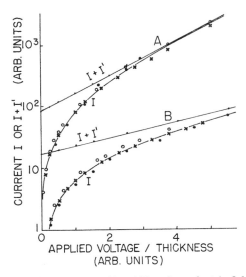

FIG. 16. Dependence of rms current ($f = 400$ cps) on electric field strength for phosphor-plastic layers of different thicknesses. (A) Blue-emitting ZnS:Cu,Cl; (B) Yellow-emitting ZnS:Cu,Mn,Cl. The solid curves represent Eq. (13) of the text. (From Thornton, 333.)

* Zalm (2) also reported dc excitation of a phosphor film only if the metal electroPe was negative. The polarity effect shown by Thornton in his first publication on films (270) is opposite to that found in the majority of later samples.

except that V' is always proportional to temperature (*333*). Equation (13) is, of course, the normal forward-biased diode characteristic and thus indicates the presence of rectifying barriers in these phosphors (see Section III,J). In many cases the output for dc excitation of powders or films was found to vary as the square of the current, but the relationship was more complicated for ac excitation.

Zalm (*2*) showed that in the case of ZnS phosphors dispersed in tricresyl phosphate the light output is decreased when dc is super-imposed upon sinusoidal or square-wave excitation. However, Thornton (*368*) and later Favorin and Kozina (*369, 370*) showed that with a small amount of plastic binder or with no binder (powders or films) the light output may be considerably enhanced by superposition of ac and dc under suitable conditions. Some results obtained by Thornton are shown in Fig. 17. It will be

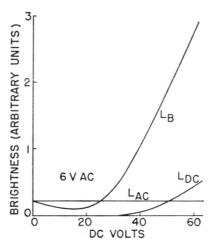

Fig. 17. Light output of special electroluminescent powder layer (with low plastic binder content) for excitation by ac or dc alone and with superimposed ac and dc (L_B). (From Thornton, *368*.)

seen that the output in this case may be many times that produced by the same value of alternating or direct voltage applied alone and indeed greater (by a factor of 120 in some cases) than the sum of the individual outputs, so that true enhancement occurs. The effect may be appreciable for values of the voltages such that one applied alone would produce no noticeable output. For low voltages quenching rather than enhancement is sometimes observed, as shown in the figure.

Although Favorin and Kozina indicate that the effect is greatest in manganese-activated phosphors, Thornton found a much larger effect in ZnS:Cu. The magnitude of the enhancement seems to be correlated with the value of the parameter V_0 in the ac characteristic of the phosphor [Eq. (8)]; the higher V_0 the greater the attainable enhancement. Since V_0 for ZnS:Cu,Mn phosphors is usually lower than for ZnS:Cu, this explains the greater enhancement of the latter. The emission spectrum in the ac-dc case is identical to that for ac excitation rather than the bluer dc emission, and occurs during the half-cycle when the alternating and direct fields oppose each other (see Section III,*I* for a further discussion). Thornton also found that the phosphor can be "presensitized" by applying the dc first, removing the dc, and then applying the ac*; in this case, of course, the effect is transient. This last observation is particularly valuable in showing that the enhanced output is not due simply to nonlinearity of the brightness-voltage characteristic.

E. Effects of Frequency and Temperature

It was pointed out in Section III,*A* that Cu can produce efficient blue or green electroluminescence in ZnS. As distinguished from ZnS:Cu,Mn phosphors, where the emission color is independent of frequency (at least for sufficiently high Mn content)†, ZnS:Cu phosphors generally show a shift in emission color as the frequency of the alternating exciting voltage is varied. This change is caused by combination of the blue and green bands in different proportions rather than by a major shift in wavelength of the bands themselves. The degree of color change observed depends on the phosphor composition and may therefore be accentuated or minimized as desired. A similar color shift is also observed in (Zn,Cd,Hg)S:Cu phosphors. In each case the shorter wavelength (more energetic) emission is favored at high frequencies.

A simple explanation of such color shifts has been given by Zalm et al. (*212*). If the so-called Schön-Klasens model for the blue and green centers shown in Fig. 18 is accepted, empty low-lying (blue) centers will be filled by electrons from filled higher (green) centers via the valence band and the emission will be predominantly green if sufficient time and activation energy (temperature) are available (the arrows in the diagram refer to the motion of the positive holes responsible for the transition and hence are in the opposite direction to the electron flow). At high frequencies and low temperature this will not be the case and blue emission will predominate. Fok (*370a*) has recently given a theoretical treatment of the kinetics for this situation. Waymouth and Bitter (*371*) also showed that the emission following the

---

* An effect with a similar result has been described for phosphor powders suspended in a liquid (*234*). In this case the dc causes alignment of the particles in "bridges" between the electrodes and consequently higher output upon application of ac.

† See Fig. 9 for the effect of operating conditions on the emission color of ZnS:Cu,Mn phosphors with low Mn content.

application of a direct voltage to an electroluminescent phosphor increases in wavelength the longer the voltage is applied. In this case emission occurs when the voltage is removed and the electrons can return to the excitation region (Section III,I); the shift is consistent with the mechanism of Fig. 18.

The change in emission color with frequency may also be viewed in another way. It is well known (372) that such phosphors with two emission bands also show a shift toward the blue if the intensity of ultraviolet excitation is increased, for example. This effect can also be explained on the basis of the kinetics appropriate to Fig. 18 (149). Since the electroluminescence

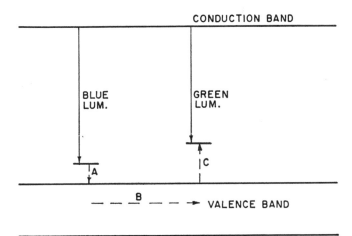

Fig. 18. Energy level diagram for a ZnS phosphor with blue and green luminescent centers. The mechanism for the transport of energy from blue to green centers by hole migration is shown by the arrows A, B, and C. (From Zalm, Diemer and Klasens, 212.)

output increases in intensity as the frequency is increased (see below), the two types of changes may therefore be considered as manifestations of a single effect. Some visual observations by Thornton on the influence of temperature on the color of electroluminescence and photoluminescence of the same phosphor at different excitation levels are shown in Table V (see also 2). It is seen that the result for excitation by field and by ultraviolet are almost exactly parallel.

It should be noted, however, that these considerations do not apply at all if the electroluminescence output is varied by changing the applied voltage rather than the frequency; in this case there is no change in emission color for ZnS:Cu phosphors. That this should be true can be explained on the basis of the hole migration discussed above only if it is assumed that this migration occurs in regions of the phosphor or at times during the cycle when the field is low and hence has no effect on the migration. It apparently can be fitted into the "intensity variation" picture only if it is taken into account that when the voltage is increased the region of excitation increases in size whereas the opposite is true if the frequency is increased (see Sections III,*B* and III,*G,3*) so that the intensity of excitation (as distinguished from total amount of excitation) is more drastically affected in the latter case; however, one would probably still expect some spectral shift with voltage.

It may be noted that if the model of Fig. 18 is accepted for the green and blue luminescence centers in ZnS, and if it is assumed that they are directly excited by collision of accelerated electrons, then it appears from Eq. (2) that the two types of emission should depend differently on the

TABLE V. DEPENDENCE OF EMISSION COLOR OF ZnS:Cu PHOSPHOR
ON OPERATING CONDITIONS

Type of excitation	Excitation intensity[a]	Temperature	Emission color
Electroluminescence	Low	Room temperature	Yellow-green
	High	Room temperature	Blue
	Low	Liquid air	Blue
	High	Liquid air	Dark blue
Photoluminescence	Low	Room temperature	Yellow-green
	High	Room temperature	Blue-green
	Low	Liquid air	Blue
	High	Liquid air	Dark blue

[a] "Low" excitation in the case of electroluminescence was at 60 cps, while "high" was at 10,000 cps. The ultraviolet intensity in the case of photoluminescence was controlled by varying the distance between source and sample.

applied voltage. Since such a shift is not observed it apparently must be concluded that the centers are excited by some other mechanism (perhaps by collision excitation of the lattice; see also Section III,*J*) or that some other model for the two types of centers involving a common ground state must apply (*179, 180, 190, 193–202*). In either case one would then have to establish that the observed change in color with frequency is in accord with the new picture.

The interrelation between frequency and temperature in electroluminescence discussed above in connection with Fig. 18 and Table V is a fundamental one. The release of electrons from electron traps or of holes from luminescence centers ("hole traps") depends on both temperature and time. Alfrey and Taylor (*262, 373*) Thornton (*334*), Haake (*374–376*), and Johnson *et al.* (*377*) have therefore emphasized the necessity for considering the effects of both variables simultaneously. They showed that any combination of f and T which satisfies the relation

$$f = C \exp\left(-E/kT\right) \qquad (14)$$

produces essentially the same condition in the phosphor; high frequency is "equivalent" to low temperature and may therefore be counteracted by increasing the temperature. The fact that the emission color may change with changes in either variable also requires that the spectral selectivity of the detector be carefully considered in interpreting results on phosphors with multiple emission bands.

If an electroluminescent ZnS powder is suspended in a conducting medium (tricresyl phosphate) the output is essentially independent of the frequency of the alternating voltage (2). The effect of frequency on the output of a single-band ZnS phosphor powder embedded in an insulating dielectric is, however, quite different (Fig. 19). It will be noted that the effect of frequency is more pronounced the higher the applied voltage (2, 82, 334, 357). For very low field strengths (1.7 volts rms across a film about one micron thick) Thornton (363) observed a change in output of only 10% when the frequency was increased from 100 to 10,000 cps. In terms of the parameters of Eq. (8), L_0 (which is the hypothetical output for infinite voltage) is approximately a linear function of frequency, if the latter is not too high (corresponding in the limit to constant output for each alternation of voltage), while V_0 also increases as the frequency increases but at a slower rate. At the field strengths which can be safely sustained in practical electroluminescent lamps and for frequencies in the low audio range normally employed, the quantum output may therefore vary slightly less than linearly. Since the emission of ZnS:Cu phosphors shifts to shorter wavelengths (corresponding to lower luminosity) as the frequency is increased, the brightness may increase less rapidly than the quantum output and a power law with exponent in the range 0.7–0.8 is sometimes observed. For phosphor powders embedded in a dielectric the increase in permittivity of the phosphor at high frequency may also affect the variation of output with frequency because of the division of voltage between phosphor and dielectric.

The curves of Fig. 19 show a tendency to saturate for frequencies above about 10,000 cps, especially at low voltages. This can be understood in a qualitative sense since the characteristic decay times of these phosphors is of the order of 10^{-4} sec (see Section III,G,2). Curie (4, 157) assumed bimolecular recombination kinetics and that the same number of excited centers are produced per half-cycle [corresponding to the observed linear dependence of L_0 in Eq. (8) on f at low frequencies]. On this basis he showed that the frequency dependence of the output should be given by the relation

$$L = \frac{S}{1 + K(\gamma S)^{1/2}/f},$$ (15)

where K is a constant, γ is the recombination coefficient (inversely related to the decay time), and S is the saturation output for high frequency. Although admittedly an oversimplification, this relation does correctly

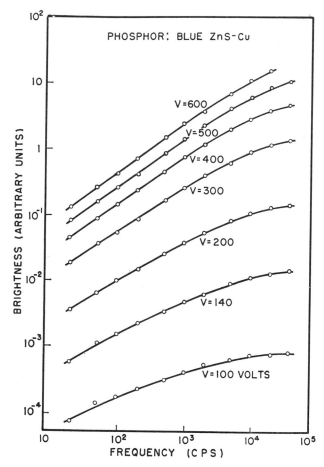

FIG. 19. Frequency dependence of the brightness of a blue-emitting electroluminescent ZnS:Cu phosphor for various applied voltages. (1, data from Lehmann.)

predict that a higher frequency should be required to approach saturation at high voltage (which increases S) and also that in the case of multiband emission the blue component should increase faster with increasing frequency than the green component (because of the longer decay time or lower value of γ in the latter case). Thornton (334) considered the recombination rate to be determined by field-controlled release of electrons from traps. In this case, and again assuming a constant number of excited centers (N_0) for each half-cycle of voltage, the frequency dependence should be given by

$$L = N_0 f[1 - \exp(-A/f)], \qquad (16)$$

where the quantity A increases as the voltage is increased.* For very high frequency the output is given by $N_0 A$, with N_0 obviously a function of voltage. This result also correctly predicts the effect of voltage on the frequency dependence of output. Zalm (2) has also made a calculation in which the rate-determining factor for the recombination is not detrapping as assumed by Thornton or natural recombination as assumed by Curie, but the effect of the voltage in driving electrons back to the empty luminescence centers. If monomolecular kinetics are assumed then the result is the same as Eq. (16) except that A is now directly proportional to V; Zalm points out, however, that other effects of frequency and voltage on N_0 should be considered (see Section III,J).

Harman and Raybold (378) and Lochinger (343) have made measurements up to frequencies of 3.7×10^8 and 2×10^7 cps, respectively. The output may actually decrease above frequencies of the order of 10^5 cps but measurements in this range are not very reliable due to heating of the sample, voltage losses in the transparent conducting electrode, and other experimental difficulties. Studies have also been made using sawtooth voltages at frequencies as low as 0.02 cps by Fredericks (379) and with sinusoidal voltages as low as 0.01 cps by Thornton. The latter found the linear dependence on frequency to hold as low as one cps, but for lower frequencies the output decreased more rapidly; this may be attributed to non-radiating transitions or thermal quenching (see below).

The normal frequency characteristics of ZnS:Cu can be markedly modified by the addition of "killers" such as Fe, Co, or Ni (249, 257), as discussed in Section III,A. The "superlinearity" that can be obtained in some cases is shown in Fig. 20, Curve D. The decreased output at low frequencies is presumably due to transfer of energy from emitting (Cu) centers to "killer" (Fe) centers, in the manner of Fig. 18 and as observed also for ultraviolet excitation (381). At high frequencies there is not sufficient time for this transfer of energy and the phosphor behaves essentially as though the killer were not present. Samples B and C in Fig. 20 are normal ZnS:Cu phosphors, while A is a special ZnS:Cu,Mn sample; although the frequency dependence of ZnS:Cu,Mn is normally less than that of ZnS:Cu

---

* $A \sim \displaystyle\int_0^{2\pi} \exp(aV \sin x)dx.$

sample A is an extreme case. Figure 20 thus represents the wide variety of characteristics which may be achieved by control of composition.

The effect of temperature on electroluminescence output has been studied by a large number of workers (*20, 244, 262, 263, 269, 334, 340,*

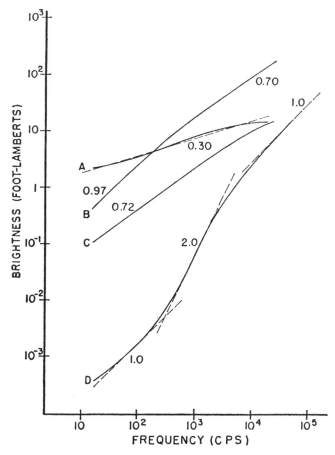

Fig. 20. Dependence of output on frequency for several electroluminescent phosphors. The numbers on the curves indicate the slope of the logarithmic plots. Samples B and C are normal ZnS:Cu, A is a special ZnS:Cu,Mn, and D is ZnSe:Cu, Fe. (*380,* data from Lehmann.)

373–377, 382–390), sometimes with discordant results, perhaps again attributable in some cases to the different phosphors employed. Roberts (*340*) in early work observed only a small effect when the temperature was varied between −100 and +50°C and concluded that "whatever the mechanism for electroluminescence may be, in these experiments, it does not depend on a thermal activation such as is encountered in conventional semiconductors." Most later workers, however, agree that electron trapping is very important in determining the output and other characteristics of electroluminescence (*334, 376* and Section III,*I* and III,*J*). Since electrons released from luminescence centers during one half-cycle of the applied voltage will be swept away by the field and can return only after the direction of the field has been reversed (for a discussion of the delayed nature of the emission see Sections III,*H* and III,*I*), it is not unexpected that in the meantime they may become trapped, most probably in regions of the crystal where the field strength is lower.

Thornton (*334*) has shown that many of the effects of frequency and temperature on the output of electroluminescent ZnS phosphors may be explained by considering that the return of the electrons to the excitation region is controlled by their thermal release from such traps and that the trap depth is decreased by the electric field. The number which are successful in returning is a function of the release rate (voltage and temperature) and also of the time available (frequency) (see Eq. 14). For sufficiently high voltage, high temperature, and low frequency all the traps (and excited centers) will be depleted. On this basis alone, with no consideration of the effect of these variables on the excitation process and therefore on the number of empty luminescence centers and trapped electrons, he was able to show that the temperature dependence of output should be a maximum at low voltage and high frequency, the frequency dependence should be a maximum at high voltage and high temperature, and the voltage dependence should be a maximum at low temperature and high frequency. These conclusions are in general agreement with experimental observations but exceptions may arise if appreciable concentrations of traps of more than one depth are present or if other effects depending on temperature occur (see below and Section III,*J*). Thus it is found that the value of V_0 in Eq. (8) for the voltage dependence of output usually increases at low temperature (*334, 373*), but maxima and minima may also occur (*2*). It has already been commented above that V_0 usually increases slightly with increasing frequency. The dependence of output on frequency predicted by this model has also been discussed earlier in connection with Eq. (16). It will be shown later (Section III,*I*) that it also satisfactorily explains many features of the output waveform ("brightness wave").

Mattler (*383*) and Haake (*375*) have emphasized that in studying the effect of temperature on electroluminescence care should be taken to avoid complications resulting from changes with temperature of the properties of the dielectric used to embed the phosphor. Irreversible changes due to excessive temperature must also be avoided. Curie (*157*), Haake (*375*), and Alfrey (*384*) have shown that the effect of temperature on the electro-

luminescence excitation should also be separated from that on the recombination (emission). The latter may be determined by measuring the
temperature dependence of the photoluminescence of the same phosphor.
As is well known, the photoluminescence efficiency is essentially constant
at sufficiently low temperatures but declines at higher temperatures because of competing nonradiating transitions ("thermal quenching"). The
electroluminescence output should therefore also be expected to decrease
at high temperatures for the same reason. In the case of electroluminescence the quenching factor may be written

$$Q = [1 + (A/f) \exp(-q/kT)]^{-1}, \qquad (17)$$

where q is the quenching energy, and account has been taken of Eq. (14).

In Fig. 21 are shown some results obtained by Haake (375, 376). It is
seen that in this case each curve has two peaks. Since the magnitude of the
output increases rapidly as the frequency is increased, the scales of the
different curves of Fig. 21 have been arbitrarily changed to fit them all on

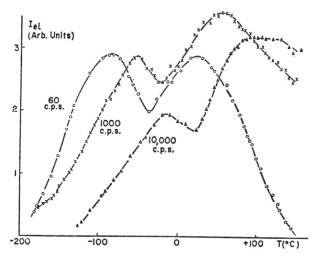

Fig. 21. Temperature dependence of electroluminescent output for different frequencies of excitation (constant voltage). The vertical scale is not the same for the three
curves. (From Haake, 376.)

the same plot. These peaks are produced by the combined effects of electron
liberation from a set of trapping levels (of which two exist in this phosphor),
which obviously increases with increasing temperature until the latter is
high enough to empty all the traps, and a decrease in emission efficiency
with increasing temperature [Eq. (17)]. Since at high excitation frequency
less time per cycle is available to empty the traps, the temperature to

obtain maximum output shifts progressively to higher values as the frequency is increased (262, 373–376, 384), in accordance with Eq. (14). This obviously has an effect on the frequency dependence of output at constant temperature. Thus at −100°C the curves in Fig. 21 are in order of decreasing frequency, while at +120°C the situation is reversed and at 0°C that for an intermediate frequency is highest. Such effects are superimposed upon the normal increase in output with increasing frequency and will cause "sublinearity" at low temperatures and "superlinearity" at high temperatures (374). Depending upon the particular phosphor and the frequency, increasing the temperature may cause either increased or decreased output.

From such studies of the effect of temperature on electroluminescence output the effective trap depths may be determined (345, 375, 377, 384) and correlated with similar data from thermoluminescence experiments. It is usually found that increasing the applied voltage causes the output-vs-temperature curve to shift to lower temperatures (334, 375, 383, 385) which is indicative of a decrease in trap depth by the electric field or of direct release of electrons from the traps by the field. On the other hand, Alfrey (384) found no effect of voltage on the temperature for maximum output, while Morehead (345) found it to shift to higher values for higher voltages. Figure 21 and the above discussion indicate that the electroluminescence output should disappear at very low temperatures where electron traps cannot be emptied thermally. With some phosphors, however, it is observed (377, 383) that the output is high or even increasing at the lowest temperatures used for measurement (as yet only liquid nitrogen seems to have been employed). Wide variations in output may also occur in temperature regions where thermal quenching of photoluminescence is not observed (377). Such behavior may be explained by other temperature effects, including that on holes trapped at empty luminescence centers, and is discussed further in Section III,J.

Neumark (263) found the dc electroluminescence of ZnS single crystals (at constant voltage) to decrease at low temperatures while Matsumura and Tanabe (387) found the electroluminescence to increase although the current decreased. Vlasenko (388) studied the ac electroluminescence of thin films of ZnS:Mn and found that the emission increased as the temperature was increased above room temperature despite the fact that the photoluminescence decreased; at high temperatures the dependence of output on frequency became much smaller than at low temperatures. Thornton finds that the current through a film of ZnS:Cu,Mn,Cl for a constant direct voltage may decrease by a factor as high as about 50 when the temperature is reduced from 300°K to 100°K but that the electroluminescence output under the same conditions decreases by only a factor of 3–10. If the current is maintained constant the output may increase by a factor of 3–10 at low temperatures. (The current-voltage characteristic and its dependence on temperature was discussed in Section III,D.)

Gobrecht et al. (244) observed an irreversible effect in their studies of the temperature dependence of the electroluminescence output of ZnS powders. As the temperature was reduced the output varied in a regular manner, but when it was subsequently increased (with constant exciting voltage) a series of peaks resembling thermoluminescence curves were obtained (it should be noted that the peaks of Fig. 21 are observed, on the contrary, for either increasing or decreasing temperature). This effect has been called "electrothermoluminescence." Hahn (390) later studied this effect further and stated that it seemed to depend to a large extent on the nature of the embedding material; this observation, the fact that it has apparently been observed only in poorly emitting phosphors, and has not been observed by other workers make it appear that the effect is probably spurious.*

Neumark (263) observed what has been called "thermally stimulated electroluminescence." ZnS crystals were cooled to low temperature, irradiated with ultraviolet radiation, irradiation stopped, phosphorescence allowed to decay, and then warmed. The emission observed with a constant field applied was greater (by a factor of 10 or more) that the sum of that observed with field off (normal thermoluminescence) or the normal electroluminescence observed without irradiation at low temperature. The effect was observed only in electroluminescent crystals and could also be obtained following a long period of field application at low temperature as well as for ultraviolet excitation. The current flowing was also measured and found to have little correlation with the "stimulated" output. Neumark concluded that the additional output was electroluminescence produced by electrons liberated thermally from traps and accelerated by the field. However, the fact that this enhanced output was obtained only for direct voltage, although ac electroluminescence was observed, requires further explanation (268 and also Section III,J).

F. Electroluminescence Efficiency

The efficiency of electroluminescence is of interest from both fundamental and practical viewpoints. The efficiency obviously follows directly from the ratio of the light output (discussed in Sections III,D and III,E) to the power input (Section III,C). The higher the applied alternating voltage the higher the light output, but for high voltages the power input in-

---

* Gobrecht et al. (391) also observed a similar effect called "cathodothermoluminescence" with cathode-ray excitation. However, this effect has also been shown to be spurious (392).

creases faster than the output so that the efficiency, as distinguished from the output, is a maximum at some intermediate value of voltage (212, 393). Maximum output and maximum efficiency thus cannot be achieved simultaneously. At low frequency the voltage required for optimum efficiency is about half the maximum safe operating voltage, and shifts to higher values as the frequency is increased (see Fig. 22). According to Lehmann (393,

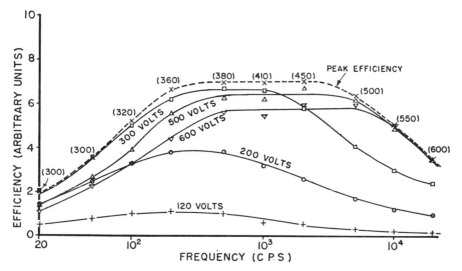

FIG. 22. Effect of frequency and voltage on electroluminescence efficiency. The dashed curve gives the maximum efficiency as a function of frequency while the figures next to this curve correspond to the voltage at which this maximum efficiency is observed. (Data from Lehmann.)

394), optimum efficiency is obtained when the output varies as about the fourth power of the applied voltage*; this is a consequence of the bimolecular recombination (285, 314, 315, and Sections III,C and III,J). At high frequency, power losses in other cell components cause the efficiency to decrease. The efficiency will also be depressed at low frequency if the phosphor is quenched thermally (or by impurities) but the effect of quenching will disappear at higher frequencies [Eq. (15)]. Many phosphors therefore show maximum efficiency at intermediate frequencies although in some cases the variation may be small over a wide range of frequency (see Fig. 22). There is usually also an optimum temperature for maximum efficiency (see Section III,J); as in the case of brightness studies, however, care must be taken that the measurements are not affected by changes in the dielectric used for embedding the phosphor or by other effects.

* According to Eq. (8) this occurs when $V = V_0/64$.

Lehmann (*325*) has also shown that the efficiency is higher for small particles of normal ZnS phosphor powders than for large particles (see Fig. 23). As in the case of the effect of particle size on the dependence of brightness on voltage (Fig. 14), Thornton (*359*) has shown that statistical effects play a role here also. The field in the particles, embedded in a dielectric of different permittivity, will differ from the applied field and also from point to point depending on the number of particles between the electrodes in the random dispersion of powder. Since there is an optimum field

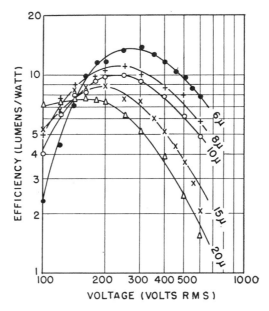

Fig. 23. Dependence of electroluminescence efficiency on voltage for phosphor fractions of different mean particle diameter. (From Lehmann, *325*.)

for maximum efficiency, the probability of many particles being situated in a favorable field is greater the larger the number of particles or the smaller their diameter. Morehead (*345*) on the other hand assumes that in small particles a larger fraction of the applied voltage appears across the potential barrier.

Figure 23 also shows that a maximum efficiency of 14 lumens/watt has been achieved for a green-emitting phosphor. If correction is made for optical absorption in the cell used, the phosphor efficiency is found to be 18–19 lumens/watt. On an energy basis this corresponds to an efficiency of 4.5%, which is not very high. This figure, however, is to be compared with those for other light sources (100-watt incandescent lamp, 16 lumens/watt; 40-watt fluorescent lamp, 75 lumens/watt, for white light in each case).

Unfortunately in practical electroluminescent lamps, where high brightness is a major requirement and operation is therefore at high field strength, the efficiency is usually of the order of 3 lumens/watt.

The efficiency which can be expected theoretically for electroluminescence, which obviously depends on the mechanism assumed, has also been discussed. On the basis of an injection-recombination mechanism, where thermal energy may be extracted from the surroundings, Weinstein (155) calculated the maximum for ZnS as

$$\eta \leqslant [1 - (1 - 0.09 \log L)(T/1050)]^{-1}, \tag{18}$$

where T is the ambient temperature and L the brightness in foot-lamberts. For $T = 300°K$, $\eta \leqslant 157\%$ for $L = 10^{-3}$ ft-L and 130% for $L = 100$ ft-L. The experimental values are obviously much below these values. If an acceleration-collision mechanism is assumed then the efficiency is limited by the following factors:

(1) Excitation and emission are confined to small regions of the crystals while voltage drop and electrical losses occur (although certainly to a different extent) in other regions as well*: such low-field regions are presumably necessary, however, in order to prevent dielectric breakdown.

(2) Of the electrons which are accelerated, only those with energy above a critical value can excite luminescence centers; those with lower energy will contribute, however, to the power losses.

(3) Not all the electrons with sufficient energy will excite luminescence centers; some will lose their energy in collisions with impurities, defects, and the base lattice itself. If the activator concentration is increased too far in order to overcome this competition then "concentrating quenching" will occur and the recombination efficiency will be reduced (395).†

(4) Nonradiating transitions may be introduced by the presence of the field as a result of the spatial separation of electrons and excited luminescence centers; a similar situation is known to exist in the quenching of photoluminescence by electric fields (135, Section V,B) and is not unreasonable in electroluminescence as well (212) (see also Section III,I).

Zalm et al. (212) suggested that if luminescence centers in electroluminescent ZnS are excited by electrons which have been accelerated by the field, a correlation should exist between the electroluminescence efficiency and that of cathode-ray excitation at low voltages, which is not high. Be-

* This comment applies equally well to injection electroluminescence.
† Concentration quenching is related to thermal quenching. The quenching energy q in Eq. (17) is lowered by high activator concentration, thus explaining the fact that most electroluminescent ZnS phosphors show thermal quenching at or near room temperature.

cause of the small penetration depth of low-energy electrons the latter is confined to the surface of the particles, which is presumably less efficient; these workers believe that electroluminescence is also a surface effect and should therefore be correspondingly inefficient. They also suggested that most of the available luminescence centers become excited, similar to the case of current saturation in cathodoluminescence, with a resultant low efficiency. A calculation concerning this last point seems in order. Perhaps the highest brightness reported to date for green emitting ZnS:Cu powder phosphors is 2000 ft-L for 10,000 cps excitation and a layer thickness of 75μ containing about 33% phosphor (*380*). In the case of ZnS:Mn thin films Thornton (*364*) has obtained 600 ft-L for ac or dc excitation for a film thickness of 2μ. For a visibility factor of 0.7 these figures correspond to emission intensities of 6×10^{18} and 2×10^{19} quanta/cm^3-sec, respectively, roughly comparable to an activator concentration of 2×10^{19} cm^{-3}, equivalent to 0.1% Cu. If one considers that the lifetime of the luminescence centers is 10^{-3} to 10^{-4} sec (see Section III,*G*,*2*) while the emission may be limited to a volume which is only 10^{-3} or 10^{-4} of the phosphor volume, it may be concluded that saturation of the centers is approached for these rather unusual conditions. For operating conditions which lead to the highest efficiency, however, the brightness is much lower and it seems unlikely that saturation then enters the picture.

Simply on the basis of activator concentration Burns (*215*) predicted an electroluminescence efficiency of 2.5%. Bowtell and Bate (*396*) give a theoretical value of 12 lumens/watt for a green-emitting phosphor but with no details of the calculations. Zalm (*2*) has concluded that only about 13% of the applied voltage occurs across the potential barrier responsible for accelerating the electrons and that, taking other factors into account, the maximum theoretical efficiency should be about 14 lumens/watt. Neumark (*356*) also made calculations on a barrier model which are in essential agreement with Zalm's results. Maeda (*319*) by a quite different argument estimated a value of 13 lumens/watt. Maeda also suggested that local heating in the high-field region might result in thermal quenching. Morehead (*346*) has obtained theoretical values ranging between 5 and 38 lumens/watt depending on the assumptions made. Although these various theoretical values are far from rigorous, they are at least in the same range as the efficiencies actually observed.

Thornton has observed that the electroluminescence efficiency of thin phosphor films, at least at the present stage of development, is usually lower than that of corresponding powder phosphors. Furthermore, the efficiency for dc excitation is much lower than that for ac excitation; figures of 0.01–0.02 and 1–2 lumens/watt, respectively, are typical. For the dc case the efficiency is found to increase the higher the applied voltage; this is a result of the fact that the output increases with increasing voltage considerably faster than does the current.

G. *Time Effects*

There are five types of variation with time which are of both practical and fundamental interest in electroluminescence. These are:

(1) variation of the output with time after application of voltage to a previously unexcited phosphor ("buildup");

(2) variation of the output with time after removal of voltage from a phosphor ("decay" or "persistence");

(3) dependence of output excited by voltage pulses on pulse duration, spacing, and shape;

(4) variation of the output with time during one cycle of the applied alternating voltage after equilibrium average output has been achieved ("brightness waveform");

(5) variation of the average output with time for long periods of sustained excitation ("maintenance of output").

Excitation by pulses and the shape of brightness waves will be discussed in the next two sections while the other three effects will be considered in the present section.

1. Buildup. It has been known for a long time (*20*) that the output of an electroluminescent cell does not reach its equilibrium value immediately after application of the voltage. This may be partially due to realignment of the phosphor particles if a liquid dielectric is used but occurs also with solid dielectrics. Typical examples of buildup following application of a sinusoidal voltage are shown in Fig. 24. A similar behavior is observed with pulse excitation (*2, 397, 398*). Buildup is also observed with ultraviolet or cathode-ray excitation and is there well explained on the basis of electron trapping; it is not surprising, therefore, that electroluminescence buildup may be explained on the same basis (*332, 376, 399*),* although there are some additional complications. If the phosphor is heated or irradiated with infrared radiation before the voltage is applied so as to empty all remanent filled traps, the buildup is slower than if some traps remain filled from previous excitation. A similar effect of trap emptying might be expected upon increasing the temperature while the field is applied, as in the case of photoluminescence. However, Haake (*332*) found the buildup at 160°C to be essentially the same as at room temperature and explained the lack of dependence upon the action of temperature on trapped electrons in the

---

* Zalm (*2*), on the other hand, suggests that build-up results from accumulation of positive space change which enhances the potential barrier (see Section III,*J*).

high-field (barrier) region as well as in the low-field region. However, the buildup time was found to increase slightly for temperatures below room temperature. In such experiments thermal quenching probably also plays a role.

Haake (*332*) found that the magnitude of the applied voltage had little effect on the buildup. If the frequency of the alternating voltage is increased the buildup time is reduced. If the time for buildup is expressed in terms of number of cycles then the effect is much less marked and in the reverse order; thus buildup to a given percentage of the equilibrium value requires about twice as many cycles at 500 cps as at 50 cps. As seen from Fig. 24,

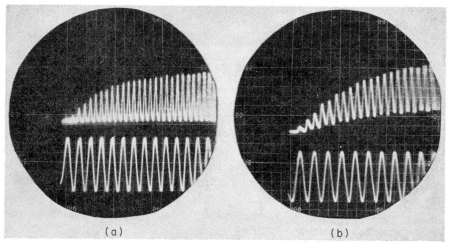

Fig. 24. Buildup of output of a typical electroluminescent phosphor after application of sinusoidal voltage at two different frequencies. (a) 400 volts, 50 cps; (b) 400 volts, 500 cps. (From Haake.)

five to ten cycles of the applied voltage may be required to reach an output close to the equilibrium value. Haake also studied the effect of previous electroluminescence excitation on photoluminescence buildup and vice versa. In the case of photoluminescence the effect of traps filled by previous electroluminescence was negligible, while prior ultraviolet excitation greatly speeded buildup (the opposite effect to infrared quenching). Although previous ultraviolet irradiation had some effect on electroluminescence buildup, the effect was much greater for prior electroluminescence excitation. This may be explained on the basis of the limitation of electroluminescence to very small regions of the phosphor (*328*).

Frankl (*264*) has observed that the equilibrium is reached much more rapidly if half-wave rectified alternating voltage is used rather than ordinary alternating excitation. Johnson (400) has also shown that the output rise time may be reduced to the voltage rise time (one half the period of the alternating voltage) if a bias voltage equal to half the peak-to-peak voltage is superimposed on a burst of alternating voltage pulses applied to a normal dielectric-embedded phosphor powder. In all these cases the applied voltage is, of course, unidirectional. This method affords the opportunity for fast buildup where needed in technical applications of electroluminescence. A somewhat similar result may be obtained with dc pulses (2, 398). Hoffman and Smith (401) obtained a rise time of less than 0.2 μsec using voltage pulses.

Thornton (367) has shown that in the case of thin phosphor films the rise time for the emission resulting from a direct voltage pulse is independent of the brightness (i.e., the magnitude of the pulse) and varies from 1.0 msec at 20 pps to 0.2 msec at 600 pps. The decay time, however, is independent of the pulse repetition rate and decreases from 8.0 msec for 10^{-2} ft-L output to 1.0 msec at 10 ft-L. On the other hand, if instead of unidirectional pulses the polarity is reversed, the response is much slower and several seconds may be required to reach the new equilibrium condition. It seems obvious therefore that for excitation by alternating voltage the same condition is never reached in the phosphor as for dc excitation. The time lags observed may result from space charge accumulation (2) or (much less likely) from ionic migration (267, 327, 347).

2. Persistence. Persistence of output after cessation of excitation, or phosphorescence, is well known for photoluminescent or cathodoluminescent phosphors and may be due either to a very long life for the excited state of the luminescence center or to electron trapping. Destriau (20) very early pointed out that electroluminescence emission, however, was of short persistence,* even with phosphors whose photoluminescence showed long persistence (see Section III,B). In the case of an electroluminescent phosphor embedded in a conducting medium, Zalm et al. (212) have shown (see Fig. 30) that the decay of the light pulse obtained when a voltage pulse is applied is faster than that of the light pulse emitted when the voltage is removed and suggested that this effect is responsible for the fast decay for normal excitation by alternating voltages or square waves. Solomon and Goldberg (219) have shown that in ZnS:Cu,Cl phosphors made with variable amounts of Cu and a fixed amount of Cl, low Cu concentration produces nonelectroluminescent but green photoluminescent materials with long persistence; when the Cu/Cl ratio in the finished materials approaches unity, however, electroluminescence appears simultaneously with a change in photoluminescence to short-persistence blue emission.

---

* There seem to be only two reported exceptions (247, 332) to this rule, which seems to hold universally for highly efficient electroluminescent phosphors.

This in agreement with general experience and the observation that deep electron traps are not favorable to electroluminescence (see Section III,J).

Destriau (*402*) and others have made measurements of the decay of emission following electroluminescence excitation. Hahn and Seemann (*308*) and Lehmann (see *380*) have shown that the emission of ZnS:Cu,Mn electroluminescent phosphors shows exponential decay with a time constant of about 500 μsec when the voltage is removed. This time constant is presumably characteristic of the Mn center and temperature independent. Electroluminescent ZnS:Cu,Cl (*380*) or ZnS:Cu,Al (*308*) phosphors, on the other hand, exhibit a power-law decay (exponent between 0.5 and 1.0) and require, respectively, about 20 or 150 μsec to decay to 50% of their initial output, about 50 or 250 μsec for 37%, and roughly 200 or 900 μsec for 10%. Although measurements have apparently not been made, it is to be expected that the decay in this case will be faster at higher temperatures, as in the case of photoluminescence.

Bonch-Bruevich and Marenkov (*403*) and Johnson (*400*) have observed a decay times as short as 10 μsec for ZnS:Cu,Cl phosphors. Johnson suggests that the measured decay time may be influenced by the construction of the cell used for testing (thicker cells giving longer decay times) and by the impedance of the external circuit. Contrary to the results of Zalm, Diemer, and Klasens for a conducting medium, Bonch-Bruevich and Marenkov found that for an insulating medium the emission obtained upon application of a voltage pulse decayed slower than that upon removal of the pulse but that both decays were independent of the duration of the pulse. Hoffman and Smith (*401*) found the decay following pulse excitation to vary from 2–3 μsec at a repetition rate of 50,000 cps to 100–200 μsec at 200 pps. Zalm *et al.* (*212*) have shown that the blue electroluminescence in multiband ZnS:Cu phosphors decays faster than the green emission (see also *371*). This is consistent with transfer of excitation from blue to green centers by hole migration as discussed earlier in connection with shifts in color as the exciting frequency is varied (Fig. 18).

3. Maintenance of Output. All electroluminescent phosphors show a loss in output during operation for long periods; the rate of decrease is greatest early in life and gradually declines for longer times. This effect has been variously referred to as aging, fatigue, decay, deterioration, and maintenance. It is obviously of practical importance and also affords some additional insight into the electroluminescence process. Quantitative studies of the changes during life and the factors affecting them have been made primarily by Roberts (*404*) and Thornton (*331, 337, 405*). A very significant observation is the fact that the photoluminescence remains essentially unchanged although the electroluminescence may decrease to a small percentage of its original value (*404, 405*). No change in emission color is observed even in double-band (green and blue emitting) ZnS:Cu phosphors (337).* Both these observations are consistent with the view that the electroluminescence centers themselves are unaffected during aging and that changes occur only in the mechanism responsible for exciting them or in the electron traps. Even if the centers were affected, the lack of a noticeable decrease in photoluminescence could be explained by limitation of electroluminescence to a very small fraction of the phosphor volume. The

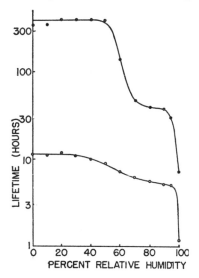

FIG. 25. Effect of relative humidity on lifetime (hours of operation at 4000 cps to reduce output to half of initial value) of electroluminescent ZnS:Cu,Cl phosphor embedded in polyvinyl chloride-acetate copolymer. The upper curve is for a phosphor which has been specially treated to improve maintenance of output. (From Thornton, 337.)

lack of a color change implies either that the luminescence centers are not affected or else that the blue and green centers are not independent entities.

The loss in output is greatly accentuated by the presence of moisture (see Fig. 25); effective sealing of commercial electroluminescent lamps is therefore a necessity. Even in the absence of moisture, however, deterioration still occurs. In this case under ideal conditions the nature of the dielectric seems to have no effect on the maintenance of output (337). This statement does not hold, however, in the case of plastic dielectrics if all solvents are not carefully removed or if volatile plasticizers are present (both of which lead to poor maintenance) or to glass dielectrics which require heating to high temperatures so that changes may be produced in the

* The only exception to this observation seems to be that of Grigor'ev and Kulyupin (405a), who used a silicone oil dielectric and a Zn(S,O):Cu,Cl,Al phosphor.

phosphor itself. Roberts (404) showed that the main portion of the curve of output as a function of operating time can often be represented by the relation

$$L = L_i/[1 + (t/t_0)], \tag{19}$$

where L_i is the initial value; since $L = L_i/2$ at $t = t_0$, t_0 represents the "halflife" of the phosphor. Thornton (337) has shown that a sum of two terms like Eq. (19) with different values of L_i and t_0 is often necessary to fit experimental data. Nudelman and Mudar (406) have used an equation similar to (19) but with an exponent for t different from unity.

It has been known for a long time that the rate of decrease of output is greater the higher the operating frequency (404, 405). Sack and Thornton (337) have shown that for high-frequency operation the total number of cycles which the phosphor has experienced (frequency times time) is the determining factor rather than the frequency or time alone. Thus the half-life (the time to reduce the output to half the initial value) is most conveniently expressed in number of cycles in order to characterize a phosphor. For low-frequency operation (below 1000 cps) deviations from this simple behavior are often observed; the actual life under these conditions is usually greater than predicted from high-frequency measurements, but this is not always the case. The deterioration increases with increasing temperature; at liquid nitrogen temperatures no loss in output is observed (405). Thornton (337) has shown that the halflife obeys an exponential dependence on (E/kT); for the phosphor tested the value of E was approximately 0.1 ev.

During aging, changes are observed in the way in which the electroluminescence output depends on the applied voltage (or field strength) as well as in the magnitude of the output (331, 337, 404). An example is shown in Fig. 26. It is seen that the effect of aging is observed only at low voltages; if the voltage is sufficiently high the output is unaffected. The effect of aging on output therefore depends on the voltages employed for measurement and for the aging. If the output is measured at the same voltage used for aging it is found that the effect of voltage on maintenance is relatively small; in some cases maintenance may even be better at high voltage than low (337, 404). The effect shown in Fig. 26 may be explained on the basis of the limitation of electroluminescence excitation to small regions of the phosphor and the expansion of these regions when the voltage is increased, as suggested by Roberts and Thornton. Data presented by Thornton (337) also indicate that the deterioration is more localized for operation at high frequency.

The phosphor composition has a large influence on maintenance of output. Figure 27 shows some results obtained by Thornton for ZnS:Cu,Cl phosphors made with various amounts of Cu and Cl added before firing (brightness data for the same phosphors are shown in Fig. 8). It is seen that the maintenance is generally better the higher the amounts of Cu and Cl used. Since the emission color also varies in roughly the same way, it is seen that in general the maintenance is better the longer the effective emission wavelength; the two sets of contours are not coincident, however. Thornton found that the maintenance characteristics of $ZnS:Cu,Mn,Cl$ phosphors were much like those of corresponding phosphors without Mn and changed with Cu and Cl concentration in the same way. Thornton also found that the maintenance of output of small particles was poorer than that of large particles separated from the same parent phosphor.

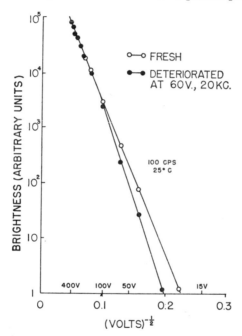

FIG. 26. Effect of aging on brightness-voltage characteristics of an electroluminescent phosphor. The effect of aging is observed only at voltages below those at which aging occurred. (From Thornton, *337*.)

The changes in electroluminescence output during life are accompanied by changes in electrical properties. As was discussed in Section III,*C*, both the capacitance and the conductance of electroluminescent phosphors increase with applied voltage. During aging, the capacitance, the conductance, and the photoconductance all decrease, but in different ways (*404, 405*); the dependence of capacitance and conductance on voltage also largely disappears (*337*). Because of these changes the efficiency is often observed to increase during the early stages of life and then to decrease again (*404*).

The optimum voltage for maximum efficiency (see Fig. 23) also shifts to higher values during aging (*337*); this is another manifestation of the localization of the deterioration.

Since the impedance of an electroluminescent lamp increases during life, the life may be artificially increased by connecting a fixed (capacitive or resistive) impedance in series (*337, 407*). The voltage across the lamp then increases continuously during life and compensates, at least partially, for the deterioration. Improved maintenance may therefore be obtained

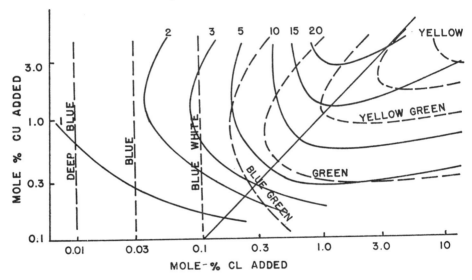

Fig. 27. Color and maintenance (percent of initial brightness) as a function of amount of Cu and Cl added before firing. The composition of the finished phosphor will differ due to losses during firing and cyanide treatment. (From Thornton, *337*.)

simply by incorporating a layer of dielectric free of phosphor in the lamp of by lowering the phosphor/dielectric ratio (*337*); the output (for a fixed voltage) will, however, be reduced by such means. If the series impedance is great enough, overcompensation may occur and the output will increase with time early in life before a decline sets in (*407*). Such an increase is sometimes observed in normal lamps (*396, 404*) and is probably there also to be attributed to series internal impedance rather than to a real effect in the phosphor. Because of such effects of lamp structure, care must be taken in comparing maintenance data for lamps of different construction. Since temperature also affects the output (Section III,*E*), changes in lamp temperature due to the power dissipation may also influence the output characteristics for a time after the voltage is applied.

Nudelman and Mudar (*406*) found that if a lamp containing phosphor powder with no dielectric was aged and then shaken so as to rearrange the particles, the output could be partially restored; successive aging and shaking resulted in a smaller degree of recovery. This result may be interpreted as indicating that only potential barriers oriented in the proper direction suffer deterioration [compare the observations of Destriau on the effect of rotating crystals on the output (284)]. Grigor'ev and Kulyupin (405a) came to a similar conclusion with a liquid dielectric. Frankl (408) also observed that annealing deteriorated ZnS single crystals in pure ZnS powder at 750–800°C restored the output of some crystals, but not others. In this laboratory I. E. Buck has also shown that the output of phosphor powders embedded in glass may be restored to more than 90% of their initial output by heating at 500–600°C and that this process may be repeated 10 or more times. This is, of course, not possible with plastic-embedded phosphors but it has been observed (first by D. C. Bell) that even in this case there is a slight recovery upon standing overnight or longer at room temperature. Such recovery effects have as yet been little explored.

Apparently the first attempted explanation of electroluminescence deterioration was due to Waymouth et al. (382), who suggested that it was associated with agglomeration of particles under the action of the electric field, perhaps similar to that observed in liquid dielectrics (278, 285). They supported this idea with the observation that the less plastic the dielectric the better the maintenance of output. Since loss in output is also observed in ceramic dielectrics where particle movement is most unlikely, it seems more probable that the "harder" plastic may also have had better resistance to moisture penetration. The use of nonacidic plastics or the addition of acid-neutralizing materials such as sodium bicarbonate have also been claimed by Mager (409) to result in better maintenance.

The fact that the deterioration is localized, as is the emission, caused Thornton (405) and Roberts (404) to assume that ionic motion is involved. They pointed out that Eq. (19) is consistent with $dn/dt = -kn^2$, where n is associated with the number of deep traps (coactivators) responsible for barrier formation. Roberts therefore interpreted deterioration as resulting from migration of coactivator atoms to different states of association with activator atoms (179). Thornton (405) emphasized the importance of trapping in the low-field regions of the phosphor and postulated that the traps might migrate to the particle surfaces under the action of the field. He also pointed out that the observed temperature dependence is consistent with ionic migration. Although it is normally assumed that ionic mobilities in ZnS are extremely low, here one is dealing with very high field strengths (particularly in the barrier regions), very long times (hundreds or thousands of hours), and very small distances (barrier widths may be expected to be of the order of 100A, reference 2) so that electrolytic action is not unreasonable. According to Thornton (*331*) a mobility of 10^{-14} cm²/volt-sec is sufficient to explain the observed deterioration. Ionic migration in ZnS has also been considered by Ince and Oatley (*327*), Ratner (*347*), and Luyckx (*267*) in connection with other properties of electroluminescent phosphors. Thornton (*333*) has also suggested that the number of active sites in the phosphor may increase with time rather than decrease; the loss in output would then be a result of the lower voltage at each region of excitation.

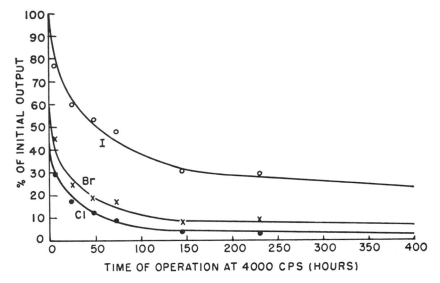

Fig. 28. Maintenance of output during life of ZnS:Cu electroluminescent phosphors coactivated with different halides. 0.1% Cu and 0.3% halide added before firing. (Data from Jaffe.)

Microscopic observation (*279*), however, although indicating some irregular fluctuation in the emitting spots, does not support this suggestion.

Jaffe (*410*) has shown that the nature of the coactivator does indeed have a pronounced influence on the maintenance characteristics of electroluminescent phosphors. As shown in Fig. 28, the larger the halide ion employed the better the maintenance, as would be expected if ionic migration is involved. The effect is actually more pronounced than shown in the figure as chemical analysis revealed that less of the halide added (0.3%) was retained in the fired material in the case of I(0.04%) than for Br and Cl (0.06%); according to Fig. 27 the reduced coactivator concentration in the case of I should be unfavorable to good maintenance. Furthermore, the emission of the sample coactivated with I was blue rather than green as for Br and Cl. The ZnS:Cu,I sample therefore has much better maintenance than a ZnS:Cu,Cl phosphor of similar emission color (see Fig. 27).

That electron traps in the phosphor are affected by aging is also shown by several experiments. Thus Thornton (*331, 405*) has shown that the brightness waves change during aging in a manner indicating the appearance of deeper traps (see Section III,*I*), which are usually assumed to be deleterious for electroluminescence as discussed previously. Jaffe (*410*) and Thornton (*331*) both have shown that thermoluminescence curves give the same indication. Thornton (*331*) also showed that the brightness-voltage characteristic of an aged phosphor could be restored to its original state, so that all evidence of aging was removed, simply by raising the temperature during measurement; this is not a permanent recovery and upon cooling the characteristic is returned to that obtained after aging. This effect too is consistent with the introduction of deep traps during aging. Changes in brightness-voltage characteristics similar to those observed after aging (higher value of V_0 in Eq. 8) can also be produced (*331*) by purposely adding to the phosphor impurities such as O, Cd, In, or Ga which are known to produce deep traps (*254*).

Thornton (*331*) has assumed that oxygen is a major factor in producing electroluminescence deterioration by means of introducing deep electron traps as discussed above. Oxygen ions are smaller than those of sulfur and hence might be expected to migrate rather easily.* The position of the thermoluminescence peak (at about $+30°C$) which appears during aging was also identified with that produced by oxygen (*254*). A monomolecular absorbed surface layer of oxygen on a particle 5 microns in diameter would correspond to a density of 10^{19} ions/cm³ if diffused into the particles and is therefore of the order of the concentration of Cu in the phosphor. Jaffe (*410*), however, has pointed out that the glow peak at $+30°C$ appears late in life, after most of the loss in light output has occurred. He further showed that the first effect of aging on the thermoluminescence is the appearance of a peak at about $-50°C$ which has been ascribed by Hoogenstraaten (*254*) to sulfur vacancies. Because of this and his results with different coactivators (Fig. 28), Jaffe assumed that the major loss in output is due to migration of halide ions and resultant formation of sulfur vacancies which serve as deeper traps; the minor loss late in life he ascribed to filling of these vacancies by oxygen, as assumed by Thornton, or to their association in clusters. W. Lehmann more recently has assumed that it is sulfur vacancies themselves which migrate into the phosphor from the surface under the action of the field. The effects of heat treatment in restoring the output of deteriorated phosphors, as observed by Frankl and Buck, could obviously be explained on the basis of annealing of sulfur vacancies.

* Woods (*315*) has ascribed the decline in photosensitivity of CdS crystals containing sulfur vacancies to migration of oxygen even at room temperature and in the absence of a field.

That moisture is bad for electroluminescent phosphors is generally acknowledged. That the reaction involved may be complicated is shown by Fig. 25, where the curves seem to show two steps. Thornton (*331*) assumed that water serves as an additional source of oxygen. He also found that exposure to moisture is harmful only if voltage is applied; if the phosphor is thoroughly dried before voltage is applied, the maintenance is unaffected (*337*). Smith *et al.* (*411*) have suggested that the deterioration process in the presence of water is similar to the photolysis of ZnS by ultraviolet radiation, which apparently requires electronic excitation of the ZnS and also involves moisture (*412, 413*). Their suggestion that an electrochemical process may be important would also explain Thornton's observation that moisture and field must be simultaneously present. Smith, Potter, and Aven were able to detect the presence of free zinc following electroluminescent deterioration of ZnS phosphors in the presence of water; in this case the phosphor became grey and optical absorption of the output also occurred. Thornton (*331*) also was able to show that small amounts of free zinc are formed even in the absence of moisture, but in this case no darkening is normally observed (*404*).

The exact role of oxygen in maintenance of electroluminescence output is still uncertain. It is well known that electroluminescent phosphors may be embedded in glass dielectrics, which are essentially mixtures of various oxides, by heating to the softening point of the glass with no harmful effect on output or maintenance (the particular glass used, however, does require some selection). On the other hand, some action of traps seems indicated and the experiments of Jaffe indicate clearly that the coactivator plays an important role in maintenance. Some kind of electrolytic process seems quite likely; vacancies apparently play a role but they would be important for any diffusion process. Unfortunately, little information seems available on the maintenance of phosphors coactivated with trivalent elements (such as Al) rather than the halides. Maintenance of output for dc excitation also has been little explored. Improvement of the maintenance characteristics of electroluminescent phosphors is possible, however. The upper curve in Fig. 25 is for a phosphor similar to that for the lower curve except that it was given a special treatment (due to Thornton) to improve the maintenance. Lehmann has also prepared on a laboratory scale a green-emitting phosphor which retained 89% of its initial output after a time corresponding to 8000 hours of operation at 60 cps (1.7×10^9 cycles); the corresponding figure for a standard fluorescent lamp is about 84%. Extrapolation shows that 10^{12} and perhaps even as many as 10^{13} cycles would be required to reduce the output of this phosphor to half the initial value.

Some comment on the usually observed correlation of maintenance of output and the total number of cycles of alternating voltage to which the phosphor has been subjected is perhaps in order. In any dielectric subjected to an alternating field the power dissipated is proportional to the frequency (constant loss per cycle). If the frequency is not too high, the light output from an electroluminescent phosphor is also proportional to the frequency; the departure from linearity at higher frequencies is believed to be related to the emission process rather than to the excitation or energy absorption process (Section III,E). Thornton has therefore suggested that it is not strange that the deterioration in output, which also depends on absorption of energy from the field if an electrolytic process is involved, should also vary linearly with frequency.

H. Excitation by Nonsinusoidal Voltages

The effect of voltage waveform on electroluminescence brightness has been studied by several workers. Waymouth and Bitter (216) reported that the integrated light output for a single pulse seemed to be independent of the rise or decay time if the latter was between 50 μsec and 50 msec. Piper and Williams (160) found that the output produced by a triangular voltage pulse depends only on the peak voltage and is independent of the width of the pulse if the latter is between 50 μsec and 0.5 sec. Early experiments by Lehmann in this laboratory also indicated that sinusoidal and square-wave voltages of equal peak-to-peak amplitude and frequency produced equal output. Kilburn et al. (398) and Johnson (400), however, obtained higher output with square waves than with sinusoidal waves under the same conditions,* while Georgobiani and Fok (see 247) found that the output produced by trapezoidal voltage pulses increased with the steepness of the pulses. Rajchman et al. (414), using pulses 40 μsec long or shorter, found that the output excited by pulses with exponential rise and decay is higher the "squarer" the pulse; the rising edge in this case is much more important than the trailing edge.

Some light is shed on this confused situation if the effect of the pulse length is considered (268, 397, 401, 403, 414). For very short pulses the output (for a constant repetition rate) increases as the pulse length is increased. If the pulses are sufficiently long, however, the output becomes independent of their duration. The pulse length required for saturation depends on the phosphor [it may be as short as 10 μsec (397, 403) or considerably longer] and also on the temperature, becoming shorter the higher

---

* The comparison of sinusoidal and square waves given by Nudelman and Matossi (415) must be treated with reserve since they refer only to the blue emission of double-band phosphors and changes in color with frequency could therefore affect the results (see Section III,E). Furthermore, the results they obtained with two different phosphors are quite different.

the temperature (397). This effect of pulse length may be understood on the basis of the formation of a polarization field, opposite in direction to the applied field, by accumulation of mobile carriers in a phosphor not in contact with electrodes (20, 216, 401). The relaxation time of the phosphor is determined by its resistivity* and permittivity ($t = \rho\epsilon/4\pi$) and will obviously decrease with increasing temperature. Once the polarization field is completely formed the effective field in the phosphor is zero; the light output will therefore not increase for longer times of external field application and the output will depend (at least to the first approximation) only on the peak applied voltage and not on the details of its variation with time. For shorter pulses, however, the output will be greater the longer the maximum voltage is applied and will therefore be greatest for the case of square waves.† In either case the output will usually depend upon the applied voltage according to Eq. (8) (397, 401, 414), as for the case of sinusoidal excitation.

Some of the earliest experiments on pulse excitation of electroluminescent phosphors were made by Waymouth and Bitter (216). If a direct voltage (or what amounts to the same thing, a voltage pulse) is applied to a ZnS:Cu phosphor embedded in an insulating medium and which has been allowed to rest for a very long time since the last excitation or has been de-excited by infrared radiation, then essentially no output is observed upon application of the voltage, but only at its removal. In the case of single crystals in contact with the electrodes, emission is observed during the voltage pulse as well, but this is followed by a burst of emission when the voltage is removed (264, 268). These results can easily be understood on the basis of the charge separation discussed above. Electrons released from the centers upon application of the field are swept away from the excitation region by the field to other regions of the crystal and can return to the empty centers and recombine with them to emit light only when the voltage is removed. These electrons can become trapped in regions where the electric field is lower than in the excitation region and their release is then facilitated by infrared radiation or by increased temperature. The existence of the polarization field thus produced was demonstrated by Waymouth and Bitter (216) by means of measurements with a ballistic galvanometer; it has been discussed by several workers (157, 268, 305, 401, 416–419). The fact that the emission in this case is delayed with respect to the excitation seems clearly established. In the case of manganese-activated phosphors, however, some or most of the light is also emitted upon initial

---

* Electroluminescent phosphors are nonlinear and hence the effective resistivity is difficult to specify.

† The fact that Johnson (400) obtained greater output for square waves even at 60 cps remains a problem.

application of the field (216, 236, 265, 420), in accord with the view that excitation of Mn centers involves only excited levels of the center and not complete ionization (see Section III,A).*

If the applied voltage (and the polarization) is maintained sufficiently long, radiationless transitions may occur and the output upon removal of the field will be consequently reduced (371). Waymouth and Bitter (371) and Zalm (2) have shown that maintaining the polarization also causes changes in the spectrum of the emitted light, the short wavelength emission disappearing more rapidly than that at longer wavelengths; this may be explained on the basis of readjustments between luminescence centers as shown in Fig. 18. If the voltage pulses are repeated, the relative heights

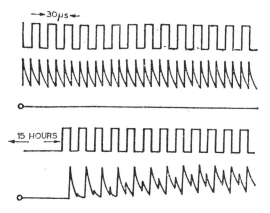

FIG. 29. Light output waveforms of electroluminescent cell excited with unidirectional voltage pulses. Top, after equilibrium has been established; bottom, when voltage is first applied. In each case the upper curve is the applied voltage and the lower curve is the light output. (From Kilburn et al., 398.)

of the two light pulses (at voltage application and removal) depends on the period between pulses; the shorter this period the larger the output at voltage application (216, 420, 421). Temperature also plays a role in this case (420, 421). For square-wave excitation (off-time and on-time equal) an equilibrium state of polarization is reached with essentially equal output pulses upon voltage application and removal, as shown at the top of Fig. 29. In this case the internal field is no longer unidirectional but alternates in direction about a "zero level" established by the polarization, similar to the case shown at the bottom of Fig. 30. When the voltage is initially applied

* Nudelman and Matossi (416) and Burns (215) concluded that the blue-emitting transitions in ZnS:Cu are also confined to the centers and that only the green emission involves the conduction band. This, however, does not seem in accord with the photo-conducting properties of such phosphors.

the output at the leading edge of the pulse builds up slowly from zero to its equilibrium value, as shown at the bottom of Fig. 29 (*2, 398*).

In Fig. 30 are shown some results obtained by Zalm (*2*) for a phosphor embedded in a conducting medium (tricresyl phosphate) for both unidirectional pulses and pulses of alternating polarity. In the former case very little light is emitted when the voltage is applied (the dc electroluminescence of this material is low). Most of the emission occurs in the absence of the voltage and the decay is very slow. When the same phosphor, however, is excited by alternating pulses of the same peak-to-peak amplitude and frequency, the output is more than twice that for unidirectional pulses.

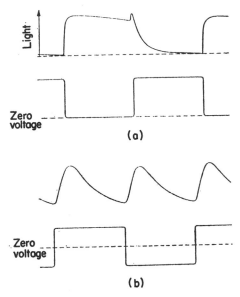

FIG. 30. Light output waveforms for electroluminescent ZnS:Cu,Cl phosphor suspended in tricresyl phosphate. (a) Excitation by square-wave unidirectional field; (b) Excitation by alternating square-wave field with same peak-to-peak amplitude and frequency. (From Zalm, *2*.)

The two half-cycles are identical as is to be expected and the decay of the emission is much faster than in the previous case. After reversal of the voltage the field is in such a direction as to aid return of the electrons to the centers emptied during the previous half cycle, while with unidirectional pulses (and a conducting medium) this return occurs under nearly field-free conditions and is therefore slower. Zalm (*2, 212*) and Frankl (*265*) showed, in accordance with this view, that reapplication of voltage in the opposite direction after removal of the original exciting pulse enhanced the output while reapplication in the original direction reduced it. Patek (*422*) states that the decay of the emission contains two components, the first being controlled by the voltage and the second by temperature.

These experiments of Waymouth and Bitter, Zalm, and Frankl afford evidence for the delayed character of the emission; other evidence will also be presented in the next section on sinusoidal excitation. Matossi and Nudelman (416, 417) and Zallen et al. (420) ,however, suggest as an alternative that upon removal of the external voltage additional excitation is produced by the presence of the polarization field which has been formed and that the emission in each case is concurrent with the excitation.* Kallmann et al. (423a) recently have apparently come to the same conclusion. They consider that the field due to "persistent internal polarization" (594) adds to the applied field when the latter is reversed to give a large enhancement of output; this effect they call "stored electroluminescence." In the case of sinusoidal excitation this stored polarization is probably dissipated before the applied voltage reaches its maximum value.

Many electroluminescent studies have been made with more complicated waveforms, including exponential (414, 416), trapezoidal (247), sawtooth (312, 416), half-sinusoidal (264, 304, 592), double pulses (305, 401, 422), and more complicated waveshapes (2, 345, 421). Some results obtained by Harper (312) with low-frequency sawtooth excitation of a thin phosphor film are shown in Fig. 31. Note that three light peaks occur for each half-cycle of applied voltage. The presence of these three peaks was observed earlier by other workers (265, 345, 392, 416), using other waveforms but they are most clearly resolved in Harper's work. The "in-phase" peaks, which occur when the voltage and current are a maximum, disappear if a sufficiently thick insulating layer is inserted between the film and the metal electrode so that carriers cannot enter the film. As discussed previously, "in-phase" peaks were also observed much earlier by Piper and Williams (158) in single crystals; although their "out-of-phase" peaks showed some structure they were not resolved into "primary" and "secondary" peaks. Since it is just these two types of out-of-phase peaks which are normally observed with sinusoidal excitation of phosphor powders embedded in dielectrics, discussion of them will be deferred to the next section.

Piper and Williams (158) attributed the out-of-phase peaks to excitation by electrons released by the field from centers within the crystal and the in-phase peaks to electrons tunneling from the electrodes; the in-phase peaks appeared only when the applied voltage was sufficiently high. On

---

* The statement of Piper and Williams (158) that they observed emission at a particular electrode on a ZnS crystal when it was becoming negative is inconsistent with a picture of delayed emission and also contrary to the results of Thornton (423) and Harper (312) with thin films.

this basis one would expect the out-of-phase peak to occur sooner in the cycle than the in-phase peak. With sinusoidal excitation the question of which peak occurs first is difficult to answer. However, when Watson *et al.* (*304*) and later Frankl (*264*) applied half-wave rectified sinusoidal voltages to ZnS single crystals they found that the out-of-phase-peak occurred on the decreasing side of the voltage pulse and, therefore, after the in-phase peak. As distinguished from the results of Piper and Williams, these workers found that the region of emission did not change location upon reversal of

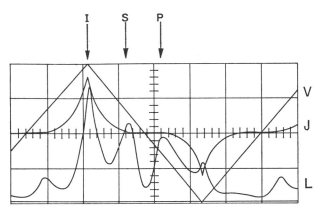

FIG. 31. Light output (*L*) and current (*J*) waveforms for 1.5μ electroluminescent ZnS:Cu,Cl film excited by sawtooth voltage (*V*). Repetition rate = 30 cps. Upward direction corresponds to transparent (tin oxide) electrode positive with respect to metal (Al) electrode. The three light peaks per half-cycle are designated in-phase (*I*), primary (*P*), and secondary (*S*). (From Harper, *312*.)

polarity, implying the existence of internal rather than cathodic barriers in their crystals. They explained the in-phase (90°) peak as due to immediate recombination and the out-of-phase (150–170°) peak* as due to "delayed emission." Watson, Dropkin and Halpin ascribed the delay to charge separation and trapping as discussed above. Since he observed no reverse current, which would be expected to accompany decay of space-charge polarization, Frankl originally assumed that the electrons are trapped in the immmediate vicinity of the luminescence centers and that this trapping is in some way aided, not hindered, by the field.† This view was later abandoned (*265*, *424*), however, and the out-of-phase peak was attributed to recombination at "centers left over from the previous half cycle," i.e., charge separation. The reverse current due to the returning electrons was later observed in single crystals (*268*).

* It may be noted that Frankl also observed other peaks at 30° and 180°.
† Neumark (*263*) also assumed that the field fills traps rather than emptying them.

It is of interest to note that Harper (*312*) found that the in-phase peaks exhibited no buildup when the voltage was first applied while the primary and secondary peaks did, implying the importance of electron trapping for the latter only (see Section III,*G,1*). The number of light peaks per second is obviously proportional to the alternating frequency. Harper found that the amplitude of the in-phase peaks is almost independent of frequency but that the area of the peak is inversely proportional to frequency (i.e., the in-phase peaks occupy a constant fraction of a cycle), so that the integrated light output arising from these peaks is essentially independent of frequency (at least for frequencies up to 500 cps), comfirming an earlier observation of Piper and Williams (*158*). The output due to the other two peaks increases with frequency as discussed earlier (Section III,*E*). Harper also observed, again in agreement with Piper and Williams, that the voltage dependence of the in-phase peaks is greater than that of the primary peaks (see Section III,*D*); he found the former to obey Eq. (9) and the latter Eq. (8). It is of interest, however, that he found the peak he identified as the secondary to vary in the same manner as the in-phase peak, not the other out-of-phase (primary) peak. In accordance with Thornton's observations of emission color for ac and dc excitation of films (Section III,*D*), Harper found the in-phase component of ZnS:Cu,Cl films to contain more shorter wavelength emission than the out-of-phase components.*

I. Output Waveshape for Sinusoidal Excitation and the Recombination Process

The detailed variation of the light output of an electroluminescent phosphor during one cycle of the applied alternating voltage, after equilibrium has been reached, is an interesting, although complicated, subject which also provides an insight into the mechanism of recombination in electroluminescence. Destriau (*1, 20, 308, 402, 425, 426*) always accorded great importance to the study of these "brightness waves"; Hahn (*308, 427–430*) and others have also studied them in detail. Unfortunately most of the experiments have been done on phosphors which are not typical of modern efficient electroluminescent materials. For conventional ZnS phosphor powders embedded in an insulating medium, in addition to the two main or "primary" output peaks observed per cycle of alternating voltage there are generally also two minor or "secondary" peaks. Several features of these waveforms are of interest and will be discussed below:†

---

* Frankl (*264*) states that the similar earlier observations of Watson *et al.* (*304*) on single crystals were due to accidental excitation by ultraviolet due to electrical breakdown; Frankl found no differences in emission color for the two peaks.

† The effect of irradiation (by ultraviolet, for example)on electroluminescent waveforms is discussed in Section V,*B,3*.

(1) the position of the primary peaks with respect to the alternating voltage;

(2) the relative heights of the alternate primary peaks occurring during successive half cycles;

(3) the position and height of the secondary peaks relative to the primary peaks for various operating conditions and the effect of phosphor composition;

(4) differences in emission color for primary and secondary peaks;

(5) the presence of a continuous component.

1. The Primary Peaks. The difference in height of successive primary peaks has been discussed by several workers (2, 212, 307, 308, 426, 427, 431). Unfortunately the experimental results are very conflicting. Both Destriau (307) and Zalm (2) found that the relative height of the two primary peaks depends on the applied voltage and reversals can occur. These workers, however, still disagree on details, Zalm stating that at high voltage the emission is greater on the cathode side and Destriau on the anode side. Hahn and Seemann (308) and Mattler (431) also found a similar reversal in some cases, while Vlasenko and Popkov (271) observed it in a thin phosphor film. Nonlinear voltage distribution in the phosphor-dielectric layer, field emission from the electrodes, and absorption and scattering of the emission have all been evoked to explain these effects but the situation is not clear; apparently many factors are involved (2, 157, 277, 287, 308, 426). Hahn and Seemann (308) found the peak heights to be equal if the output is taken from the side of the cell rather than through one electrode; in geometricaly dissimilar cells (one transparent and one metallic electrode, for example) additional complications arise.

Concerning the position of the primary peaks, Destriau (1, 20, 425) emphasized that in the case of phosphor powders embedded in a dielectric the field in the phosphor particles may not be in phase with the applied voltage. In support of this view he showed (307) that as the thickness of a layer of dielectric in the cell devoid of phosphor (often used for added protection against voltage breakdown) is increased, the position of the light peaks is shifted to earlier times relative to the voltage maximum, as is to be expected from simple electrical considerations. Burns (215) considered it more likely that the voltage in a dielectric-embedded phosphor was in phase with the current, i.e., out of phase with the applied voltage. Thornton (334) showed that the waveforms for powders with air, vacuum, or plastic dielectric are identical and later (423) that the application of a thin insulating layer to a phosphor film produces no change in the position of the peaks. He therefore concluded, in agreement with Zalm (2), that the voltage across the excitation region in the phosphor is in phase with the applied voltage.

Destriau (1, 20, 425) observed very early that the primary peak in ZnS:Cu phosphors usually precedes the voltage maximum and occurs earlier in the cycle the higher the applied voltage. This latter fact he explained on the basis of increased conductivity of the phosphor, using the relation $\tan \varphi = 4\pi/\epsilon\rho\omega$ (ϵ = permittivity, ρ = resistivity, and $\omega = 2\pi f$). This shift has been observed by many other workers (2, 334) but explained on different bases, to be discussed later. Destriau also observed (20, 307, 426) that as the alternating frequency of the applied voltage is increased the primary peak occurs later in the cycle. It may be noted that this is also in the direction predicted by the equation above. Destriau found that at very high frequencies the shift could be so great that the output peak occurs after the voltage maximum. Haake (419) also shows the brightness wave lagging the voltage at 10,000 cps. Destriau ascribed this lag to the decay time of the recombination process. Zalm (2) and Thornton (334), on the other hand, state that the emission never lags the voltage, but is at most in phase with it. Zalm assumes that the lag observed by Destriau was due to the series impedance of the transparent electrode of the cell.

Zalm (2) has explained the observed dependence of the position of the primary emission peak on voltage and frequency in terms of the delayed nature of the recombination. After the field is reversed the electrons must return to the empty luminescence centers for emission to occur. This return is obviously facilitated if the driving voltage is higher and also if sufficient time is allowed. The emission peak should therefore occur earlier in the cycle for high voltage and low frequency, as observed. On the basis that this is the rate-determining step and that the recombination is monomolecular, he obtained for the location of the peak the relation

$$\cos (\omega t)_m = \left[\left(\frac{\omega}{CV}\right)^2 + 1\right]^{1/2} - \frac{\omega}{CV}, \tag{20}$$

where C is a constant. Zalm considered neither electron trapping nor the effect of space charge in this calculation. It is difficult to understand, however, why the transit time for the returning electrons should be the determining factor. Since experimentally $(\omega t)_m$ may be about 45°, $(\omega/CV) = 0.36$ (2). If the distance to be traversed is 10μ (roughly the particle diameter), the field strength is 5×10^4 volt/cm, and $f = 100$ cps then, since $C = \mu/d^2$, the required mobility μ would be only 3.5×10^{-5} cm²/volt-sec. This figure is very small compared to the value 120 cm²/volt-sec measured for ZnS by Kröger (432).

Thornton (334) and later Georgobiani and Fok (432a), on the other hand, assumed that the rate-determining step is the field-controlled thermal release of trapped electrons. The brightness wave is therefore a kind of field-controlled glow curve. Thornton developed a model based on reduction of the trap depth by the field. This mechanism also leads to facilitated return of the electrons to the excitation region, and hence an earlier primary peak, for high voltage and low frequency as well as for high temperature. He experimentally observed such a shift for increasing temperature but it was small compared to that for changing the voltage or frequency. This last fact is somewhat difficult to understand since one would expect the usual exponential dependence of release rate on temperature to have a greater effect than that of voltage or frequency. However, since it is known that trapping is important for other aspects of electroluminescence (temperature dependence of integrated light output, secondary waves, etc.) it is to be expected that it should also play a role here. Furthermore, since Thornton's model is in good agreement with many observations concerning the dependence of the integrated output, which is due mainly to the primary peak (see Section III,E), it is reasonable to expect that it should also apply to the output as a function of time.

Morehead (*345*) has considered this problem further. He applied a complicated wave shape consisting of a negative pulse for producing the excitation following by a positive-going sawtooth to control the recombination. It was found that the primary peak occurred at a critical voltage (V_m) on the sawtooth; although changing the magnitude or duration of the ionizing pulse altered the size of the primary peak, its position was unaffected. The value of V_m increased with increasing rate of rise of the sawtooth voltage, which corresponds to increasing the frequency in the sinusoidal case, and also with decreasing temperature; the total light output during the primary, however, was unaffected by these variables. Georgobiani and Fok (*433*) also observed a similar critical voltage with a trapezoidal waveform. Figure 32 shows the results obtained by Morehead with a more complicated waveshape and a ZnS,ZnO:Cu,Cl phosphor apparently having more than one kind of trap. The peaks 1, 1′, and 1″ all occur at the same voltage and presumably arise from the same kind of traps; the peaks 2 and 3 appear at progressively higher voltage and are ascribed to deeper traps. From an analysis of the shape of the emission peak for sawtooth excitation Morehead concluded that the experiments were not in agreement with Thornton's model of a field-reduced trap depth but were consistent with sweeping away by the field of electrons released thermally from traps, i.e., a modification of Zalm's picture which introduces temperature as a factor. In Eq. (20) the factor C is now replaced by $C \exp(-E/kT)$, where E is the trap depth, so that the dependence of the position of the primary peak on temperature is also explained. Trap depths calculated on the basis of this model were in good agreement with those obtained from thermoluminescence measurements.

As discussed above, it is difficult to understand that transport of the electrons to the centers should be the rate-determining step, as assumed by Zalm (2) and Morehead (345), even at very low frequencies. Thornton (435a) has made observations at frequencies as low as 0.01 cps and finds that light is emitted over most of the cycle and has the shape characteristic of the primary peak at higher frequencies. This indicates that recombination can be retarded until at least a minute after the excitation even though a low field in the right direction has been present for many seconds. The conclusion seems to be that trapped electrons are not released until a field of the proper magnitude is present. Thornton (435a) has also shown that if a small voltage of 5 volts, 400 cps is superimposed on a potential of 100

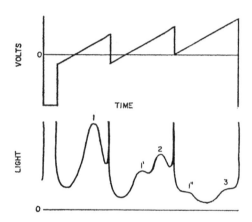

FIG. 32. Brightness waveform for ZnS,ZnO:Cu,Cl phosphor produced by pulse and multiple sawtooth voltage waveform. The peaks 1, 1', and 1'' all occur at the same voltage. (From Morehead, 345.)

volts, one cps used for exciting an electroluminescent phosphor, almost 100% modulation of the light emission is observed. This can be understood on the basis of an exponential dependence of release rate on field strength, but it would appear that a much higher variation in voltage would be required to give such a large effect if transit time were the determining factor. The multiple peaks observed by Morehead (Fig. 32) also seem to indicate an effect of the field on electron release from traps despite his contrary opinion. It should also be noted that the shape of curves giving the output as a function of time calculated from Thornton's model (334) also resemble the experimental curves for sinusoidal excitation quite well and better than do those from Zalm's model (2). The value of the trap depth required to give proper fit to the observed shape was also in reasonable agreement with that obtained from thermoluminescence measurements. In addition, Thornton's model leads directly to the presence of a continuous component (to be discussed below), whereas Zalm's (even modified for trapping) does not.

At sufficiently low temperatures Morehead found that the value of the critical voltage V_m no longer increased but reached a limiting value which seemed to be directly related to the major trap depth (at least for the two phosphors used). Morehead therefore concluded that under these conditions, where thermal release becomes negligible, electrons are released from the traps by collision of accelerated conduction electrons as proposed by Curie (157, 434) for the Gudden-Pohl effect. Georgobiani and Fok (433) found a very complicated variation of the critical voltage V_m with temperature. They also concluded that below room temperature the release of electrons from traps is due to a collision mechanism; for higher temperature they ascribed the release to tunneling. These workers therefore agree with Thornton that detrapping is the rate-controlling process and that this rate is determined by the field. In an early paper (433) they differ from Thornton, however, in saying that the field is the only important factor and that temperature has no direct effect. They reached this conclusion because in their phosphors neither temperature nor frequency affected the position of the primary peak appreciably. As seen above, however, this is not usually the case. Later (432a), however, they accepted Thornton's model.

Kuchar (435) has also given a model for the primary peak of the brightness wave on the basis of back-to-back Mott-Schottky barriers. Electrons penetrating these barriers are assumed to recombine with empty activator centers. The mechanism by which the activator centers were emptied is not discussed, nor is electron trapping or delayed emission assumed. The effect of temperature enters only through the barrier penetration factor. Although this model differs markedly from those due to Thornton or Zalm, as modified by Morehead, and apparently neglects many important factors, it gives brightness waves in surprisingly good agreement with experiment.

If the primary peak is due to electrons released from traps, then the question arises as to what happens when traps of more than one depth exist. Although it seems quite likely that the multiple peaks observed by Morehead (345) (see Fig. 32) result from such an effect, until recently multiple primary peaks had not been observed for conventional sinusoidal excitation. Thornton (435a) has, however, now observed an additional peak which behaves very much like a primary peak. It may occur very early in the cycle, before the usual primary, near or even before the voltage zero in some cases; this is taken as an indication that it arises from relatively shallow traps. With decreasing temperature it occurs later in the cycle while its amplitude first increases and then decreases. Since the normal primary peak decreases in size continuously in this range, the "additional primary" peak may predominate at low temperatures. In one case a third peak was observed at very low temperatures. The fact that the additional peaks are usually seen only for high voltage excitation also seems consistent with the idea that the responsible traps are shallow; for lower excitation intensity only the "normal" deep traps are filled. Because the traps involved are so shallow, this peak is also favored by low temperature and high frequency, which limit the return of the trapped electrons to the luminescence centers. This new peak is distinguished from the usual secondary peak (to be discussed below) by the fact that the former consists predominantly of blue emission and the latter of green; the secondary peak is also favored by the opposite conditions of low voltage and high temperature (but also by high frequency).

2. The Secondary Peaks. We turn now to a discussion of the more complicated, and often elusive, secondary peaks of green or blue emitting ZnS:Cu phosphors. These normally minor peaks are often not well resolved. They occur near (and usually before) the time the applied voltage passes through zero. Destriau (*426*) first observed that the secondary may appear either on the descending side of one primary peak or the ascending side of the following primary. Later he reported (*1, 307*) that as the voltage is increased the secondary peak may shift from the descending position to the ascending position, i.e., later in the cycle. It should be noted that the direction of this shift is opposite to that for the primary peak. Some workers seem to note no affect of voltage on the position of the secondary peak, perhaps because of its occurrence in the cycle near zero voltage. Thornton, however, states that the secondary shifts in the same direction as the primary peak. Destriau (*1, 307*), working with early and relatively poor phosphors, concluded that the secondary peak occurs only when one electrode is metallic and in contact with the phosphor or separated from it by only a thin insulator, or when many particle-to-particle contacts occur.* He also used electrodes of various metals and concluded that the work function of the electrode has an effect on the phase position of the primary peaks, on differences in height of successive primaries, and on the secondary peaks. Hahn and Seemann (*308*) also made somewhat similar observations.

Although Destriau (*307*) states that the secondary peak disappears for operation at high frequency, this probably arose from observations on

---

* It seems quite possible that what Destriau observed in these cases was really an "in-phase" peak rather than a true secondary. Confusion in the identification of secondaries seems also to have arisen in other cases. Thus Nudelman and Matossi (*416*), Morehead (*345*), Hahn and Seemann (*305, 430*), and Patek (*422, 436*) consider the emission peak occurring at removal of a voltage pulse as a secondary; it seems quite possible that such a peak combines the properties of the primary and secondary peaks observed with sinusoidal excitation.

phosphors where it coalesced with a primary peak and could not be separately resolved. Zalm (2), Matossi (418), and Thornton find that its amplitude increases with increasing frequency. Zalm (2) also states that it increases with decreasing applied voltage. Jerome and Gungle (341) observed that the primary peak occurs when the voltage and current are in phase and hence the phosphor is absorbing power from the field while the secondary occurs when they are out of phase, corresponding to release of stored energy. If the phosphor is irradiated with ultraviolet the secondary peak disappears (418, 437, 439a); Matossi (418, 439a) found that after removal of the ultraviolet radiation several minutes might be required for the secondary peak to reappear.

A secondary peak is normally not observed in ZnS:Cu,Mn phosphors (236, 334, 431)*, where the transitions are normally considered to be localized in the luminescence centers, and this is suggestive that it is related to the action of the field on trapped conduction electrons, as apparently first proposed by Zalm et al. (212). Mattler (431) also pointed out that the position of the light peak (primary) for ZnS:Cu,Mn is only slightly dependent on voltage or frequency, again in accord with the model of the Mn center; this, however, does not always seem to be the case. A secondary peak is also absent in red-emitting ZnS:Cu (2), other phosphors with small trap depth (212), organic materials (1), or SiC (442) (for SiC only an in-phase peak is observed). On the other hand it is very pronounced in phosphors containing oxygen (2, 20, 425), which is known to introduce deep traps in ZnS (254), and in weakly emitting (Zn,Cd)S:Ag phosphors (334). Narita (253) found that single crystals of ZnS:Cu showed only small out-of-phase peaks unless Cl (which introduces traps) was also present, in which case the emission was also quenched by infrared radiation.†

The secondary peak usually disappears at high temperatures, where the lifetime of trapped electrons is very short, and at very low temperatures, where the lifetime is very long (212, 419, 429, 431). Zalm et al. (212) and Hahn and Seemann (428) observed that as the temperature is varied the height of the secondary may grow and then disappear more than once, corresponding to traps of different depths. Patek (436) found that the height of the secondary is a minimum relative to the primary at the same temperature at which the thermoluminescence curve shows a maximum. Haake

---

* It may be noted that if Mn emission is sensitized by Cu centers a secondary peak should apparently occur; its absence may therefore be taken as indicating direct excitation of Mn centers. Zalm (2) has shown, however, that with ZnS:Cu,Mn,Al in a conducting medium a small out-of-phase peak is also observed.

† Destriau (20) very early commented on the absence of quenching of electroluminescence by infrared radiation. Although Heckscher (443) later reported such quenching, it seems to be great only in phosphors containing Pb.

(419) also observed that the temperature for maximum secondary amplitude shifts to higher values as the frequency is increased similar to the behavior of the integrated output which is due mainly to the primary peak (Section III,E), and also to higher values as the voltage is decreased.

Not only the amplitude, but also the position of the secondary peak is a function of temperature. Mattler (431) and Haake (419) observed that if the frequency is kept constant and the temperature is decreased the secondary moves continuously from the decending side of one primary peak to the ascending side of the next primary (see Fig. 33). The reverse sequence is also seen if the temperature is maintained constant and the frequency decreased (419), as also shown in Fig. 33. Similar shifts of the secondary have also been observed by Patek (436) and Hahn and Seemann (429).

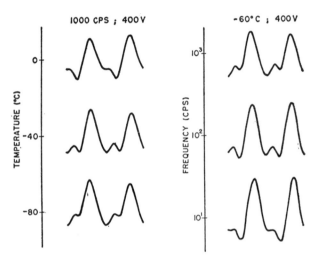

FIG. 33. Effect of temperature and frequency on position of secondary peak of brightness waveform. (From Haake, 376.)

Thornton, however, has never observed a secondary peak on the ascending side of a primary peak; it is probably significant that the phosphor used by Haake in his studies had very deep traps and exhibited persistence after electroluminescence excitation, which is in strong contrast to modern highly developed materials. Hahn and Seemann (429) show a more startling example which on first sight seems to indicate that for a small temperature increase of only 8°C (−86 to −78) the secondary peak shifts from the ascending side of the primary peak to the descending side of the same primary peak, a position about 70° later in the cycle. As they point out, however, careful observation indicates that what really happened is that the secondary peak actually shifted to a position slightly (20°) earlier in the cycle but increased greatly in size while at the same time the primary became drastically reduced so that on the basis of size rather than position the primary now appears to be a secondary, and vice versa. Fortunately situations such as this are not common.*

Matossi (418) attempted to explain the presence of the two brightness peaks for each half cycle of voltage on the basis of polarization. In his words: "Transitions to traps are not included. These are not important in electroluminescence, as indicated by the much faster decay with field excitation compared to that with ultraviolet excitation." As discussed above, however, the importance of traps in determining the shape of the brightness waves (as well as other properties) is shown by many factors (effects of composition, temperature, etc.) and had been pointed out earlier by Zalm et al. (212). Haake (419) made an analysis on the basis of trapping action and polarization which easily explains the shift in position of the secondary peak with temperature and frequency (Fig. 33). Both high temperature and long times (low frequency) favor detrapping and hence cause the secondary peak to occur earlier in the cycle. Haake and later Patek (436) showed that on this basis it was possible to obtain trap depths from measurements on the secondary peaks which were in good agreement with those obtained from conventional thermoluminescence experiments. Haake's analysis is deficient, however, in that it does not include the effect of voltage. It would seem that the theory developed by Thornton (334) originally for primary peaks, based on field controlled thermal release from traps, might apply to the secondary peaks as well. As mentioned previously, however, not only is data on the effect of voltage on the secondary peaks scarce, but it seems contradictory to what one might expect; for example, increasing the voltage is reported in some cases to cause the secondary to occur later in time (307) and at higher temperatures (419).

Since the secondary peak may occur either on the ascending or the descending side of a primary peak, or equidistant between two primary peaks (see Fig. 33), it was initially difficult to know to which primary it was logically related. Much confusion has arisen, and still exists, on this point. Thus Frankl (265), Morehead (345), and Harper (312) (see Fig. 31) show the secondary preceding the primary, while Thornton (334) assumed, without discussion, that it follows the primary; Patek in two papers (422, 436) published a year apart took first the latter and then the former view with no apparent notice of such a drastic change in viewpoint. A definite answer to this question seems first to have been given by Zalm (2). As shown in Fig. 34, he superimposed a small voltage pulse on the sinusoidal exciting voltage at various positions in the cycle (although the effect of several pulse positions is shown in the figure, during the experiments the pulse was

---

* It is possible that the peak recently identified by Thornton (435a) as an "additional primary" may in some instances have been confused with a secondary peak.

applied at only one position at a time). The first few pulses shown only add to or subtract from the effect of the sinusoidal voltage. Of great interest, however, is the pulse shown at t_a, in phase with the sinusoidal voltage. Although it produces a momentary increase in output, its major effect is seen as a general enhancement during the following half-cycle, including both the primary and the secondary peaks. It seems clear that the secondary peak belongs to the primary preceding it. The last pulse shown, of opposite polarity, causes exactly the opposite effect. Haake (*376*) later repeated

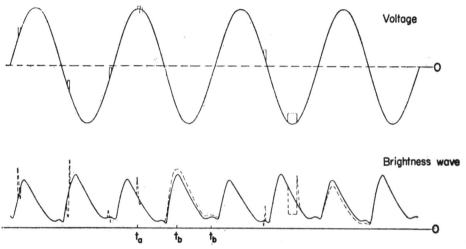

FIG. 34. Influence of a small test pulse on the electroluminescence brightness waves excited by sinusoidal voltage. Solid curve, light output without pulse; dashed line, output with pulse. (From Zalm, *2*.)

these experiments with better resolution of the primary and secondary peaks and obtained the same results. The effect of such a "probe pulse" is seen for a complete cycle, clearly demonstrating the delayed nature of the emission. That the secondary follows the primary rather than vice versa is also shown by the observation of Haake (*376*) that the first peak emitted during buildup of emission after initial application of a sinusoidal voltage is a primary peak, followed by a secondary. Patek (*444*) also later used a "probe pulse" superimposed on excitation by pulses of alternating polarity.

Thus far it has been concluded that the secondary peak is due to traps, but there still remains the questions as to where these traps are located in the phosphor crystal.* If return of free electrons is responsible for the

* Because of the low intensities, no observations have been made of secondary peaks in the light from single emitting spots, which should simplify matters if it were possible. As it is, one must bear in mind that the waveforms observed represent the combined emission of many spots and hence some details may be lost.

primary peak, as assumed by Zalm (2), then the most obvious location of the traps responsible for the secondary peak would be in the region which was the instantaneous anode ("low-field region") during excitation; this was the original view taken by Haake (419). If, however, it is assumed that the primary peak is also produced by detrapping, as emphasized by Thornton (334), then one must explain the difference between the action resulting in the primary and that which causes the secondary. Because of the delayed nature of the emission, the traps which are responsible for the primary peak are assumed to be in that part of the crystal which was the "low-field region" during the excitation process in the "high-field region." They not only determine the shape and position of the primary peak but are also important, since the primary is the major part of the emission, in determining the frequency and temperature dependence of the integrated light output (Section III,E). But why does the secondary peak occur? One obvious suggestion would be to ascribe the primary peak to electrons, thermally released from these traps, which can return to the excited centers in what was formerly the high-field region when the field (including polarization effects) is reversed; the secondary peak could arise from electrons liberated from the same traps later when the internal field has become high enough to influence the release rate. This simple model is, however, most likely not correct since it does not seem to give the correct phase positions for the primary and secondary peaks relative to the applied voltage. The phase relationships are more plausible if the secondary is ascribed to thermal release and the primary to field-controlled release as proposed by Georgobiani and Fok (433) but then the secondary would precede the primary rather than follow it as observed.

Zalm (2) has, however, attributed the secondary peak to electrons which, in returning to the excitation region to form the primary peak, "overshoot" the empty centers and become trapped in what was the high-field (cathodic) region during excitation. They can then return and have a second try at recombination only after the internal field is reversed. This model was later also accepted by Haake (376), who noted that "During the previous excitation process the electrons had to travel a certain distance before they acquired sufficient energy to collision-ionize luminescence centers, thus leaving behind a small region with virtually no empty luminescence centers." That at least some of the returning electrons can pass through the cloud of ionized centers without recombining is reasonable in view of the recombination coefficient of 10^{-14} cm^3/sec given by Zalm (2).* Figure 35 is a diagrammatic representation of this model, due to Patek (436). It will be noted that according to this picture the traps responsible for the

---

* The low efficiency of dc electroluminescence is also explained by the very low recombination predicted on this basis.

primary and the corresponding secondary peak are in different regions of the crystal. The electrons responsible for the secondary peak have in fact been trapped twice, as pointed out by Patek (*436*) in commenting that not only the absolute magnitude of the secondary but also its ratio to the primary can be correlated with the glow curve. According to this model the secondary naturally follows the primary, in agreement with Fig. 34.

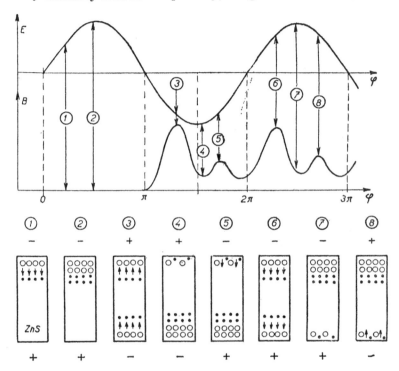

FIG. 35. Schematic representation of Zalm's model (2) for origin of secondary peaks in brightness wave. *E*, applied voltage; *B*, electroluminescence brightness. Below, the empty circles denote ionized luminescence centers and the black dots denote trapped electrons. (From Patek, *436*.)

Frankl (*265*) presented a model in which the variable width of the barrier responsible for the excitation as a function of the applied voltage is an important factor. Figure 36 is a schematic representation of the process as given by Patek (*422*). The upper diagrams show the situation for no applied voltage and represent two back-to-back barriers, as assumed also by Piper and Williams (*160*). When voltage is applied (second row of diagrams) the cathode barrier widens and the anode barrier disappears. During this period luminescence centers in the barrier are emptied by impact of electrons entering from the cathode and recombination of some of the incoming

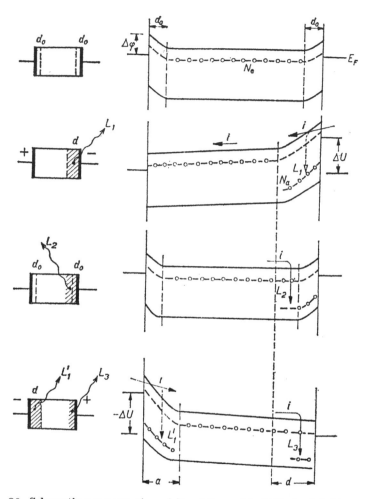

FIG. 36. Schematic representation of Frankl's model (265) for brightness waves. The drawings on the left indicate the barrier widths (dotted lines) and area of ionized luminescence centers (shaded) at four points during the voltage cycle as indicated. The drawings on the right indicate the potential distribution across the crystal. L_1 and L'_1 correspond to the in-phase peak, L_2 to the secondary, and L_3 to the primary peak. (From Patek, 422.)

electrons produces the in-phase peak, still in agreement with Piper and Williams. While the applied voltage is decreasing (third row), electrons recombine with the empty centers in the diminishing (but still present) cathode barrier region and cause the secondary peak. When the voltage (bottom diagrams) is reversed this barrier disappears and recombination in the region immediately adjacent to the electrode produces the primary peak; at the same time the barrier at the other end of the crystal is growing and in-phase emission occurs later in time. The situation in insulated crystals is assumed to be the same except for the absence of the in-phase peak; internal barriers in this case may serve as the source of electrons.

According to Frankl's model (265) the in-phase and out-of-phase peaks result from the same accelerated electrons rather than electrons released from the electrode and from donors inside the crystal, respectively, as assumed by Piper and Williams (160). The out-of-phase peaks also follow the in-phase peaks as observed by Watson et al. (304). The attempt to explain the occurrence of both primary and secondary peaks is also an improvement over Piper and Williams and Thornton (334), who did not consider the secondary peak. The primary and secondary peaks both occur near the electrode which was the cathode during excitation, although not precisely in the same region. In this model, however, the secondary precedes the primary peak, which is contrary to the observations of Zalm (2) and Haake (376). The expression obtained for the primary peak is similar to that of Thornton (334) and predicts the correct shift of the peak to later times for decreasing voltage or increasing frequency. In developing the theory for this model, Frankl neglected the action of traps or of temperature. He, however, did obtain the result that the secondary peak should occur later in the cycle the higher the voltage. As noted above, this seems to be in agreement with some observations and opposite to any effect of the field on trapped electrons. Patek (422) has also used a similar model including the effect of temperature on the returning electrons.

Thornton (423) has recently performed some interesting experiments on the brightness waves obtained from thin ZnS:Cu,Cl phosphor films (about one micron thick). In these films the emission occurred almost entirely when the metallic electrode (Al) was positive (see also 312). No in-phase emission peak was observed. A plastic coating several microns thick under the metallic electrode produced no change in the waveform. Thicker ZnS films (6–8μ thick) gave equal emission on both half-cycles. Except for the fact that emission occurred during only one half-cycle, the waveforms produced by these thin films were identical to those obtained for powder suspensions. Since only one primary and one secondary occurred per cycle the order was apparent; the secondary always followed the primary (see also 368), in agreement with Zalm (2) and Haake (376). The currents in these films were independent of polarity. Thornton points out that the waveforms for the resistive component of current and for the emission are similar in shape and in phase.

Thornton (423) found that clipping the sinusoidal voltage applied to these films on either polarity resulted in a drastic reduction in output but, of course, also a reduction in voltage. Addition of dc voltage component while maintaining the ac component constant showed, however, that the reduced output is not due only to the magnitude of the voltage. Either direction of dc reduced the output strongly; positive bias on the metallic electrode also shifted the primary peak to earlier times in the cycle while negative bias affected only the amplitude of the peak. (These experiment were done at voltages below those at which the ac-dc enhancement effect (368) occurs.) This shows that a process necessary for light emission occurs during each half cycle even though the actual emission occurs only when the metal is positive. The results are consistent with a model in which excitation occurs when the metal is negative* while the emission is delayed and occurs during the next half-cycle. Positive bias reduces the voltage during the negative half-cycle and hence reduces the number of excited centers and the output which occurs later. Because of the larger positive voltage swing, however, recombination occurs sooner; in this case all the trapped electrons and excited centers recombine. Negative bias increases the number of centers excited during the negative half-cycle but reduces the voltage available to return the electrons during the positive half-cycle. The excited centers are therefore not completely filled so that the emission is reduced and maximum emission occurs nearly in phase with the voltage. This result is consistent with that of Frankl (265) on the effect of voltage in driving electrons back to the excitation region.

Numerous experiments have been discussed above which support the view that the emission in electroluminescent phosphors is delayed by half a cycle or so with respect to the excitation process. It has also been pointed out that Matossi and Nudelman (416, 417) and Zallen et al. (420) disagree with this point of view, although they are definitely in the minority. Loebner and Hegyi (447) studied the electroluminescence waveforms in crystals of GaP-GaN, containing predominantly GaP, which possessed striations similar to those observed in ZnS crystals. In this case the output was always symmetrical about the voltage maximum. However, increasing the applied voltage resulted in either one, two, or three peaks in a half-cycle. These they interpreted on the basis of superposition of three different phenomena, all occurring in phase with the voltage and the current: (1) electroluminescence at low fields, (2) quenching of electroluminescence by the field at intermediate strengths, and (3) another electroluminescence mechanism at high fields. Such effects could obviously lead to the sequence of peaks as observed.

---

* For a discussion of the emission of these films for dc excitation see Section III,D. Cusano (445) also observed that the X-ray excited luminescence of ZnS:Cu,Mn,Cl films is enhanced by a field (see Section V,D,1) only if the metal electrode is negative; Williams (237, 446) interpreted this as indicating that only in this case is a potential barrier formed. Even in Cusano's experiments, however, the current showed no such effect of polarity (see Fig. 72).

Loebner and Hegyi (*447*) also suggested that a similar situation holds true in ZnS. The secondary peak would then not have a distinct origin but would appear only as a result of quenching in the region between the primary and the secondary where the voltage is highest, since the primary peak usually occurs before the voltage maximum. The secondary would not be the result of trapping, although its height relative to the primary might be affected in this way, thus explaining the asymmetry of the output in ZnS. Thomsen (*346a*) also believes that the secondary peak is caused by competing nonradiative processes. It is true that the application of a field to a nonelectroluminescent phosphor will in most cases result in quenching of photoluminescence (see Section V,*B*) and a similar result would not be unexpected in electroluminescence as well.* Studies of brightness waves when both an electric field and radiation are applied to a phosphor, however, seem to indicate distinct differences between the behavior in the quenching effect and in electroluminescence (Section V,*B,3*). The experiments of Goldberg (*249*) on the differential action of Co and Ni on the secondary peaks also seem difficult to explain if they are due to an instantaneous quenching process, as would the delayed effect due to probe pulses observed by Zalm (Fig. 34).

Various observers have noticed a difference in emission color for the primary and secondary peaks in ZnS:Cu. Destriau (*426*) commented on such a difference without giving any details. Other workers (*212, 334, 448*) have found that the content of green emission, relative to blue, is higher in the secondary peak than in the primary peak. This is, of course, consistent with the usual model of transfer of excitation from blue to green centers and may, indeed, be considered as additional evidence that the secondary peak follows the associated primary peak, rather than vice versa.

3. The Continuous Component. In addition to the primary and secondary peaks in the output waveform when a phosphor is excited by a sinusoidal voltage, there may also be a continuous component, i.e., the emission may never become zero during the cycle except for very low frequency. Experimentally, however, it is often difficult to separate the primary, secondary and continuous components. Destriau (*1, 425*) found that the continuous component continues to increase in magnitude with increasing frequency while the height of the alternating component of the output (determined mainly by the primary peak) reaches a maximum value at some intermediate frequency. He concluded that the continuous component was

* Such quenching seems to have been observed for pulse excitation by Bonch-Bruevich and Marenkov (*403*) and in the ac-dc effect (Fig. 17). Care must be taken, however, to distinguish between true quenching (a decrease in integrated output) and the effect of a field in determining when the emission occurs without changing the total amount of emission (*2, 265*).

correlated with the decay time of the emission as measured after removal of the exciting voltage; phosphors which had a long decay time had a small periodic component compared to continuous component. Unpublished studies by Thornton and the writer confirm this view. The continuous component is greater in ZnS:Cu,Mn than in ZnS:Cu under the same conditions and is also greater in green-emitting phosphors than for blue. In these experiments, however, the maximum periodic component was reached at a frequency of 5000–10,000 cps, which is much higher than indicated by Destriau's data. It is also found that the continuous component increases relative to the periodic component as the applied voltage is increased (334); however, the periodic component always increases in absolute magnitude with increasing voltage.

Georgobiani and Fok (247, 449) also studied the continuous component with excitation by trapezoidal voltage pulses and found it to become large compared to the average brightness for high repetition rate, low peak voltage (small effect only), and high rate of rise of voltage. They also state that infrared radiation quenches the constant component but barely affects the periodic component. These workers conclude that the excitation diffuses from the high-field region into the volume of the crystals (probably by hole migration) and that this is the origin of the continuous component (see also 370a); this conclusion, however, seems unlikely.* It may also be noted that the presence of a continuous component follows directly from Thornton's model of field-controlled thermal release from traps of the electrons responsible for the recombination (334). This model also predicts that the continuous component should decrease as the temperature is lowered according to the usual exponential factor involving the trap depth. The experimental variation is in the predicted direction. Kuchar's model (435) also predicts that the continuous component should increase with increasing voltage.

Goldberg (249) has studied the effects on the brightness waves of the addition of Ni or Co to ZnS:Cu,Cl. He found that $1 \times 10^{-2}\%$ Ni was sufficient to suppress both the secondary peak and the continuous component of the emission, even at frequencies as high as 10,000 cps. For lower concentrations of Ni the height of the secondary peak is reduced and it occurs earlier in the cycle. On the other hand, Co does not affect the continuous component. At as little as $3 \times 10^{-4}\%$ Co, however, the secondary is completely suppressed but reappears again at the same phase position for higher amounts of Co. These results are generally consistent with a picture of the secondary peak and of the decay as due to traps and the

* One fact on which this conclusion was based is their observation that the continuous component builds up much more slowly than the periodic component. Figure 24 indicates that this is, however, not necessarily true.

effects of Ni and Co on such traps (*194, 254*); many details have yet to be explained, however.

The study of brightness waves in the ac-dc enhancement effect observed by Thornton (*368*) has also given information concerning the mechanism for this process. The light is emitted predominantly during the half-cycle when the alternating voltage opposes the direct voltage. The position of the light peak in the ac-dc effect is observed to shift to later times for high frequency or low ac voltage in the same manner as for the normal primary peak for ac excitation. These facts were interpreted as indicating that the action of the alternating voltage is mainly to force electrons (including those trapped in other regions of the crystal) to return to excited luminescence centers (primarily in the cathode region) produced by the direct voltage. The probability of capture by these centers of electrons flowing through the crystal (dc efficiency) is low but is increased by an appreciable factor by the bucking action of the alternating voltage. The increase in output is similar in origin to the burst of emission observed by Frankl (*264*) and by Steinberger *et al.* (*268*) when a direct voltage is removed from a single crystal; in the ac-dc case the effect of the direct voltage is removed or reduced during each negative swing of the alternating voltage. That the spectrum of the enhanced emission is identical to that of the normal ac electroluminescence rather than the bluer emission observed for dc excitation alone also indicates that the emission occurs in a low-field region.

J. Mechanism of Electroluminescence in ZnS, Particularly the Excitation Process

It has been shown in the previous sections that many of the detailed characteristics of electroluminescent ZnS phosphors (dependence of integrated light output on temperature, deviation of output from linear dependence at high frequency, position of primary and secondary output peaks, build-up, etc.) can be explained reasonably well by considering only the recombination process with no regard for the mechanism responsible for emptying the luminescence centers into which the recombination occurs. Obvious exceptions are the voltage dependence of the output and the nominally linear dependence of output on the frequency of the alternating excitation. The principle features of the recombination process are the transport of carriers away from and then to the region of excited luminescence centers, giving rise to the delayed nature of the emission, and the influence of electron trapping in the "low-field" regions of the crystal. Some of the possible mechanisms of electroluminescence excitation have already been reviewed in Section II; in this section the considerations will be restricted to ZnS phosphors.

Excitation by the Zener effect or field ionization of luminescence centers, although suggested as a possibility by Destriau (*20*) and by Ueta (*74*), does not seem likely because of the very high field strengths required for such processes due to the high energy separation in ZnS (*2, 5, 157, 159, 160* and Section II,*D*). It has been customary to assume that the luminescence centers in electroluminescent ZnS:Cu are excited (actually, ionized) by collision of electrons accelerated in the conduction band by the applied field, as also suggested by Destriau (*20*). The theory of the acceleration-collision process was developed by Curie (*157*) and by Piper and Williams (*5, 160*). Curie considered the acceleration to occur in the volume of the phosphor although he conceded that potential barriers at the surface might serve as the source of the initial carriers. Piper and Williams, however, considered the acceleration and ionization to occur within potential barriers. They, and also Waymouth and Bitter (*216*), pointed out that since the field strengths in electroluminescent ZnS are not far below those for dielectric breakdown, a system consisting of such a barrier in series with a wider region of low field would contribute to electrical stability. The experimental evidence for the existence of small regions in the phosphor where the excitation and emission are localized have been reviewed in Section III,*B*.

In their detailed calculation (*160*), Piper and Williams assumed that the potential barrier is of the Mott-Schottky exhaustion type and arises from ionization of shallow donors either thermally or by very low voltages. For the source of electrons accelerated by the field they assume the presence of another set of deeper donors with concentration much lower than the shallow donors; various distributions of such deep donors were assumed for the analysis. These deep donors were assumed to be ionized by the action of the field if the latter is above a critical threshold value. This last assumption seems unwarranted in view of what is now known concerning the nonexistence of such a threshold (Section III,*D*), but was believed to be consistent with the experimental data available at the time. For the case of the in-phase or dc emission, tunneling of electrons from the electrodes was assumed. This theory resulted in complicated algebraic functions for the dependence of output on voltage, depending on the deep donor distribution assumed, rather than the exponential dependence [Eq. (8)] which is now found to describe the experimental results. However, fair fit to experimental data over a range of three decades in brightness was achieved. The shape of the brightness wave was also calculated, although the delayed nature of the emission was not considered.

Waymouth and Bitter (*216*) emphasized the importance of charge separation and delayed emission. These authors, as well as Burns (*215*), discussed qualitatively the barrier model for electroluminescence excitation. The origin of the initial electrons which are accelerated has always seemed to be a troublesome point in the acceleration-collision model. Garlick (*9*) suggested liberation of trapped electrons by the field. As noted above, Piper and Williams assumed complete field ionization of deep donors above a certain critical field strength; on this basis the output should be strictly proportional to the number of field reversals, i.e., to the frequency. Curie (157) also assumed that the initial electrons were released by the action of the field rather than thermally, largely because the existing experimental data did not indicate a large temperature dependence of output.

Alfrey and Taylor (262, 373) modified Piper and Williams' model by considering the smaller probability of ionization of donors for field strengths lower than the critical value in order to account for the less than linear dependence of output on frequency at low voltage where the time-dependent ionization should be more important. They attributed the action of temperature to its effect on the resistance of the crystal bulk in series with the barrier. Due to the complications of this model they could not derive an explicit equation for the dependence of output on voltage. They also pointed out, however, that a model assuming a space-charge barrier and initial electrons thermally released from traps can lead to a result in which the principal factor is $\exp[-(V_0/V)^{\frac{1}{2}}]$, as observed experimentally. On the other hand, they decided that such a model could not explain the details of the observed dependence of output on frequency without arbitrary and probably unwarranted assumptions concerning the distribution in depth of the traps. The effect of trapping in the low-field region seems to have been ignored by these workers.

Zalm et al. (280) showed that Eq. (8) for the voltage dependence of output holds experimentally over seven decades in brightness but pointed out that it could be explained on a simple basis, if a Mott-Schottky barrier ($F \sim V^{\frac{1}{2}}$) exists, by several processes: (1) ionization of activator centers in the barrier region by impact of accelerated electrons [Eq. (2)], (2) field ionization of activators in the barrier [Eq. (4)], or (3) penetration of the barrier by electron tunneling [Eq. (4)]. The result of several consecutive processes each varying as $\exp(-C/V^{\frac{1}{2}})$ will be a similar dependence on V but with a constant C equal to the sum of the individual C's. Zalm, Diemer, and Klasens pointed out that straightforward application of Eq. (8) to a sinusoidally varying instantaneous voltage would lead to a predicted output independent of frequency, which is actually observed if a phosphor powder is embedded in a conducting medium (2). Some additional features must therefore be introduced to give the observed essentially linear dependence of output on frequency [constant number of excited centers per half-cycle, N_0, in Eq. (16)]. In Piper and Williams' model (160) this is supplied by the assumption of a threshold field above which donors are completely emptied; thus a constant charge is released for each half-cycle. Zalm, Diemer, and Klasens, however, object to the details of the model used by Piper and Williams. They do not believe that the shallow donors assumed by the latter for formation of the barrier exist in reality as experimentally it is found (by glow curves) that empty traps of considerable depth exist. Furthermore, they point out that if the deep donors of Piper and Williams existed in the phosphor bulk the electrical conductivity would be much higher than observed.

Zalm et al. (280) suggested instead that the donors responsible for the positive space charge barrier are the ionized activator centers themselves and that the initial electrons are supplied by a surface layer of Cu_2S. The Piper-Williams mechanism of complete field ionization of donors was retained to account for the frequency dependence. This model was later extended by Zalm (2). For the case of a powder phosphor embedded in a dielectric he showed that space-charge limitation is not important in the interior of the particles and that consistent fields and barrier voltages can be obtained only if the excitation restricts itself to small regions (linear dimensions of 1000A on 10μ particles), as observed experimentally. As soon as electrons penetrate the potential barrier from a "sensitive spot" at the Cu_2S-ZnS* interface where the field strength for some geometric reason is higher than elsewhere, they begin to produce secondary electrons and excited activator centers. The electrons are swept away to the opposite side of the grain and a positive space charge left behind. Because of this positive space charge the field strength at the sensitive spot increases and other electrons penetrate the barrier or are released from surface donor levels. The process continues until the positive space charge is such that electrons can no longer leave the barrier region, i.e., until the applied field is counteracted by the space charge field. The detailed calculation predicts that only about 10% of the applied voltage appears across the barrier and that only 10–30% of the initial electrons succeed in exciting luminescence centers and producing secondaries. It was also shown that the results are rather insensitive to the donor distribution assumed in the Cu_2S phase.

If the source of initial electrons is limited by the depletion of donors as assumed by Piper and Williams or by polarization as assumed by Zalm, several other assumptions must still be met to assure a linear dependence of output on frequency (2):

(1) The electrons must traverse the particles in a time which is only a fraction of a cycle. The transit time of a free electron will normally be far below this value (450), but if deep traps are present the effective mobility may be low; in the latter case an increase in temperature will

* Tunneling of electrons from Cu_2S is also emphasized by Georgobiani and Fok (449a).

reduce the effect of trapping. Trapping will also impede formation of the positive space charge responsible for the barrier.

(2) The time between successive excitations must be large in comparison with the time for the electrons to return to the excitation region and recombine with empty centers (see Section III,E). The latter will increase with decreasing voltage, thus explaining the earlier saturation with increasing frequency at low voltage. Zalm apparently did not consider the influence of trapping in this case.

(3) The mean time of escape to the valence band for holes trapped at luminescence centers must be long compared to the time between successive excitations; temperature also plays a role here.

Zalm also considered that in the case of dc excitation the probability of injection of carriers from the cathode and of excitation of luminescence centers both involve a factor of exp $(-C/V^{1/2})$.

Thornton (334) and Haake (376) have devoted considerable attention to the action of electron traps in electroluminescence. Haake pointed out that in the high-field (barrier) region they could serve as donors of initial electrons while in the low-field region they could impede the return of the electrons to the excitation region. The latter effect is important for determining the temperature dependence of the output (375), as discussed earlier by Thornton. Haake (376) also pointed out a similarity to the picture used by Alfrey and Taylor (262) in which temperature controls the resistivity in the low-field region; in either case the effect of temperature is to increase the rate of return of electrons. Johnson et al. (377) suggested that trapped electrons also have other effects on the temperature dependence. Traps in in the barrier region enhance the barrier when they are thermally ionized early in the voltage cycle at high temperature. On the other hand, at low temperature they may be emptied by the field and serve as the source of additional initial electrons.

Zalm (2) differs from Thornton (334), Alfrey (384), Johnson et al. (377), and Haake (375) in considering that the positive space charge which enhances the barrier plays a role in determining the temperature dependence of output in addition to the effect of trapped electrons (and thermal quenching). As the temperature is increased electron promotion to empty luminescence centers will reduce the barrier height and hence the output. This may be offset by electron release from traps so that a complex behavior results. The effect of electron trapping is also interpreted, however, in terms of an effect on the barrier height rather than on the return of the electrons to the excited centers. Zalm interpreted successive decreases in output (superimposed on a general increase to produce two maxima in output similar to Fig. 21) as the temperature is increased to hole escape first from deep (blue) centers and later from higher (green) centers. He made no mention, however, of the expected correlation of the emission color with the temperature, nor did he attempt to correlate the temperature dependence numerically with the energy separation of the activator centers from the valence band as Haake (375), Alfrey (384), Johnson et al. (377), and Morehead (345) did for trap depths in the electron-trapping model.

Morehead (345, 346) treated separately in a barrier model the returning electrons which recombine radiatively (α), those which fill shallow traps or donor sites in the high-field region (β) and those which fill deep traps or donors in the high-field region (γ).* Field ionization of shallow traps was assumed to be responsible for producing the exhaustion barrier, while the deep traps are the source of the initial electrons. Trapping in the low-field region was considered to be important in controlling the return rate of electrons to the excitation region; only a fraction ψ are able to return. The action of the voltage in the return process was assumed to be sweeping out thermally released electrons for high temperatures or emptying the traps by means of accelerated electrons at low temperatures, with little or no effect on the trap depth. To fit the experimental data it was also necessary to assume weakening of the barrier by hole diffusion at high temperature and an effective mobility for returning electrons which varies as $(dV/dt)^{0.4}$ and $f^{0.4}$ due to retrapping. Morehead also applied this model to the power absorption in the phosphor as well as to the light output and thus calculated the efficiency (346). Neumark (256) has also made calculations of the efficiency to be expected on the basis of the barrier model.

The following different effects have therefore been suggested as being important, under appropriate conditions, in determining the effect of temperature on the electroluminescence output:

(1) thermal quenching of luminescence at high temperature (which probably also involves escape of holes from excited activator centers) (Curie, Haake, Alfrey and Taylor);

(2) temperature dependence of resistivity in the low-field region as controlling the voltage across the barrier (Alfrey and Taylor);

(3) action of electron traps in the low-field region in controlling the rate of return of electrons to the excitation region (Thornton, Haake, Morehead);

(4) field ionization of electron traps in the barrier region as the source of initial electrons for acceleration at low temperatures (Johnson, Piper, and Williams);

* Note that in Morehead's second paper (346) β is omitted while γ is called β.

(5) thermal ionization of electron traps in the barrier region as responsible for enhancing the barrier (Johnson, Piper, and Williams);

(6) thermal escape of holes from empty activator centers as responsible for decreasing the barrier (Zalm, Morehead);

(7) trapping of electrons in the low-field region as impeding the growth of the barrier (Zalm).

Haake (332) also explained the buildup of the emission after application of the voltage on the basis of traps in the high-field region serving as sources of initial electrons; this explanation had, as a matter of fact, been given some years earlier by Curie (157). Zalm (2), on the other hand, attributed buildup to the accumulation of positive space charge which enhances the potential barrier.

Lehmann (217) has assumed that the high-field region responsible for the excitation arises from geometrical concentration of the field due to segregations of high conductivity material (probably Cu_2S) in the phosphor. He arrived at this conclusion largely from microscopic observations and "contact electroluminescence," in which a normally nonelectroluminescent phosphor becomes electroluminescent when mechanically mixed with a metallic or semiconducting powder. Lehmann showed that in this case the dependence of output on voltage is the same as for conventional phosphors and therefore suggested a similarity in excitation mechanism. The internal field in this case will be a linear function of the applied voltage rather than proportional to $V^{1/2}$ as for a space-charge barrier. As discussed in Section III,D, however, this is the situation Lehmann (336) finds experimentally for single emitting spots, which yield Eq. (9) rather than (8), which Lehmann states is due to the combined emission of many individual spots. Morehead (346) decided that on the basis of a space-charge barrier model the calculated efficiency would be less than that observed, while an exciting field proportional to the applied voltage would allow more reasonable values. He therefore also suggested the influence of Cu_2S segregations in determining the field. Actually both Lehmann and Morehead used Eq. (11) rather than (9). Maeda (319, 320) made detailed calculations for the case of segregations in the shape of oblate or prolate spheroids. Using Lehmann's data (336) on voltage dependence he concluded that the maximum dimension of the conducting segregation is about 1.3μ as compared to typical particle diameters of $10-20\mu$. Lehmann (279) has observed microscopically that the segregations seem to be larger, on the average, in large particles.

Von Hippel and his co-workers (100, 101) have considered the currents which flow when a voltage is applied to an exhaustion (physical) or depletion (chemical) potential barrier. The current decays and the barrier field increases with time; eventually the field may become so high that electron tunneling occurs from the cathode and the equilibrium current corresponds to the tunneling carriers. In the case of KBr they observed tunneling for voltages as low as one volt. This is presumably the mechanism responsible for the in-phase light peak observed by Piper and Williams (*158*) in ZnS single crystals. The injected carriers may ionize centers which may further increase the barrier field as suggested by Zalm and discussed above. On the basis of such a tunneling mechanism and taking into account the changing width of the barrier as the voltage varies, Frankl (*265*) made calculations for the case of a sinusoidal applied voltage. In this way he was able to explain the existence of the in-phase, primary, and secondary peaks by one excitation process without any assumptions as to field-ionized donors being responsible for the out-of-phase peaks (see Section III,*I* and Fig. 36), contrary to the picture of Piper and Williams (*160*). This model also explains the faster rate of increase of the in-phase peak with increasing voltage but takes no account of trapping or temperature effects. Patek (*422*) has presented a similar model for excitation by voltage pulses.

Neumark (*263*) interpreted her observations of "thermally stimulated electroluminescence" (see Section III,*E*) as resulting from acceleration and avalanche multiplication of electrons thermally released from traps followed by impact excitation of luminescence centers. Steinberger (*451*) also reported what he considered to be a direct proof for the existence of carrier multiplication in electroluminescence. The current through a single crystal of ZnS due to a small direct voltage was found to increase by a factor as high as 100 when a high alternating voltage was also applied; the effect was greater than expected from the observed nonlinearity of the dc characteristic and was observed only in electroluminescent crystals. Since, however, these crystals showed no luminescence even for the highest applied direct voltage there was no corresponding enhancement of luminescence; only the normal ac electroluminescence was observed. Both the "multiplied current" and the brightness were found to obey the same relation, Eq. (8), but the value for V_0 was larger in the case of the light output. Both the multiplied current and the brightness increased with increasing frequency. It was therefore concluded that these currents, and the electroluminescence, resulted from avalanche multiplication of the carriers and impact ionization of luminescence centers. If electrons which tunnel through a barrier with a probability $\exp(-C_1/V)$ then excite luminescence centers with a probability $\exp(-C_2/V)$, one would expect (*2*) that the brightness would increase more rapidly with increasing voltage ($C = C_1 + C_2$) than the direct current through the crystal, as observed by Thornton (*233*), Alfrey et al. (*311*), and Steinberger et al. (*268*).

Steinberger and associates (268) considered both the magnitude of the emission (B) of single crystals while a voltage pulse was applied and the total amount of light emitted (the "light sum," S) arising from delayed recombination after the voltage was removed. Both B and S varied with the duration of the pulse in the same way and it was concluded that both quantities were proportional to the concentration of excited activator centers. It was found that B increased faster than S when the amplitude of the voltage pulses was increased. If the tunneling electrons excite luminescence centers as assumed above, S should also increase faster than the current I when the voltage is increased. This was found experimentally not always to be the case, however. Steinberger, Bar, and Alexander therefore concluded that one must either reject the impact ionization model altogether or at least assume that no ionization of luminescence centers is produced by the tunneling electrons. In the latter case one must then assume that the accelerated electrons responsible for ionization of centers have been liberated from donors or traps, thermally or by field action. These authors therefore believe that the earlier "proofs" of impact ionization by Steinberger (451) and Neumark (263) must be reinterpreted, in the latter case in order to explain the fact that the effect was observed mainly only with direct voltage.

On the basis of the acceleration-collision mechanism for electroluminescence Curie (157) concluded that electron traps may have both a beneficial effect (as a source of initial electrons for the acceleration process) and a detrimental effect (impeding the acceleration process by acting as obstacles). It is reasonable that which effect predominates would depend on the depth of the traps. Haake (376) agrees that the first effect (traps in the high-field region) is important in affecting the rate of buildup but concludes, in agreement with Thornton (267), that once equilibrium is reached traps in the low-field region are detrimental since they impede the return of the electrons to the excited luminescence centers. The experiments of Lehmann (257) and Goldberg (249) clearly show the effects of introducing Co or Ni into ZnS and these have been interpreted on the basis of trapping action (252). Zalm (2) believes that not only should the traps be as shallow as possible but that the activation energy for escape of holes from excited luminescence centers should be as large as possible (see the discussion of the effect of temperature on output above). He explained the poor electroluminescence properties of $(Zn,Cd)S:Cu$ by the presence of the deep traps introduced by Cd, and the superiority of Cu as an activator over Ag or Au on the latter basis.* Ballentyne (242, 243) states that the deeper traps

---

* If this explanation is true then ZnS:Ag and ZnS:Au should be electroluminescent at low temperature; this however, is not the case according to observations by Lehmann at liquid nitrogen temperature.

in hexagonal ZnS compared to the cubic form explains the preference for the latter, although other explanations have also been offered (see Section III,B). Thornton (*331, 405*) and Jaffe (*410*) have also shown that electron traps appear in electroluminescent phosphors as they deteriorate in output during life.

Lehmann (*394*) has shown that many features of the integrated output of an electroluminescent phosphor may be predicted on a simple model which involves electron traps but makes no detailed assumptions concerning the nature of the excitation process (although an acceleration-collision mechanism is assumed) nor the variation of the recombination process with time during the voltage cycle. The basis of this model is a dynamic equilibrium between the excitation process and the recombinatoin process. Luminescence centers (concentration N) are assumed to be ionized by impact of accelerated conduction electrons (concentration n). It is considered that the centers are far from saturation so that the ionization rate is $P_1 = \alpha_1 nN$, a monomolecular process. The type of barrier, the relationship between α_1 and the voltage V, or the source of the initial electrons is not considered. The recombination rate is assumed to be $P_2 = \alpha_2 nm$, where m is the concentration of filled traps which is assumed to be equal to the concentration of empty centers because n should be small compared to m and electrical neutrality must apply; this is a bimolecular process. The rate of trapping is given by $P_3 = \alpha_3 nM$, where M is the concentration of traps. The rate of thermal release of electrons from traps is $P_4 = mp$, where p is the usual expression $p = \exp(-E/kT)$ and E is the trap depth. This simple model does not provide for thermal promotion of electrons from the valence band to empty activator centers, for nonradiating transitions, for an effect of the voltage on trapped electrons, or for frequency effects. Detailed balancing requires that at equilibrium $P_1 = P_2$ and $P_3 = P_4$. The result for the light output L (given by P_2) is

$$L = \frac{\alpha_2 \alpha_3 n^2 M}{p} = \frac{\alpha_1^2 p N^2}{\alpha_2 \alpha_3 M}. \tag{21}$$

Since the power is proportional to $ne\mu V^2$, where μ is a mobility and V the applied voltage, the electroluminescence efficiency is (in appropriate units)

$$\eta = \frac{\alpha_1 N}{\mu V^2} = \left(\frac{\alpha_2 \alpha_3 M}{p}\right)^{1/2} \frac{L^{1/2}}{\mu V^2}. \tag{22}$$

The effect of voltage on the output in this simplified model is given by the coefficient α_1, which is unspecified.* The effect of frequency also enters

---

* Actually Lehmann gives it the usual exponential form but this is unnecessary for the argument.

mainly through this factor since transport from centers to traps and back is assumed to be instantaneous. Temperature enters, at least mainly, through the quantity p, the thermal release rate from traps, in agreement with several other models discussed previously. Equation (21) indicates that the concentrations of activator centers and traps affect the brightness

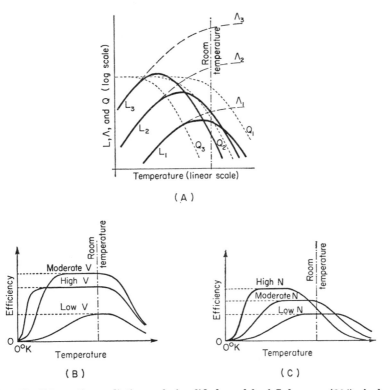

Fig. 37. Schematic predictions of simplified model of Lehmann (394), including thermal quenching. (A) Dependence of light output on temperature and activator concentration: Λ is the ideal emission intensity, Q the quenching factor, and $L = Q\Lambda$ the actual output for three activator concentrations $N_1 < N_2 < N_3$. (B) Dependence of efficiency on voltage and temperature. (C) Dependence of efficiency on activator concentration and temperature.

in the ratio N^2/M, i.e., the concentration of activators should be large compared to that of traps. Lehmann, however, noted that in practice N cannot be increased indefinitely since "concentration quenching" (not included in the simple model) will occur if the temperature is sufficiently high. Since the activation energy for quenching [Eq. (17)] decreases with increasing N, the maximum brightness will increase if N is increased but the temperature at which quenching occurs will decrease (see Fig. 37A).

This may lead to an optimum activator concentration for operation at a given temperature. Equation (21) also indicates that if traps are present they should be shallow (meaning that the trapped electrons have a high probability of escaping in a time equal to half the period of the applied voltage) so that p is large.

Equation (22) shows that as the voltage is increased the efficiency will occur at or near the point where the output varies as V^4 (*320, 325*). This relation also predicts that the efficiency should be essentially independent of temperature, aside from the small temperature variation of μ. Lehmann points out, however, that at high temperature quenching (which is independent of voltage, reference *257*) will reduce the efficiency. If the temperature is sufficiently low, where the output is also low due to the low value of p, other power losses not directly associated with the electroluminescence mechanism will again reduce the output; this will be more marked the lower the output, i.e., for low voltage. The predicted behavior is shown in Fig. 37B. Equation (22) indicates that the efficiency should increase with increasing activator concentration and be essentially independent of traps, except as they affect the mobility μ. Here again, however, quenching at high temperature will lower the efficiency, and the more so the higher the temperature. As shown in Fig. 37C, this may lead to an optimum activator concentration for operation at a given temperature. At low temperature parasitic power losses also again reduce the efficiency; this effect will occur at lower temperatures the higher the activator concentration because of the higher output.

Lehmann's simple model tells nothing of the effect of frequency on the efficiency. Since, however, the power absorption increases essentially linearly with frequency (since the phosphor impedance is mainly capacitive), as does the light output if the frequency is not too high, the variation of efficiency with frequency should be fairly small over a fairly wide range. At low frequency thermal quenching can become important [see Eq. (17)] and cause decreased efficiency, regardless of the voltage, as seen by the experimental curves of Fig. 22. The loss in efficiency at high frequency is believed to be due to additional losses in the electroluminescent lamp, including those in the transparent conducting electrode. These become more severe compared to the power going into the electroluminescent excitation at lower voltages, since they are essentially ohmic while the losses associated with electroluminescence increase faster than linearly with increasing voltage.

The theories discussed thus far in this section have assumed that luminescence centers in electroluminescent ZnS are excited by collision of accelerated electrons. Goffaux (*162, 163*) and Nagy (*164*) have considered that the excitation is due to "hot electrons." This model (see Section II,*C*) differs from the collision model only concerning the way in which the electrons have gained energy from the field. Nagy has given the relation

$$L = A \exp\left[-B/(1 + CE)^2\right] \tag{23}$$

for the expected dependence of output on field strength in this case. Goffaux, on the other hand, from other considerations concerning the mobility of fast electrons obtained

$$L = A \exp\left[-B/(1 + CE^{1/2})^2\right]. \tag{24}$$

Nagy pointed out, however, that the electrons which are accelerated in the conduction band cannot arise in the bulk of the phosphor (with $np = n_i^2 = 6.25 \times 10^{38} \exp(-E_g/kT)$ one finds $n_i = 2 \times 10^{-12}$ cm^{-3} for ZnS), so that here too one must assume that the production of free electrons occurs in one region of the crystal and recombination occurs in another. Nagy suggests that the surface serves as the source of these initial electrons so that one has a picture differing very little from that of Curie (157).

Goffaux (162, 163) also derived a more complex theory on the basis of a hot-electron model and obtained for the voltage dependence of output, assuming a Mott-Schottky barrier,

$$L = A \exp(aV) \cdot I_0^2(bV), \tag{25}$$

where I_0 is the modified Bessel function of the first kind. He claims that on the basis of this model it is possible to explain many experimental facts concerning the electroluminescence of ZnS, including the saturation of brightness at high frequency and the effect of voltage on the saturation, color shifts with frequency and temperature, the decrease in the temperature for maximum light output with increasing voltage or decreasing frequency (383), the time constant for buildup, the shape (but not the position) of the primary brightness peaks, the correlation of the magnitude of the continuous component of the output with the decay time and frequency (402), and the variation of the electrical properties of the phosphor with voltage. Although most of these predictions seem qualitatively correct, the agreement is often not as good quantitatively as seems to be claimed. Thus Goffaux predicts that the output should vary linearly with frequency at low frequency, but as $f^{1/2}$ for higher values. Although Thornton (334) did indeed report such a behavior in one case, it seems far from typical. The predicted buildup time (0.01 sec) seems to be independent of frequency, contrary to experiment. Goffaux also explains the shift in T_m (the temperature for maximum output) to lower values as voltage is increased as due to the increase in the ratio of the electron temperature T_e to the lattice temperature as V is increased; he states that the T_e for maximum output is independent of V.

However, the constants given by Goffaux ($h\nu = kT_0 = 0.03$ ev, $HF^2_{max} = 0.2$ ev) when inserted in Eq. (2) give $T_e = 435°K$ as compared to $T_0 = 348°K$. It is difficult to see how the observed excitation in ZnS could be due to such a low electron temperature. It seems, however, that the hot electron mechanism for electroluminescent excitation deserves more attention than it has received in the past. Goffaux concluded that the distinction between electroluminescent and nonelectroluminescent ZnS is the high density of free electrons in the former; he states that a concentration of 10^{14} cm^{-3} is necessary to produce sufficient interelectron collisions to produce an electron temperature higher than that of the lattice.

Perhaps the most serious objection which has been raised against the acceleration-collision mechanism in electroluminescence in ZnS is the lack of a threshold voltage. On the basis of this model it would seem that to produce excitation of luminescence centers the applied voltage must be at least equal to the optical excitation energy. However, as discussed in Section III,D, Thornton (363, 364) has shown that ZnS can be excited by 2.0 volts dc, which is lower than the minimum optical excitation energy (2.8 ev) or the average energy of the emitted photons (2.1 ev), with no indication of a threshold or a change in emission spectrum. He therefore concluded that excitation by collision cannot play a role in this material and suggested either minority carrier injection or an electron temperature mechanism; in a later paper (333) he presented evidence, to be discussed below, favoring minority injection. Patek (452) has shown that the dependence on alternating voltage obtained by Thornton below 2.2 volts rms, which is not a straight line on the plot of Fig. 15A, can be fitted quite well by using the acceleration-collision mechanism but taking into account the thermal energy of the electrons at room temperature. It will be noted, however, that the deviation observed by Thornton for dc excitation (and also for a different activator) is in the opposite direction to that predicted by Patek (Fig. 15B). Unfortunately, experiments have not yet been performed at low voltage and low temperature because of the very low emission intensities (the lowest point on Thornton's curve, 10^{-10} ft-L, corresponded to 700 quanta/cm^2-sec).

That p-n junctions are responsible for the electroluminescence of ZnS has been suggested by several workers. Thus Lehovec (125) proposed that "Near the boundaries of the crystallites there is a region of distortion, causing an extremely short lifetime of minority carriers. Accordingly, also the rate of thermal creation of minority carriers is very high in this region. An applied field is able to sweep the minority carriers into the bulk of the semiconductor, where they recombine under light emission." Oranovskii and Khmelinin (266) suggested that the striations seen in ZnS crystals correspond to boundaries between regions with n- and p- type conductivity.

Ballentyne (243, $296a$, 342) also considered that emission may result from recombination at what is "essentially" a p-n junction, perhaps involving Cu_2S. Since they observed emission from single spots of electroluminescent powders for both polarities of the alternating voltage (although differing in intensity by 3–4 orders of magnitude), Bodo and Weiszburg (277) suggested that an impact ionization mechanism applies when the barriers are biased in the reverse direction and an injection mechanism for forward bias, similar to the two types of emission observed by Lossew in SiC (15).

Weiszburg (453) has carried the analogy between electroluminescence in ZnS and in SiC further. In his SiC samples the reverse current was found to vary as $\exp(bV^{1/4})$, which may be explained on the basis of image-force reduction of the barrier height. Since in this material the output is proportional to the current one would then expect the output to depend on voltage in the same way. Weiszburg then showed that Thornton's data at low voltage (363) fit such an expression about euqally well as the function $\exp(-bV^{-1/2})$ used by Thornton. It must be concluded that the fit of data to such exponential relations, even over several decades in output, is an extremely insensitive test and no rigorous conclusions concerning mechanisms should be drawn in this way. It will be recalled, however, that Thornton (333 and Section III,D) correlated his results on electroluminescence in ZnS with forward, not reverse, currents and found that the output usually varies as the square of the current. If the potential barriers effective in an acceleration-collision process arise from reverse-biased p-n junctions, this adds nothing essentially new to the mechanism as previously discussed. On the other hand, if minority carrier injection occurs at a forward-biased junction this is an entirely different process.

However, to surmise that p-n junctions are the source of excitation in ZnS and to conclusively show their presence is quite another matter. Loebner (454) observed sharp light pulses in ZnS crystals which occurred at "kinks" in the current characteristic (high d^2I/dt^2) rather than in phase with the current. He interpreted these on the basis of a "stacked barrier" model similar to a string of back-to-back diodes. The emission was correlated with abrupt local field changes preceding and following reversible electronic breakdown of the reverse-biased barriers (see also $346a$); minority injection at forward-biased junctions is not involved in this picture. Narita (253) claims to have prepared a p-n junction by diffusing Cu (acceptor) into an n-type ZnS:Cl crystal. The location of the emission in this case was independent of the polarity but emission occurred mainly when a voltage pulse making the copper side negative was applied or when a pulse making the chlorine side (indium contact) negative was removed. The emission therefore occurred when the voltage was in the direction to increase the junction barrier; if the excitation in this case is indeed due to minority carrier injection this result could be explained only on the basis of delayed recombination resulting from the previous half cycle. Zalm (2) concludes that such delayed recombination is impossible with an injection mechanism, and this is indeed a point which must be carefully explored by anyone who seriously suggests such a process. The question of buildup (Section III,G,1) should also be considered in this connection; Johnson (400) has made a start in this direction. Thornton (435a) has recently suggested that delayed emission and buildup may result from trapping of electrons and holes, respectively, in a high resistivity (intrinsic) region in the junction. Emission would then occur during the following (reverse-biased) half-cycle. The importance of p-i-n junctions has already been demonstrated in the electroluminescence of SiC and GaP (see Sections IV,B and IV,E).

That the mobility of positives holes in normal ZnS phosphors is much less (by at least a factor of 1000) than that of electrons seems to be clearly demonstrated in the experiments of Halsted (455) on modulation of photoluminescence by an electric field.* The observation of edge emission in undoped ZnS single crystals by Smith (252), however, shows that holes can be injected from suitable contacts and produce light upon recombination with electrons; this emission was reported to occur in the volume of the crystal rather than being confined to the anode. Narita (253) also observed ultraviolet emission in the case of ZnS:Cu crystals, but not for ZnS:Cu,Cl, and only "in phase" with the voltage.

Thornton (333) has shown that the resistive currents in phosphor powders and films excited by ac or dc follow the characteristic dependence for a forward-biased barrier, Eq. (13). To the objection that this relation is derived for dc conditions he showed experimentally that it is also obeyed by a standard germanium diode operated on ac. It is also conceivable (since the efficiency is low) that the measured currents do represent injection over barriers but that they have no connection with the electroluminescence process. To check this point Thornton studied the effect of phosphor composition on the parameters I_0 and V' of Eq. (13) and on the output. It was found that when contour plots for these three quantities were made (similar to Figs. 8 and 27), the shapes of the contours, although not identical, were quite similar and they closed in the same region of composition. It should be noted that the observed dependence of Eq. (13) on temperature (V' is proportional to temperature when correction is made for a "leakage conductance" which is subtracted from the observed currents)

---

* Kallmann and his co-workers (456) have recently shown that although in activated ZnS phosphors electrons are more mobile, in unactivated samples the photovoltaic effect is due to motion of holes.

is also consistent with normal diode behavior. The same type of behavior was found in a wide variety of phosphors and for different lamp constructions (films and powders in plastic, glass, or air).

On the basis of the above results Thornton (*333*) concluded that "The controlling elements in the phosphor are "forward-biased metal-semiconductor or *p-n* junctions behaving in the usual manner . . . The junctions may occur, for example, at metal or semiconducting inclusions (Cu_2S?) in the phosphor crystal, at dislocations, at interfaces between cubic and hexagonal phases of ZnS or in other minute regions of disorder." A large number of such junctions, all oriented in the same direction, must be connected in series; they must also be interconnected by some region acting as the conductor in a string of normal diodes. Each particle probably has a similar but oppositely oriented return path to account for operation on both half-cycles of an applied alternating voltage. This picture differs from that used by Piper and Williams (*160*), Loebner (*454*), and others which involves back-to-back barriers. The observed dependence of current on frequency may be duqlicated experimentally by a combination of diodes and capacitors.

Thornton (*333*) was able to calculate the number of barriers in three different ways: (1) the dependence of the parameter V' of the current Eq. (13) on the concentration of phosphor powder in a plastic dielectric layer, (2) the dependence of V' on temperature in similar plastic layers, and (3) the direct current-voltage characteristic for a thin film. The three methods agree in indicating about 15 barriers per micron of phosphor thickness. On the basis of electron micrographs and X-ray diffraction studies Goldberg (*297*) has concluded that about 1% of the planes in particles of electroluminescent powders are faulted. Since the spacing between planes in the *c*-direction in hexagonal ZnS is 6.23A, this corresponds to 16 stacking faults per micron, in startling agreement with Thornton's value. Since the breakdown voltage of thin films is normally 20–30 volts/micron, this density of barriers indicates a maximum barrier voltage during electroluminescence of two volts, i.e., about half the band gap of ZnS, which is not an unreasonable value. Thornton also observed that during long periods of operation V' increases but there is little change in I_0. He therefore suggested that the number of active barriers increases during life, resulting in a lower voltage per barrier and hence lower output; there seems to be no independent support for this view, however.

From his measured current characteristics for phosphors Thornton (*333*) was able to evaluate the "built-in" barrier voltage E of Eq. (13) as about 0.12 volts. This is a very small value compared to the band gap of ZnS and has caused some discussion of how effective such a barrier might be as a rectifier.* It seems significant, however, that from a study of the high photovoltages in striated ZnS crystals Merz (*300*) obtained a value of 0.15 volts per barrier.† In view of this apparent correlation between electroluminescent properties, photovoltaic properties, and stacking faults it is tempting to connect the three effects. Unfortunately the theory of the high-voltage photoeffect (*299–303*) seems as uncertain as that of electroluminescence. In Fig. 38, however, is shown a suggested energy level diagrams for striated ZnS as proposed by Merz (*300*) ,who says it should be

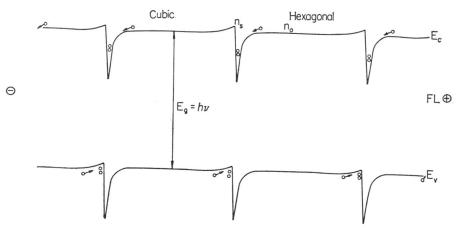

Fɪɢ. 38. Proposed energy band structure for cubic-hexagonal transition in ZnS. (From Merz, *300*.)

considered only as a schematic and not taken literally. In this figure, the barrier height ΔE is drawn much larger than the observed value of 0.15 ev.

One must explain, however, why the potential barrier is in the same direction when going from cubic to hexagonal regions or vice versa; this is obviously necessary for the photovoltages to be additive and to prevent back-to-back barriers in order to be consistent with Thornton's observations of forward currents. As discussed by Merz (*300*), the answer seems to lie in the crystal structure of ZnS (see Fig. 39). Both cubic and hexagonal structures consist of the same tetrahedral groups, but with different stacking schemes (two-layer for hexagonal and three-layer for cubic). Transitions from one structure to the other require only a rotation of the tetra-

* Aven and Cook (*457*) have made junctions of ZnTe (E_g = 2.2 ev, *p*-type) and CdS (E_g = 2.4 ev, *n*-type) and obtained a maximum photovoltage of 0.5 volts.

† This figure was obtained by dividing the observed photovoltage by the number of striations as seen in an optical microscope. The last figure was 2000 cm^{-1}, which is a factor of 100 below Goldberg's value. The crystal used by Merz, however, was presumably not electroluminescent which might easily explain this difference.

hedra by 60° about the hexagonal c-axis or the [111] direction in cubic material. Because of the symmetry, however, clockwise or counterclockwise rotations are identical; the lattice strains produced at the fault are therefore identical for either type of transition. The bonds directed along the principal axis always go from Zn to S, or vice versa, and hence the barrier voltages are additive. The origin of the oppositely oriented barriers

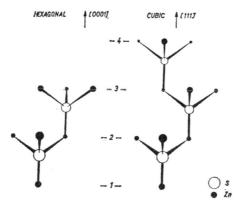

FIG. 39. Model for crystallographic structure of cubic and hexagonal ZnS. The two positions of the tetrahedra represent rotation by 60° about the vertical axis. The hexagonal structure corresponds to a two-layer sequence with rotation of the tetrahedra and the cubic structure to a three-layer sequence without rotation. (From Merz, *300*.)

forming the return path as assumed by Thornton, however, must still be explained. Furthermore, if stacking faults are responsible for the potential barriers which are effective in electroluminescence, then one would expect to find maximum output when the applied field is perpendicular to the striations, i.e., parallel to the c-axis in hexagonal crystals. As discussed in Section III,*B*, however, it is found experimentally that a field perpendicular to the c-axis is most effective (*2, 213, 248, 282, 283*).

Goldberg (*297*) has suggested that rather than the striations themselves, the partial dislocations which may be presumed to be the cause of the etch pits which are observed in conjunction with the striations are the important factor for producing electroluminescence. Chynoweth and Pearson (*458*) have shown that dislocations may be sites at which avalanches are initiated and result in the formation of microplasmas in reverse-biased silicon junctions. In this case the light emission is also restricted to small spots, as in the case of ZnS. This hypothesis would be conrtary to Thornton's assumption of forward-biased barriers. Goldberg emphasizes, however, that as yet there is no independent evidence for the existence of dislocations peculiar to electroluminescent ZnS; the etch pits may have some other origin.

Thornton's observation (*333*) that under some conditions the dc-excited light output of both powders and films is proportional to the square of the current might be taken as indicating bimolecular electron-hole recombination (through activator centers, because of the emission spectrum). However, it has been shown by Duboc (*151*) and Klasens (*152*) that one must be extremely cautious in any such conclusion based solely on the intensity dependence; the presence of trapping or other competing processes may completely obscure the real kinetics.

Piper and Williams (*160*) in presenting their acceleration-collision mechanism gave three reasons for rejecting an injection electroluminescence mechanism in ZnS: (1) the observation of a threshold voltage, (2) emission not concentrated at the anode,* and (3) no evidence for the necessary minority carrier injecting regions. Thornton (*333*), however, has pointed out that: (1) it is known today there is no threshold voltage; on the other hand, the excitation of emission at very low voltages makes the acceleration-collision mechanism seem unlikely, (2) in the case of edge emission in ZnS as observed by Smith (*252*), and where hole injection almost certainly occurs, the emission is not localized at the anode but occurs throughout the crystal, and (3) the existence of edge emission, photovoltages larger than the band gap, and currents typical of forward-biased conditions all afford evidence for the existence of normal semiconductor junctions and minority carrier injection. Thornton also observed that although the absence of an effect of an intense magnetic field on electroluminescence (*20, 328*) is commonly interpreted as implying that the field is concentrated across a (reverse-biased) barrier, if the essential mechanism is minority carrier injection or some other mechanism not involving acceleration (e.g., field ionization or hot electron excitation) then no effect of a magnetic field should be expected either.

The present status concerning the mechanism of electroluminescence in ZnS is very uncertain. There is no agreement as to which of the major mechanisms is responsible for the excitation, and many divergences of experimental observation and interpretation exist. As W. Lehmann has said, there is the danger of "explaining everything and understanding nothing." However, because the brightness and efficiency obtainable with ZnS are still greater than those with other materials which are presumably simpler and more completely understood, it is of great technological importance and therefore deserves further study in an effort to understand the processes involved and hopefully to improve its performance to a level useful for purposes of illumination, as well as the more specialized applica-

---

* It seems that the polarity at which one would expect the emission to occur depends upon whether one assumes delayed emission or not; Piper and Williams (*158*) apparently did not.

tions for which it is now used. Any acceptable theory for ZnS must explain why Cu is the preferred activator, the effect of crystal structure, the existence of delayed emission and buildup, and a host of other experimental observations summarized above. It must also take into account the important role which seems to be played by electron traps in this material.

K. Practical Considerations in Design of Electroluminescent Cells

In practical electroluminescent cells or lamps the ZnS phosphor powder is usually embedded in a plastic or glass dielectric. Equation (8) represents the dependence of the output of a particular cell on the applied voltage. It is logical to expect that the light output will also be proportional to the amount of phosphor in the cell, that is, that the parameter L_0 should be proportional to the product of c and d, where c is the phosphor concentration (fraction of the total volume occupied by phosphor) and d is the cell thickness. If the cell thickness is increased the applied voltage must be increased by the same factor if the field strength in the phosphor is to be maintained the same; this means that the parameter V_0 in Eq. (8) is also a linear function of d. Furthermore, Eq. (7) and Fig. 12 indicate that the field strength in the phosphor produced by a given applied voltage also depends on the phosphor concentration and the relative dielectric constants of the phosphor and the embedding medium; since V in Eq. (8) is the applied voltage, V_0 will also depend on these factors.

The predicted linear dependence of the parameter L_0 and V_0 on the cell thickness d has been verified experimentally (360). Under these conditions differentiation of Eq. (8) leads to the fact that maximum output should be obtained if d is adjusted so that $V = V_0/4$ (see also 20). In practice, however, such small values of d cannot be employed because dielectric breakdown occurs at the resultant high field strengths; in many cases the safe operating voltage falls between $V_0/30$ and $V_0/10$. Practical lamps are therefore normally made as thin as possible consistent with a reasonable safety factor against breakdown at the rated voltage. The breakdown voltage is also usually a linear function of the layer thickness. Since the margin of safety between operating and breakdown voltages is normally smaller (at least on a percentage basis) the greater the thickness (396), the practical benefit to be obtained from use of thick layers, and therefore high operating voltages, is greater than that predicted solely on the linear dependence of L_0 on d. Plastic-embedded phosphor layers for operation at 120 volts are normally about one mil ($= 25\mu$) thick, while those for operation at 600 volts are about three mils. With a normal average phosphor particle size of about 10μ, technical difficulties (pinholes, etc.) are usually encountered in making such lamps for operation at voltages much below 120 volts. On the other hand, the breakdown voltage of thin phosphor films is usually 20–30 volts/micron and films for operation as low as 20 volts may be prepared relatively easily.

Since the dielectric breakdown strength of a dielectric is normally higher than that of the same material in which an electroluminescent phosphor has been incorporated, practical electroluminescent lamps are often made with a "clear coat" for added protection against breakdown. Introduction of additional dielectric in this way also increases the value of V_0 with no effect on L_0. Experimentally it is found (360) that if the added layer thickness is not too great the increase in breakdown voltage is proportionately greater than that in V_0 so that the output achievable from a given phosphor layer may be increased, although obviously with an increase in operating voltage. The voltage appearing across the additional layer will obviously be minimized if its dielectric constant is made as high as possible; additions of high permittivity material such as $BaTiO_3$ have been used for this purpose with both plastic and glass dielectrics.

If it is assumed that L_0 is a linear function of phosphor concentration, as discussed above, and that Eq. (7) expresses the effect of concentration on V_0, then differentiation of Eq. (8) yields for the optimum phosphor concentration

$$c_m = \frac{k_2}{k_2 - k_1} \frac{6V}{V_0} \left[1 + \left\{ 1 + \left(2 + \frac{k_1}{k_2} \right) \frac{V_0}{3V} \right\}^{1/2} \right], \qquad (26)$$

where k_1 is the dielectric constant of the phosphor (see Section III,C for a discussion of the meaningfulness of this value) and k_2 that of the surrounding dielectric. There will be a real (positive) value for c_m only if $k_2 > k_1$ (see Fig. 12). Furthermore, since c by definition cannot exceed unity, a meaningful value of c_m will exist only for small values of V/V_0; even for $k_2/k_1 = \infty$ and $c_m = 0.74$ (close-packed spheres of equal size), $V = V_0/67$. For normal operating voltages the phosphor concentration should therefore be as high as possible without producing other disadvantages. If c is too high, for example, then the breakdown voltage is lowered (see Table VI) and the obtainable output adversely affected. As discussed in Section III,G,3, the presence of the dielectric, whose electrical properties remain essentially constant during life, can improve the observed maintenance of output during life by serving as a series impedance. The maintenance will therefore be better for low phosphor concentration, as also shown in Table VI; superimposed "clear coats" improve the maintenance for the same reason.

Table VI also shows that the parameter L_0 in Eq. (8) does not vary linearly with the phosphor concentration c as assumed above on a simple basis of no interaction between particles. For the "optimum" concentration of $c = 0.48$ the particles seem to contribute to the emission by a factor of

3.1 more than for very dilute suspensions. Halpin and Goldberg (281) have made similar observations and concluded that this effect indicates higher emission (by about a factor of 3.5) when phosphor particles are in contact with each other than when they are separated. Such an influence of particle-particle contacts is rather surprising since it is usually assumed (except by Zalm (2)) that electroluminescence excitation is not a surface effect. "Contact electroluminescence" (217) seems to play a role even in normal powder cells.

TABLE VI. EFFECT OF PHOSPHOR CONCENTRATION ON PERFORMANCE OF ELECTROLUMINESCENCE CELLS ($f = 400$ CPS)[a]

Phosphor concentration, c	V_0 (volts)	L_0 (ft-L)	L_0/c	Breakdown		Lifetime[b] (hours)
				V_B (volts)	L_B (ft-L)	
0.009	3500	6	666	300	0.19	230
0.029	3800	32	1103	300	0.85	210
0.083	4100	110	1325	300	2.6	230
0.23	4700	370	1608	400	12.0	200
0.48	5400	1000	2083	400	26.0	130
0.75	4700	830	1107	250	4.0	100
0.90	5400	900	1000	150	2.3	90

[a] Data primarily from reference (360). Dielectric constant of embedding medium about 5.

[b] These values should not be taken as representative of present day improved phosphors.

Obviously one electrode of an electroluminescent cell must be transparent in order for the generated light to escape. The material most often used for this purpose is a thin coating of tin oxide on glass. The effects of the resistance of this electrode on the operating characteristics of the cell have been discussed by Destriau (459), Ivey (460), and Coerdt (461). A complete analysis is difficult because of the nonlinear electrical characteristics of electroluminescent phosphors (Section III,C). Application of linear transmission line theory to the problem as a first approximation shows, for the case where contact is made to one side of a rectangular cell, that the controlling parameter is (460)

$$K = L(\rho \epsilon f/2d)^{1/2}, \tag{27}$$

where L is the width and d the thickness of the cell, f the frequency, ϵ the effective dielectric constant of the phosphor/dielectric layer, and ρ the resistivity of the transparent electrode. The need for low resistivity is obviously greater the higher the frequency or the larger the dimension L.

Finite resistivity of the transparent electrode will produce several effects if the frequency is high enough (460):

(1) There will be a voltage drop across the cell; the brightness will vary from one edge to the other by a factor appreciably larger than that for the voltage. If the voltage variation is not to exceed 10% and if the phase angle φ of the phosphor/dielectric layer is 75°, then K cannot exceed 0.8.

(2) Because of losses in the resistive electrode the over-all efficiency of the lamp may be appreciably reduced. For 10% variation in voltage over the cell and for $\varphi = 75°$ the losses in the electrode and the dielectric layer will be roughly equal. The extra dissipation will also increase the phosphor temperature and further affect the brightness and efficiency.

(3) The measured capacitance will be less than that for low frequency or for $\rho = 0$. The phase angle of the cell will also be less (corresponding to the increased dissipation) than its value φ at low frequency; at very high frequency the phase angle will approach the value $\varphi/2$. These effects may have a serious influence on measurements made on electroluminescent cells at high frequency.

The nontransparent or rear electrode may also influence the output of an electroluminescent cell by virtue of its optical reflectivity. If the principal optical effect in the phosphor/dielectric layer were due to simple absorption, then the fraction of light generated in the cell which would escape is given by

$$L/L' = (1 - e^{-\alpha d})(1 + re^{-\alpha d})/2\alpha d. \tag{28}$$

where α is the absorption coefficient for diffuse radiation,* d the cell thickness, and r the reflectivity of the electrode. In actual electroluminescent cells optical scattering is usually more important than absorption. In this case

$$\frac{L}{L'} = \frac{(1 - T - R)}{2ad}\left[1 + \frac{rT}{1 - rR}\right], \tag{29}$$

where R and T are the reflectance and transmittance of the phosphor/dielectric layer for its own emission. R and T are, of course, dependent on the thickness d and are given by the Schuster equations (462) as

$$T = \frac{1}{\cosh\ (pd) + [(a + s)/p]\ \sinh\ (pd)}, \tag{30a}$$

$$R = \frac{(s/p)\ \tanh\ (pd)}{1 + [(a + s)/p]\ \tanh\ (pd)}, \tag{30b}$$

---

* As an approximation the absorption coefficient for diffuse radiation may be taken as 1.9 times that for parallel radiation.

where

$$p^2 = a(a + 2s), \tag{30c}$$

and a and s are the differential absorption and scattering coefficients, respectively. If the transmittance t and reflectance r' of the transparent electrode are included then

$$\frac{L}{L'} = \frac{t}{2ad} \cdot \frac{(1 - R - T)[1 + r(T - R)]}{1 - R(r + r') + rr'(R^2 - T^2)}. \tag{29a}$$

Obviously the effects of absorption and scattering should be minimized if high output is to be realized. Both coefficients a and s should be linearly related to the phosphor concentration c. The absorption coefficient a should be independent of particle size while the scattering coefficient s should be inversely proportional to the size (463, 464); the particle shape is also an important factor. The particle size will also have an effect on the parameters L_0 and V_0 in Eq. (8) for the dependence of output on voltage (316, 325, 336). The scattering coefficient is also a function of the relative refractive indices of the phosphor and the embedding medium; according to Antonov-Romanovskii (464), $s \sim (n - 1)^2/(n^2 + 1)$, where $n = n_1/n_2$. The refractive index for ZnS is quite high, $n_1 = 2.3$ (322, 323). An increase in refractive index of the embedding medium will therefore in general decrease the scattering and increase the output; since the refractive index and the dielectric constant are related, the field strength in the phosphor will also normally be increased. Too high an index of refraction may, however, cause appreciable trapping of light inside the cell by total internal reflection. It is seen, therefore, that there are many complicated interdependent factors affecting the output of a practical electroluminescent lamp.

IV. ELECTROLUMINESCENCE IN OTHER MATERIALS*

A. Cadmium Sulfide†

Because large single crystals of CdS are relatively easy to grow compared to those of ZnS, most of the work on the former material has been done with such crystals rather than powders. Like ZnS, CdS is normally an n-type conductor, but its resistivity is considerably lower than that of ZnS and can also be controlled in a known manner by "doping."

Böer and Kümmel (21) first observed electroluminescence in CdS crystals protected by a high series impedance at direct voltages just below breakdown, where the current increases very rapidly with increasing voltage.‡ In order to raise the breakdown limit sufficiently for the liminesence to be observed it was necessary to perform the experiments at liquid air temperature. The current was of the order of one ma, corresponding to current densities of the order of one amp/cm² and the field strength was about 10^5 volts/cm. Below the breakdown limit no irreversible changes in the crystal were observed even if the high field was sustained for several hours. The emission occurred uniformly over the region where the field existed and was the same color as photoluminescence (either red or green depending on the activation of the crystals). Böer and Kümmel attributed the excitation to electrons which had been liberated from the valence band or from discrete levels in the forbidden band under the action of the field (acceleration-collision or "hot electron" mechanism) and concluded that thermal excitation was unimportant.

Diemer's (22) observations were somewhat different. His crystals were coactivated by small amounts of Cl and light was first seen (at room temperature) when the current was only a few microamperes. This emission consisted of small orange-red spots concentrated near the anode where the field was higher than in the crystal bulk because of the electrode arrangement used. Operation in this region could be sustained for hours with no change in the crystal. Diemer compared this situation to that of the Townsend region in a gas discharge, which results from electron avalanches. As the current was increased the number as well as the intensity of the emitting spots increased. At higher currents (about 100μa) a region of the current-

---

* See also Table I, p. 2.

† For other information on CdS see references (181, 465).

‡ Böer and his coworkers have studied dielectric breakdown in CdS extensively (see reference (8) for further references); Williams (466) has also recently studied this problem.

voltage characteristic with negative slope was found if the voltage and series resistance were properly adjusted; this region was also fairly reproducible if the time involved was not too long. In this region small "tongues" of orange-red light branched out from the emitting spots and formed a "curtain" of light. Optical absorption measurements showed that local heating of the crystal occurred in these regions. Diemer compared this behavior to the "streamer discharge" observed in gases at high-pressure; positive space charge plays an important function in the formation of such streamers. He concluded, however, that hole injection at the anode was not present in these experiments.

For still higher currents ($>500\mu a$) Diemer (22) observed a localized arc discharge extending from the anode to the cathode; in this region the temperature was estimated as 600°C. Following this the conductivity of the crystal at lower currents was found to have increased by a large factor. This mode of operation could be supported by fields as low as 10^3 volts/cm. During operation under arc conditions a spot of green emission ("edge emission") was sometimes seen near the boundary of the arc. Because of the measured temperatures and the time lags observed in the light output and the current for pulsed or alternating voltage, the orange-red arc emission was assumed to be thermal in origin. This view is supported by the fact that a blast of cold air caused the arc to disappear and the current to decrease. A magnetic field produced no effect on the arc.

Woods (24) perfromed experiments similar in some respects to Diemer's. In the "arc discharge" mode, however, the emission was green for currents below 0.5 ma and red for higher currents. Following this type of breakdown the photoconductivity as well as the dark conductivity of the crystals was much higher than initially. Both Diemer and Woods observed partial recovery from such changes if the crystals were allowed to rest for some time. Woods also found that recovery could be speeded up by heating or by illumination; recovery was usually not complete, however. In crystals whose initial conductivity of 10^{10} ohm-cm had been reduced to 1–10 ohm-cm in this manner Woods observed an additional emission similar to the "fireball" mode in gas discharges. This emission was red and confined to a small region of circular cross-section. The crystal operated hot under these conditions; if the current was too high vaporization occurred and a vapor arc was formed which destroyed the crystal.

Smith (23) observed two types of behavior in CdS crystals, depending on the conductivity and past history. For more conducting crystals red or straw-colored emission, independent of the electrode configuration and material, was observed at room temperature with direct voltages producing field strengths as low as 150 volts/cm and currents in the order of tens of milliamperes. These crystals were near thermal breakdown and Smith observed that the emission is "best described as incandescence"; this seems similar to Diemer's arc discharge. More insulating undoped crystals with In electrodes produced green emission (often unaccompanied by red) at field strengths of 10^3 volts/cm and currents of several hundred microamperes. This emission was most intense around the anode and tapered off in intensity over a region (about 1 mm long) comprising an appreciable fraction of the crystal; for low intensities this emission consisted of "beams" of light. Spots of yellow emission were also observed at the anode. Space-charge-limited currents were observed in similar crystals at such field strengths. Because the field strengths in these experiments were so much lower than those employed by Böer and Kümmel (21), Smith suggested that the green emission arises from hole injection at the anode and subsequent recombination rather than collision excitation by electrons; he also observed similar "edge" emission in ZnS (252). In agreement with this view it was found that highly photoconducting but nonelectroluminescent crystals doped with Cu and Cl showed long electron ($\geqslant 10^{-3}$ sec) and short hole ($\leqslant 10^{-11}$ sec) lifetimes while the lifetimes for the electroluminescent crystals were approximately 10^{-5} and 10^{-6} sec, respectively. The emission spectrum was correlated with the absorption spectrum and found to shift with temperature in the same manner, thus confirming the emission as arising from band-to-band recombination (see Table III). Smith did not discuss the origin of the yellow emission.

Potential distribution measurements on Smith's crystals (23) indicated a high voltage drop at the anode, in the vicinity of the yellow spots, and a low cathode drop. Emission was also obtained for ac operation if the crystal was first "formed" by application of a direct voltage. The function of this treatment is apparently to facilitate hole injection. The appearance of the yellow spots at the anode is accompanied by an abrupt increase in current. The emission varied linearly with the dc current and was in phase with the ac current. "Formed" crystals also exhibited electroluminescence when embedded in a dielectric and subjected to an alternating field. The decay time following removal of the voltage was less than 1μsec. The luminescence efficiency at room temperature was very low; only 10^{-8} of the electrical power appeared as radiation. This low efficiency is presumably due to the low probability for direct electron-hole recombination. In these crystals a magnetic field produced a deflection of the emission and indicated a carrier mobility of about 100 cm²/volt-sec.

Kikuchi and Iizima (467) also observed emission in CdS single crystals which they attributed to electron avalanches. The light appeared in the immediate neighborhood of the silver paste contact when the latter was positive and corresponded to a marked increase in the (forward) current. These workers believe that the avalanches were triggered by holes injected from the anode. It was also found that visible illumination triggered such avalanches but that infrared radiation quenched them; the last effect is presumably related to the infrared quenching of photoconductivity. Yamashita and his co-workers (468) have made observations very similar to those of Smith. In their case the emission increased at a rate less than linear as the current is increased. They measured the green emission as a narrow band with peak at about 5300A and the orange emission as a broad band with peak at about 6000A. The former they attributed to recombination of trapped electrons with free holes and the latter to recombination at an impurity center or a Cd vacancy.

Both thermal and electrolytic "forming" processes in CdS have been studied by Woods (469). Although CdS is normally considered to exhibit n-type conductivity (465), Woods and Champion (318) claim that doping with large amounts of Cu results in p-type crystals as evidenced by Hall coefficient and thermoelectric measurements. CdS p-n junctions were prepared by these workers and the rectification and photovoltaic effects investigated. No electroluminescence, however, was seen at these junctions. To explain the observations it was assumed that conductivity occurs through the Cu impurity levels rather than in the valence band.

The behavior of CdS crystals seems to vary greatly depending on the details of preparation and treatment. With appropriate materials and for suitable conditions it appears that the electroluminescence may result primarily from collision excitation (Böer and Kümmel, Diemer, Kikuchi and Iizima), from thermal action (Diemer, Woods, Smith), or from minority carrier injection (Smith, Yamashita). Steinberger (470) has suggested that many internal potential barriers may have existed in Böer and Kümmel's crystals. Unfortunately, not as many systematic studies have been made of the electroluminescence in CdS and the influence of composition and treatment as in the case of the technologically more important ZnS.

Electroluminescence in other II-VI compounds is discussed in Section IV,G,1.

B. Silicon Carbide*

Silicon carbide is of historical interest because it is the first material in which electroluminescence (excluding galvanoluminescence) was observed. Following his original discovery of the phenomenon (15), Lossew continued to study it for many years (136, 471).† Many of his observations were repeated and confirmed by Claus (472). Most of the early work was,

---

* For other information on SiC see references (473) and (473a).

† Earlier Destriau was referred to as the "father of electroluminescence." Lossew should then perhaps be considered the "grandfather."

of course, performed with point contacts on materials of questionable purity; long periods of time were required to select crystals with good emission and in locating the proper "sensitive spots" for the contact. It is only fairly recently that single crystals of this refractory material have been grown under controlled conditions (473) and rectifying junctions formed (474, 475).

Lossew very early established that two different types of light emission occur in SiC (15):

"Luminescence I" is usually greenish-blue and the color is independent of the applied voltage. It occurs as small points (less than one micron in diameter) in the vicinity of the contact or sometimes, according to Tetzner (476), as a "string of pearls" along a crack in the crystal. The emitting points may be surrounded by diffuse light due to reflection. The emission occurs under reverse bias conditions and usually appears for voltages in the order of 15–20 volts, but was also observed (471) as low as 1.9 volts.

"Luminescence II" occurs for forward bias and may appear at 3 to 6 volts. The emission occurs over an appreciable area in a thin layer parallel to the special "active face" of the crystal (471). According to Lossew (15) the color is orange at low voltage but shifts to violet for high voltage. The emission still appears even when the crystal is red hot.

Lossew observed that some crystals gave only Luminescence I and some either type depending on the polarity, while in some cases both types were observed simultaneously. He commented on the fast decay of the emission when the voltage was removed and the "high sensitivity" (emission for current as low as 0.1 ma).

Lossew (15) compared the spectrum of Luminescence II to that of the same crystals excited by cathode-rays. The changes in emission color were at first ascribed to heating effects; changes in absorption may have played a role. In later work (471) he stated that part of the change was due to temperature and part to the field itself. The wavelength was found to decrease for either heating or cooling (to liquid air temperature). The former was attributed to the addition of thermal energy to energy gained from the field and the latter to the higher voltage gradient at low temperature due to increased resistivity. Lossew realized the direct connection between the luminescence (15) and the rectification and experimented with contacts of various materials. As early as 1931, by grinding away the surface of the crystal, he recognized the area responsible for Luminescence II as one of low conductivity and had some idea of a junction in this region (471). He referred to ionization by electron collision and also found that an electrolyte could serve as the electrode. Lossew (471) and also Claus (472) attributed Luminescence II (and apparently also Luminescence I) to retardation of electrons, i.e., to "bremsstrahlung," similar to the continuous X-ray spectrum. Claus observed that Luminescence II became blue-green and more intense at liquid air temperature but found Luminescence I to be independent of temperature. Lossew also pointed out a correspondence between the color of Luminescence I and the absorption spectrum. Lossew (136) later studied the inverse effect of electroluminescence at a junction, i.e., the photovoltaic effect, and attempted to correlate the two.

Although Lossew (471) and Claus (472) had claimed that the change in emission color was consistent with deceleration of electrons, Tetzner (476) later disputed this and insisted that the two types of emission must have different origins. He also pointed out that the efficiency, although low, is higher than could be expected from "bremsstrahlung." Ultraviolet radiation was found to excite emission in the same areas which emit Luminescence II; Luminescence I could not be excited by ultraviolet. No emission was found in very pure crystals. The emission color was also found to vary from crystal to crystal. Tetzner therefore concluded that Luminescence II was a type of impurity-activated emission similar to that in conventional phosphors. The impurity involved was not positively identified but Tetzner suggested the presence of silicates. For the cause of Luminescence I he suggested local heating due to electrical inhomogeneities.

Modern work on electroluminescence in SiC may be said to have begun with the work of Lehovec et al. (61), who studied primarily the forward-biased emission, Luminescence II. Their first experiments were performed on a crystal which appeared dark blue and hence was apparently relatively impure. In this case the emission was yellow. The output was proportional to the current if a constant "leakage" current was assumed and subtracted. The efficiency at room temperature was found to be only about one quantum for 10^6 electrons passing through the crystal; this efficiency increased by about a factor of six on cooling to near liquid air temperature. The emission was observed at applied voltages as low as 1.8 volts and its onset corresponded to a break in the current-voltage characteristic (as also noted by Lossew and Claus). The emission extended over most of the visible range and consisted of two peaks at 5500 and 6100A; the former predominated at low temperature and the latter at room temperature. Schön (479) has pointed out that this shift is in accord with the model of Fig. 18. The spectrum was found to be independent of the current, in disagreement with Lossew. Probing of the crystal established that for reverse bias a high potential drop appeared in the same region in which the emission occurred for forward bias. Since the latter occurred when the point contact was negative, the crystal was identified as p-type with an n-type surface layer; a similar conclusion had also been reached earlier by Lossew (136). Lehovec, Accardo, and Jamgochian therefore ascribed the emission to injection of minority carriers across the junction (see Fig. 1). Since the emission predominantly consisted of quanta with energies less than the band gap of SiC (2.86 ev), recombination presumably occurred at impurity or defect centers.

In later experiments Lehovec et al. (61) used pale green transparent crystals of higher purity. In this case the color of the forward-biased emission was green with peaks at 4750A and 5250A and was independent of temperature as well as of current. Contrary to the statement of Tetzner (476), the emitting area in this case could not be excited with ultraviolet radiation. The emission efficiency increased as the temperature was lowered according to an activation energy of 0.12 ev, attributed to competing nonradiative transitions. The measured efficiency at $-134°C$ was 2×10^{-4} quanta/electron. The decay time of the emission following a voltage pulse was 1.2 μsec at room temperature and 80 μsec at $-140°C$. If the polarity was reversed, diffused yellow emission first appeared in a region different from that giving the green emission. In this case a similar reddish yellow emission was excited in the same area by ultraviolet radiation; the persistence was much greater than for the electroluminescence, however. This yellow emission was attributed to another barrier with different impurity conditions. At still higher voltages a few distinct spots of bright bluish-white emission (Luminescence I) were superimposed on the yellow emission. Lehovec, Accardo, and Jamgochian attributed these spots to either the Zener effect or ionization by electron collision; Curie (157) also considered field emission to result in Luminescence I. G. Curie and D. Curie (442) have shown that for sinusoidal excitation the emission of SiC is strictly in phase with the voltage and no secondary peak is observed.

Szigeti et al. (477) obtained a very complicated emission for electroluminescent SiC, independent of the voltage, with five peaks at 4900, 5200, 5400, 5800, and 6100A. The emission appeared bluish white. Szigeti observed that some of these peaks seem to coincide with those reported for the cathodoluminescence of BN (478, Section IV,G,2). The absorption spectrum also contained peaks at 4900, 5450, and 6200A, and a complicated energy-level diagram was advanced to explain the observed structure in emission and absorption. No photoluminescence was observed in these samples but the cathodoluminescence appeared the same color as the electroluminescence. The output was found to increase with increasing purity of the sample (contrary to Tetzner) but the emission spectrum was unchanged. For a constant applied voltage the light output was found to increase as the temperature (and therefore the current) was increased above room temperature, but the efficiency decreased. The efficiency at room temperature was 3.5×10^{-6} lumens/watt.

Schön (*479*) came to the conclusion that in the case of emission at a p-n junction in SiC the recombination occurred primarily in the n-type region. He attributed the presence of a "threshold" current which is ineffective in producing emission, as observed by Lehovec and his coworkers (*61*), to recombination in the junction region. Patrick (*62*), on the other hand, concluded from an analysis of the current-voltage characteristics of junctions in SiC that they corresponded to p-i-n or p-n*-n junctions and that the recombination occurred in the intrinsic or nearby intrinsic transition region (see Fig. 40). Patrick calculated the thickness of the n* region to be about 5μ, in very good agreement with the much earlier figure of $2\text{-}4\mu$ given by Lossew (*471*).

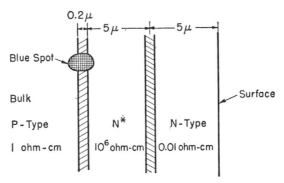

FIG. 40. Model of electroluminescent SiC junction. The "blue spot" represents a short through the p-n* junction. (From Patrick, *62*.)

The junctions grown by Greebe and Knippenberg (*475*) were also of the p-i-n type and appeared to emit "mixed white and violet light" under high forward bias. For reverse bias the usual blue spots were obtained; when the voltage was increased the number rather than the intensity of these spots increased. Hall (*474*) states, however, that both the number and the intensity of the spots increased. Patrick (*62*) found that the reverse-bias characteristics were determined by leakage currents at "weak spots" and that these were the same spots responsible for the blue Luminescence I. He suggested carbon particles as the cause of these weak spots. Patrick (*62*), Hall (*474*), and Rücker (*480*) all compared the blue spots of Luminescence I in SiC to those seen in reverse-biased silicon junctions (see Section IV,D). Patrick obtained a figure of 0.8 ev for the activation energy of the n* region while Greebe and Knippenberg obtained 1.4 ev, almost exactly half the band-gap. Patrick did not observe a break in the forward I-V characteristic at the onset of light emission as observed by Lehovec and earlier workers and states that there is no true threshold other than leakage current.

Hall (474) found the forward-biased emission of junctions formed by alloying to be yellow or green at room temperature or below, or even red in some cases, depending on the crystal used. As the temperature was increased above room temperature, however, the color became blue in all cases. The photon energy of this blue emission was found to shift in the same way as the energy gap of SiC, indicating direct recombination of free electrons and holes. A brightness of 10 ft-L was measured for an emitting area of one mm² at 0.3 amp and 3 volts, corresponding to an efficiency of 5×10^{-4} lumens/watt or 1×10^{-6} quanta/electron, in good agreement with Lehovec's results (61) on natural junctions.

Patrick and Choyke (62) have studied the spectrum of the emission at forward bias in more detail. Three different types of emission were observed: (1) band-to-band transitions with energy near E_g ("recombination radiation"); the intensity here should be proportional to np, where n is the electron density in the conduction band and p the hole density in the valence band, (2) transitions from filled levels below the Fermi level to the valence band ("impurity luminescence"); the intensity of these transitions should be proportional to p, and (3) transitions from the conduction band to empty levels above the Fermi level; this intensity should be proportional to n. In the n^* region in which most of the emission occurs the Fermi level was about 0.5 volts below the conduction band. The impurity luminescence (type 2) was observed to consist of five broad peaks in the wavelength region 0.5 μ (5000A) to 1.5 μ; no correlation of these peaks with specific impurities was made. At low temperatures (77°K) the impurity emission was many orders of magnitude higher than that at the band edge (see Fig. 41A). The shape of the spectrum for energies below about 2.2 ev was independent of current density and temperature. As shown in Fig. 41A, however, the high-energy edge (which has an exponential characteristic) moves continuously to higher energy for increasing current density. This was attributed to variation of the Fermi level with current and this emission was called "Fermi level edge emission." The absence of band-to-band transitions at low temperatures, indicating the absence of electrons in the conduction band, was attributed by Patrick and Cohyke to the formation of impurity bands, rather than isolated levels, at the impurity concentrations involved (about 2×10^{18} cm^{-3}). Electron injection into this region under these conditions therefore occurs only through these levels and not through the conduction band.

At high temperatures Patrick and Choyke (62) found the exponential edge on the spectrum to disappear and radiation with energy near and even greater than the energy gap (recombination radiation, type 1) to appear in addition to the impurity emission (see Fig. 41B). This variation seems consistent with the color changes reported by Hall (*474*). Since high temperature and high current density increase the electron concentration in the conduction band, a new infrared radiation (type 3) also appears in the region 0.5 ev (limit of measurement) to 0.65 ev. Because of the dependence on electron concentration, the intensities of type 1 and 3 emission increase faster than linearly with the current, while that of type 2 increases at a rate

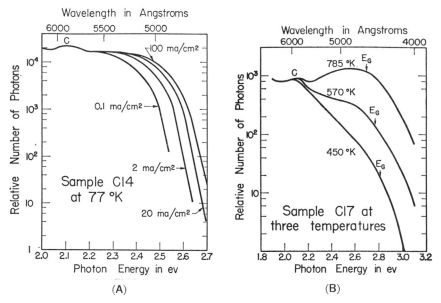

FIG. 41. Electroluminescence of SiC as a function of temperature and current density. All curves normalized at 6000A. (A) Emission as a function of current density at 77°K (E_g = 2.91 ev). (B) Emission as a function of temperature at 1 amp/cm². (From Patrick and Choyke, *62*.)

less than linear. The photoluminescence was found to include emission at energies higher than that of the low-temperature electroluminescence (higher Fermi level); that the n-region as well as the n^*-region was photoluminescent was proven by reverse biasing the junction to sweep ultraviolet-excited carriers out of the latter. It is believed that for high current densities the n-region may also contribute to the electroluminescence. The photoluminescence efficiency of the p-type material (black, Al-doped) was too low to be measured. The n-type surface doping in the crystals may have been due to nirtogen. Patrick and Choyke (*62*) obtained a value of 3 or 4×10^{-9} sec for the electron lifetime in their samples. The lifetime of positive holes at room temperature (as determined by decay measurements) was about 10 μsec and decreased as the temperature or the current density was increased. The efficiency of electroluminescence was found to vary in the same way as, and hence to be determined by, the hole lifetime. A value of one generated photon for 570 electron-hole recombinations at 77°K was obtained. However, because of internal reflections (index of refraction of SiC = 2.65) and absorption, the efficiency for the radiation which actually escapes is much lower.

Rücker (480) has also studied the electroluminescence of SiC. For his samples the spectrum of the yellow-green Luminescence II was a single broad band with peak in the region 5100–6300A, depending on the crystal and the conditions. The peak occurred at shorter wavelengths the higher the conductivity of the sample and the lower the temperature. For most crystals the spectrum was independent of voltage but, in cases where the n-type region to which contact was made was very small, increasing the current density caused a shift to shorter wavelengths. The photoluminescence of green (n-type crystals) was similar and had a peak at 5900A. Luminescence II was found to increase at low temperature according to an exponential relation exp $(-E/kT)$ with $E = 0.1$ ev. The best efficiency obtained was 10^{-4} lumens/watt or 10^{-5} quanta/electron. The decay time varied from 8 μsec at 3 ma/mm^2 to 3 μsec at 30 ma/mm^2; the long wavelength end of the spectrum was found to decay at a slower rate than the short wavelength end. Rücker relieved that the changes in emission color could be explained by assuming a p-i-n junction, similar to Patrick (62), and a continuum of activator levels. Long carrier lifetime would then lead to a shift to long wavelengths as shown by Fig. 18 (Schön-Klasens model).

Rücker (480) also studied the blue point emission (Luminescence I) which could be observed both for reverse bias on junctions consisting of n-type surface regions on blue p-type crystals (which gave Luminescence II for forward bias) and also at contacts to green n-type crystals. The emitting points were found to be less than 0.3μ in diameter and to correspond to current densities of 10^4 amp/cm^2 and field strengths of 1.5×10^6 volts/cm. As with Luminescence II, the emission was proportional to current, but the efficiency was a factor of 10 lower. The decay time was less than 2×10^{-7} sec. This emission was found to increase exponentially with increasing temperature. The spectrum was independent of voltage or temperature and was very broad, extending from the ultraviolet to the red region; the peak was at 4600–4700A in all samples. The heat rise in the spot was calculated to be only 40°C, thus ruling out a thermal origin as suggested by Tetzner (476); the fast decay also points to a nonthermal origin. The emission of energies greater than the band gap indicates the presence of very energetic electrons and holes. Rücker found the dependence of Luminescence I on voltage to obey Eq. (8) as observed for electroluminescence in

ZnS and concluded that the $V^{1/2}$ factor arose from electron-collision and impact ionization in a Schottky barrier.

Gol'dman (*480a*) has recently described a new type of emission which he calls "Luminescence III" in SiC. The forward-biased emission (Luminescence II) excited by short voltage pulses of constant width was found to increase linearly with the repetition rate of the pulses. The same was true for the reverse-biased emission at low repetition frequency, but above a certain frequency the output increased much more rapidly. The value of this critical frequency was lower the greater the pulse amplitude. Microscopic examination revealed that the increased emission (Luminescence III) arose from an extended area identical to that for Luminescence II and is thus distinguished from the usual emitting spots of Luminescence I. The intensity of this type of emission was sometimes nearly as great as that of Luminescence II but it differed in color. Since it was observed that the decay time of the new emission was much greater than that of Luminescence I (even leading to continuous emission between pulses) Gol'dman assumed that trapping of carriers was involved.

Weiszburg (*481*) studied the electroluminescence of SiC crystals in alternating-fields with no direct electrode contact, i.e., the arrangement normally used for ZnS powders. About 600 volts at 1000 cps were required to obtain the same output as for 3 volts ac without the insulator. Since no rectification existed in this case Weiszburg rejects the entire model of carrier injection at a junction commonly assumed for SiC and considers instead that surface states are important. In view of the great difference in output obtained with and without the insulator present, and the many detailed correlations which have been made between the light generation and the rectifying properties of SiC, it would seem that such a hypothesis requires further substantiation.

The decay of the electroluminescence of SiC has been studied by several workers (*15, 61, 62, 480*), as discussed earlier. If recombination occurs by several simultaneous processes, then measurement of the decay rate of any individual process will provide information concerning the lifetime appropriate to the fastest process. Electroluminescence measurements may therefore be used to measure minority carrier lifetimes in semiconductors. Eriksen (*482*) in this way obtained values ranging from 4×10^{-7} to 1×10^{-8} sec. He explained deviations from exponential decay as arising from trapping; exponential decay was obtained if the temperature was raised or if a dc bias was added to the voltage pulse. Harman and Raybold (*483*) have used measurements of output as a function of frequency of an applied alternating voltage to measure the lifetime. If the lifetime is taken as the reciprocal of the frequency required to reduce the output to 34%

of its constant value at low frequency some typical results were 1 to 4×10^{-7} sec for n-type material and 4 to 9×10^{-9} sec for p-type material.

It seems that considerable more work is needed on SiC samples which have been carefully grown and doped with controlled amounts of impurity before the details of the electroluminescence in SiC will be fully understood. Since this material exists in many crystalline polytypes (at least 40 are known), their influence on the light emission should be studied*; the band gaps for the cubic and hexagonal (6H) modifications have been reported (484) to be 2.2 and 2.86 ev, respectively, a much greater difference than for ZnS. The weaker Luminescence I observed in reverse-biased junctions also needs to be studied in more detail.

C. Germanium†

In general, four types of light emission may be expected in a semiconductor (see Fig. 42):

(1) Intrinsic electron-hole interband recombination (shown as F in the figure); in the case of germanium and silicon such transitions will be predominantly indirect (phonon-assisted),

(2) Recombination through impurities (G in the figure),

(3) Avalanche emission from energetic carriers (H in the figure),

(4) Intraband transitions or deceleration emission (not shown in the figure).

For germanium ($E_g = 0.7$ ev) the intrinsic emission is to be expected at a wavelength near 1.8μ. Impurities and intraband transitions should result in emission even further in the infrared. Only in the case of avalanche excitation is visible emission to be expected.

Electroluminescence in forward-biased germanium junctions was first observed by Haynes and Briggs (49) and later by Newman (51) and Gunn (488). This emission consisted of a symmetrical band with peak at about 1.8μ, in good agreement with calculations on the basis of interband recombination and the known absorption data for germanium (51, 143). That interband recombination is involved is also supported by the observations of Hayes and Briggs (49) that the peak wavelength decreased as the temperature was decreased, in agreement with the change in band gap, and that the half-width of the emission band was expressed by $(0.022 + 3kT)$ ev, corresponding to the kinetic energy of the holes and electrons ($3kT/2$

---

* See the recent paper by van Daal et al. (484a).

† For a review of the optical properties (absorption and emission) of Ge and Si see Pearson (485), Moss (486), and Conwell (487).

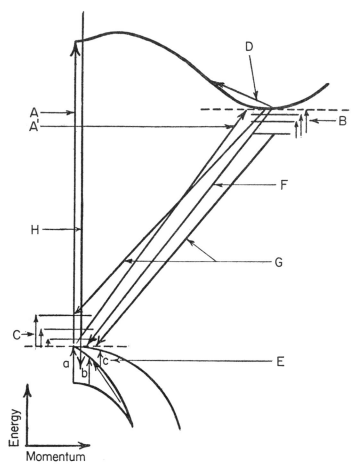

Fig. 42. Generalized energy-momentum diagram showing various optical absorption and emission processes in a semiconductor such as germanium or silicon. A—intrinsic absorption, direct; A'—intrinsic absorption, indirect; B—impurity absorption, donors; C—impurity absorption, acceptors; D—free electron absorption; E—free hole absorption; F—intrinsic recombination radiation; G—impurity recombination radiation; H—avalanche emission. (From Pearson, *485*.)

each). Newman found the output to vary linearly with the current, indicating that for the currents employed the majority carrier density was independent of the injected minority carrier density. Brill and Schwartz (*489*) found the output in germanium to vary with current as a power law with exponent between 1.3 and 1.7 over a fairly wide range. Newman (*51*) also observed that the radiation could be modulated by a magnetic field of 20,000 oersteds perpendicular to the direction of current flow.

Deflection of the carriers toward the surface decreased the output; this was ascribed to the higher probability of nonradiative transitions at the surface. Since the index of refraction of Ge is approximately 4.0 in the infrared, only the radiation which lies within a cone whose axis is perpendicular to the surface and whose half-angle is 14.5° can escape; internal trapping is therefore very important (*51*). Aigrain (*52*) used a Weierstrass sphere to reduce the effects of internal trapping.

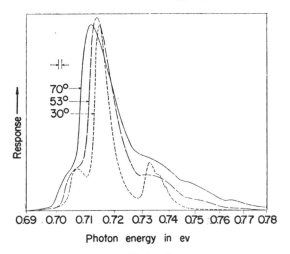

Fig. 43. Interband recombination radiation from germanium at three different absolute temperatures, showing structure due to phonon absorption and emission. (From Haynes *et al.*, *490*.)

Haynes (*50*) later (using optical excitation) observed a secondary emission peak lying near 1.5μ (0.82 ev). This more-energetic emission was ascribed to direct rather than indirect transitions (see Fig. 42). Haynes *et al.* (*490*) considered the role of phonons in the indirect transitions in more detail. Since there are four types of phonon (acoustic longitudinal, acoustic transverse, optic longitudinal, and optic transverse) and since momentum can be conserved either by absorption or emission of a phonon, in principle the spectrum should consist of eight lines. Figure 43 shows some of the structure actually observed at low temperature. Phonon energies obtained in this way are in good agreement with other determinations.* The possibility that the free electrons and holes form excitons before recombining must also be considered (*490, 491*). Benoit à la Guillaume and Parodi (*492*) have studied the Zeeman effect (at a magnetic field of 40,000 oersteds) on

---

* The effect of phonons on the radiation from Ge and Si was discussed further by Haynes, Lax, and Flood, Benoit à la Guillaume and Parodi, and Dumke at the conference in Prague in 1960 (*490a*).

the intrinsic recombination line in Ge at 1.9°K and concluded from the magnitude of the shift observed (4×10^{-4} ev) that this emission is indeed due to exciton annihilation rather than direct electron-hole recombination. They also observed one peak which appeared only below 2°K.

Aigrain and Benoit à la Guillaume (52) observed, in addition to the interband recombination emission, emission in the far infrared region from 2 to 6μ for point contacts to Ge at 90°K and 360°K but for Ge junctions only at 300°K and not 90°K. Since the decay time for this emission is less than one μsec, it is not thermal in origin. Furthermore, since the spectrum is continuous and independent of impurity content, it apparently is not due to impurities. That the presence of holes is necessary is indicated by the fact that wetting the surface with a solution of $ZnCl_2$ quenches the emission. These workers therefore attributed this emission to intraband hole transitions (actually, transitions between two branches of the valence band). Since the field near the point contact is about 10^3 volts/cm, the holes may have a temperature higher than that of the lattice and thus emit as a 500°K source even though the lattice is at liquid nitrogen temperature. Pankove (493) observed a very broad band with apparent peak at about 4.6μ which he also attributed to intraband hole transitions; the true peak, when properly corrected for detector sensitivity, is at 6.6μ (494). Kessler (495) studied the optically-excited emission of Ge and found a peak at about 10μ which he attributed to intraband hole transitions; for pure samples the intensity varied linearly with temperature in the range 20–70°C and with the number of holes for small current density. Schmidt and Church (496a) recently observed infrared radiation from an n-type Ge cathode in the electrolysis of heavy water; no emission was observed with normal water, which however absorbs very strongly in the expected wavelength region. Under these conditions hole injection occurs at the Ge surface and recombination radiation results.

Newman (497) observed another band near 2.5μ (0.5 ev) in alloyed, but not in grown, Ge junctions. It was found that this band could be introduced by mechanical deformation of grown junctions and at least partially removed by annealing, so that it must be due to some mechanical defect serving as a recombination center. Vavilov and his co-workers (496) studied the electroluminescence of Ge following electron bombardment and observed an increase in the emission peak (at 2.35μ) which they attributed to structural defects. Newman (497) also observed that introduction of Cu as an impurity resulted in an emission band at 0.59 ev. Although Benoit à la Guillaume (498) also at first suggested that an emission band he observed at 0.53 ev was due to Cu, he later reported (499) that introduction of Cu, Ni, or Co introduced no new bands. This emission he later attributed to recombination at dislocations. When measurements were made at liquid hydrogen temperature he observed a very complicated spectrum which he analyzed as consisting of peaks at 0.50, 0.545, 0.61, and 0.68 ev. The efficiency was estimated to be about 1% of that due to interband recombination. The theory of recombination at centers with more than one energy level has been considered by Sah and Shockley and by Bernard (500).

Gosnet et al. (491) observed emission bands in As-doped Ge at 0.707 and 0.734 ev which they believed to result from recombination at As centers, since the intensity depended on the As concentration. The difference in energy was explained by cooperation of a longitudinal acoustic phonon. A third band at 0.714 ev was attributed to "intrinsic emission" due to annihilation of indirect excitons. Benoit à la Guillaume (500a) has recently studied Ge doped with P, As, Sb, Ga, or In. In this case either two or three emissions (identified as A, B, and C) due to the impurities were observed, in addition to the exciton annihilation peak. Emission A had a width of $3kT$ and was attributed to recombination of free carriers with oppositely charged carriers trapped at an impurity ground state. Emissions B and C, on the other hand, were very narrow (1.3×10^{-3} ev at 14°K and 3×10^{-4} ev at 2°K) and symmetrical. It was therefore suggested that they arose from a four-particle complex consisting of an exciton and a neutral impurity; similar observations and conclusions had been made earlier by Haynes on doped Si samples (see the next section).

Pankove (494, 501) has studied the emission from a germanium tunnel diode at 77°K. At low currents only a peak near 0.6 ev was observed. As the current was increased this peak became larger and shifted to higher energy; the emission at the low-energy side showed saturation. For low currents the output due to this peak increased as the 1.83 power of the current and for higher values as the 0.93 power. Increasing current also caused the appearance of the interband radiation at 0.71 ev which increased very rapidly with current (5.35 power) so that for high currents it was the predominant peak. Pankove states that these changes are consistent with the electron occupancy of the degenerate conduction band in such highly doped material as the Fermi level is raised due to injection. He also gives one of the few figures in the literature concerning the efficiency of electroluminescence in Ge; he reports that only 10^{-4} of the input power is radiated. Sclar and Burstein (502) have calculated that for hydrogen-like impurities in Ge at 4.2°K the cross-section for nonradiative (phonon) recombination should be 2700 and 5600 times that for radiative recombination in n-type and p-type material, respectively.

Pankove (501) in one Ge tunnel diode sample observed an infrared emission varying as $I^{1/2}$ up to a certain current and as I^3 above this point. The first behavior occurred in the "excess current" region of the current-voltage characteristic and the second in the "injected mode"; the latter presumably represents band-to-band recombination but the spectrum could not be measured because of the geometry. No luminescence was observed in the tunneling region of the characteristic, indicating either that it was absent or that its wavelength was greater than 10μ, the limit of sensitivity of the detector. He also observed (*494, 501*) an infrared emission which for sinusoidal excitation was 45° in advance of the voltage maximum and which increased much more rapidly as the current was increased than did the in-phase emission. In addition he observed an emission with long time constant (0.5 sec) which was brighter than the in-phase emission and occurred for both polarities. This emission could be distinguished from that due to heating. The origins of these different types of emission have not yet been established. Koenig and Brown (*503*) have reported the presence (at liquid helium temperature) of extremely long wavelength radiation (about 100μ) in-type Ge at breakdown resulting from the recombination of "hot electrons" with ionized donor impurities. The fact that an Sb-doped Ge source ($E = 0.0097$) could produce a response in an As-doped Ge detector ($E = 0.0127$ ev) establishes the fact that the electrons involved are energetic ones. This type of recombination radiation has also been observed by Ascarelli and Brown (*504*).

Bernard and Loudette (*505*) have described generation of radiation in germanium containing no junctions. If a sample whose thickness is considerably less than the ambipolar diffusion length is subjected to electric and magnetic fields at right angles to each other and to the thin dimension, one face is impoverished of electron-hole pairs and the generation rate increases to counteract the deficit. At the other face the concentration of electron-hole pairs is higher than the equilibrium value and recombination is increased; under suitable conditions radiation will result. This "electromagnetophotonic" effect is the inverse of the photomagnetoelectric (PME) effect. The intensity of the emission generated in this way is very feeble.

Visible emission from a reverse-biased Ge junction was first observed (much later than similar observations in Si) by Nelson and Irvin (*506*) and Kikuchi and Tachikawa (*507*). The latter workers think that oxygen impurity promotes this emission; they observed it only when SiO_2 crucibles were used. This emission was investigated further by Chynoweth and Gummel (*165*). The breakdown field was estimated at 5 to 10×10^5 volts/cm. Around the edges of the junction the emission appeared white to the eye and to color photographic film; the spectral distribution measurements paradoxically showed no green or blue emission. This emission is believed to originate very near the surface. Red or orange emission which was also observed was attributed to breakdown sites at a significant distance from the surface, as affected by self-absorption. The emission was found to rise rapidly for energies less than about 1.2 ev and to reach an apparent peak at 1.09 ev; this peak, however, could be the result of the large and relatively uncertain correction factors for the photomultiplier sensitivity in this region. The rapid rise, however, is real and is not observed for the corresponding emission in silicon (see the next section). For energies above 1.2 ev the emission decreased more slowly and the highest detectable energy was about 2.1 ev. No appreciable change of spectrum with varying current was observed. Except at very low values the output was proportional to the current.

The efficiency of the visible emission in Ge (energy > 1.8 ev) was estimated by Chynoweth and Gummel (165) to be one photon for 10^8 injected carriers; the total efficiency is probably 100 times higher. No microplasma noise was observed as for silicon. Although the absence of noise is unexplained, microplasmas are believed to exist and to result in the light emission through recombination of accelerated holes and electrons. The threshold energy for electron-hole pairs in Ge is about 1.5 ev (508); this value added to the band gap gives 2.15 ev, which is very close to the observed maximum photon energy. Wolff (167) has concluded that the rapid increase in output below 1.2 ev is due to intraband transitions of accelerated holes and has discussed in detail both types of emission in terms of the complicated band structure of Ge.

D. Silicon*

Electroluminescence in silicon was observed by Haynes and Briggs (49) at the same time as that in germanium. Since the energy band gap of Si is 1.11 ev, the interband recombination radiation was observed near 1.1μ. At room temperature one photon was emitted for about 5000 injected minority carriers; this efficiency was increased by a factor of roughly five at liquid nitrogen temperature. Sclar and Burstein (502) calculated that for hydrogen-like impurities in Si at 4.2°K the cross-section for nonradiative recombination should be 14,000 and 37,000 times that for radiative recombination in n-type and p-type material, respectively. At room temperature the spectral distribution was found to have a single peak, but Haynes and Westphal (54) found that at 77°K it was resolved into other peaks lying on the low-energy side of the (sharpened) peak attributed to indirect transitions across the band gap ("intrinsic" peak). The additional peaks were attributed to recombination at impurities. The effect of various impurities on the emission is shown in Fig. 44 (the sample for the curve labeled As contained both As and B). Impurity ionization energies calculated from these curves agreed with those measured in other ways except for the case of As.

Haynes et al. (490) later studied the recombination spectrum of Si in more detail and obtained several peaks attributed to the phonons associated

* See references (485–487).

with indirect transitions (similar to Fig. 43 for Ge). It is now believed that exciton annihilation rather than electron-hole recombination is responsible for this emission (*509*). Radiation due to direct (rather than phonon-assisted) transitions across the band-gap has not been observed in Si. Haynes (*510*) has recently studied, using optical excitation, the spectrum for recombination at impurities at 25°K more closely. Introduction of As

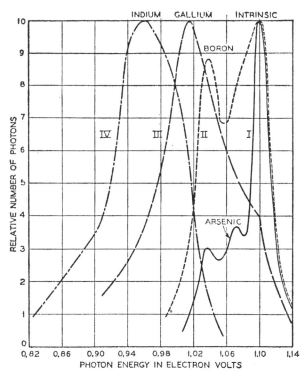

Fig. 44. Effect of impurities on the infrared electroluminescence of forward-biased silicon junctions; $T = 77°K$. (From Haynes and Westphal, *54*.)

caused the appearance of two very sharp lines at 1.091 and 1.149 ev in addition to the main peak at 1.098 ev (the exciton energy itself was 1.156 ev, with the difference accounted for by phonons). The energy difference between these two lines corresponds to the transverse optical phonon, which is also responsible for the main peak. Because of their very narrow width (<0.0005 ev), it was concluded that these lines arose from recombination of an electron and a hole both of which were immobilized. The energy in the additional lines was proportional to the amount of As added, so it appears that a single As atom is involved in the binding. Similar sharp lines were observed with other impurities (Sb,P,Bi,B,Al,Ga,In) and the separation between the impurity peak and the intrinsic peak (both phonon-assisted) was found to be a linear function of the impurity ionization energy. For acceptors $\Delta E = 0.10E_i$ and for donors $\Delta E = 0.12E_i$. If this emission were due to exciton annihilation at an un-ionized donor or acceptor, then E should decrease as E_i increases. It was therefore concluded that the complexes responsible for this emission consisted of a hole bound to a positive donor ion by two electrons or an electron bound to a negative acceptor ion by two holes. Such complexes were suggested earlier by Lampert (511).

Benoit à la Guillaume and Parodi (512) have discussed the radiative recombination at impurities in Si in detail. In Si:Sb,Al at 77°K only two peaks were observed, intrinsic radiation at 1.114 ev and recombination at Sb centers at 1.058 ev. At 20°K these two peaks occurred at 1.102 and 1.059 ev, while a new peak occurred at 0.99 ev, attributed to recombination at traps. At 77°K the intensity of the Sb radiation was proportional to np (as was the intrinsic radiation); at 20°K, however, the Sb radiation was proportional only to n due to a shift in the Fermi level. These workers also resolved the band due to In (see Fig. 44) into two peaks of roughly equal magnitude ascribed to direct and indirect transitions. The intrinsic peak was proportional to np and hence increased with current more rapidly than the peaks due to In (proportional to p only).

Davies and Storm (509) have studied the infrared emission from Si at high field strengths, using p-p^*-n junctions and current densities up to 10^4 amp/cm². The field strength in the p^* (or π) region was as high as 3700 volts/cm. A portion of the observed emission was due to impurities. Although the emission observed for high currents was slightly broader than that for low currents, the difference was in agreement with the calculated temperature rise (from 77 to 84°K) of the spectrum. Since the carrier temperature under the high current condition should have been about twice the lattice temperature it was concluded that the radiation resulted not from electron-hole recombination but from excitons in thermal equilibrium with the lattice. Similar results were obtained at 20°K.

Visible emission from reverse-biased Si junctions (analogous to Luminescence I in SiC) was first observed by Newman (53). This emission was yellowish in appearance and was detected over the range of 1.8–3.4 ev (3600–6800A). At low currents the emission appeared in small spots which seemed to reach their maximum brightness over a relatively narrow range of current; at higher currents additional spots appeared and at very high currents (4 amp/cm²) regions which seemed to emit more-or-less uniformly were observed. At a constant current the brightness decreased if the sample was cooled by an air blast, indicating a temperature effect. This emission was dependent on the state of the surface; mechanical "working" induced the appearance of emitting sports and caused the $I-V$ characteristic to be "softer." However there was evidence that the light was generated within the sample and not just at the surface. It was concluded that the emission was the result of avalanche breakdown in the silicon. In this case, however, the emission could result either from interband recombination of energetic carriers (proportional to the square of the current, minimum energy equal to band gap) or intraband transitions (proportional to the current, no minimum energy). Because of temperature effects the dependence of output on current could not be accurately determined in Newman's experiments.

Chynoweth and McKay (55) studied the visible emission in Si further. Diffused junctions only two microns below the surface permitted easy examination. A few white spots were observed where the junction intersected the surface but most of the emission was from small red spots randomly spaced over the entire junction area. As many as a thousand simultaneously emitting spots were observed; the ultimate size was too small to be determined microscopically (less than 1μ). The number of spots increased with current rather than individual spots becoming brighter. It is believed that all the breakdown current through the junctions is carried by these spots; the current per spot was about $100\mu a$. The spots always occurred in the same position and time sequence as the current was increased from zero. The emission from the spots appeared red because of self-absorption; if a portion of the surface was ground off to give varying thickness the color varied continuously from blue-white to red. The spectrum was measured from 1.0 to 3.2 ev (see Fig. 45). The emission intensity was found to increase continuously toward low energies with no structure; photons with energy substantially less than the band gap were included in the emission. Observation at 300°C, room, and liquid nitrogen temperature showed no change in the pattern of the light spots or their visual color; the spectra measured at 30°C and 75°C were identical. Heating the crystal caused the emission to decrease and to disappear when the junction became intrinsic. There was no observable change in spectrum with increasing current. It was estimated that 7×10^{-9} visible photons were emitted for each carrier traversing the junction.

Chynoweth and McKay (55) attributed the very energetic emission in Si to recombination of fast electrons with holes in equilibrium with the lattice or of fast holes with electrons in equilibrium with the lattice. Since the threshold for electron-hole pair production in Si is about 2.3 ev (513),* addition of the band-gap of 1.1 ev gives 3.4, although the existence of a definite threshold cannot be established. In principle energies as high as

---

* For other information on electron multiplication in Ge and Si see references (102, 103, 111).

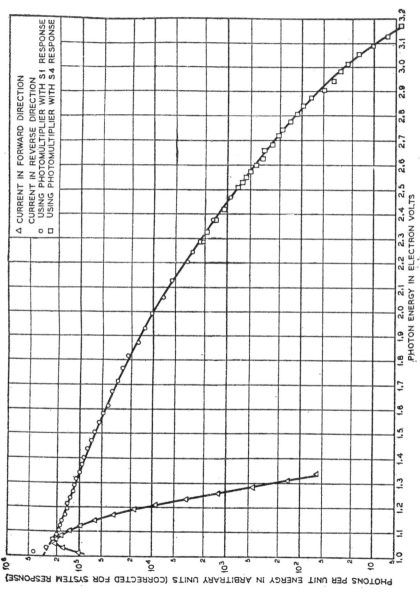

FIG. 45. Emission spectra for forward- and reverse-biased *p-n* junctions in silicon. (From Chynoweth and McKay, *55*.)

2(2.3) + 1.1 = 5.7 ev should exist, but the probability of such recombinations between fast electrons and fast holes should be very small. The emission at energies below the band gap was attributed to intraband transitions. The limitation of the breakdown to small spots has been studied theoretically by Rose (166). In analogy to discharges in gases these small regions, which are mainly controlled by space charge, are referred to as "microplasmas." Rose's analysis indicates that these regions are about 500A in diameter, carry a current density of about 2×10^6 amp/cm^2, have a field strength of about 7×10^5 volts/cm, a voltage drop of about 4 volts, and a temperature rise of perhaps 18°C. Two such space charge regions (one for holes and one for electrons) are to be associated with each microplasma. Champlin (514) has also studied such microplasmas in silicon with some results which differ from those of Rose.

Chynoweth and McKay (515) later studied the noise generated by the current flowing through the avalanche microplasmas. Direct correspondence was found between the noise and the light emission. The noise appears as the current is increased and one microplasma becomes active and then disappears at higher values when this microplasma stays permanantly "on," rather than extinguishing and re-igniting in a random manner; for even higher currents onset of more noise is observed as another microplasma begins breaking down. The light intensity was found to be directly proportional to the current. This was interpreted on the basis of increasing duty cycle for an unstable microplasma and an increase in cross-sectional area of a stable microplasma.

The first observations of visible light emission in Si were in p-n junctions. Kikuchi (516) was the first to observe it also at reverse-biased point contacts to Si crystals. Although the breakdown in Si junctions is normally of the avalanche type, Chynoweth and McKay (517) have shown that in very narrow junctions (400A wide) internal field emission (Zener effect) may be the breakdown process. In these narrow junctions the field for no applied voltage is already 4×10^5 volts/cm, while breakdown was observed at about 6 volts or 1.2×10^6 volts/cm. Analysis of the reverse current characteristics showed that multiplication occurred above about 3.6 volts[*]; after tunneling through the energy gap an electron must still be accelerated before it can excite additional carriers. Neither noise pulses nor an array of

---

[*] The forward-bias characteristic plots given by Chynoweth and McKay (517) for these Si junctions show oscillations about a straight line on a plot of logarithm of current as a function of voltage. Oscillations of this type have also been observed in currents in electroluminescent ZnS phosphors by Thornton (333). Chynoweth and McKay explained them as resulting from addition of field-emission current to the thermally generated current. It may be n oted, however, that such oscillations are also observed in the currents from thermionic cathodes in accelerating fields.

emitting spots similar to those for the avalanche microplasmas was observed. In these junctions the visual appearance of the light emission was a very faint and more-or-less uniform red glow, detectable at current densities of 2 amp/cm² or greater; the intensity was about a factor of 100 below that for avalanching junctions. Microscopic observation, however, indicated that the light came from a vast number of small spots; the current per spot was less than $10\mu a$, much below that for avalanche breakdown.

Chynoweth and Pearson (458) have studied the correlation of the light emitting spots of reverse-biased *p-n* junctions with dislocations as revealed by etch pits. It will be recalled that Newman (53) in the earliest observations on this phenomenon also noted the effect of mechanical strains in

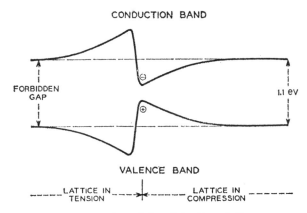

CONDUCTION BAND

FORBIDDEN GAP

1.1 eV

VALENCE BAND

LATTICE IN TENSION   LATTICE IN COMPRESSION

Fig. 46. Schematic representation of the distortion of the energy gap of silicon in the neighborhood of an edge dislocation. (From Chynoweth and Pearson, 458.)

inducing emission while Chynoweth and McKay (55) observed strong emission correlated with a scratch on the surface. Chynoweth and Pearson (458) found that microplasmas occur preferentially where dislocations pass through the junction; the emitting spots often lie on straight lines which are correlated with lines of etch pits. It is believed that the same holds true in junctions in which breakdown occurs by field emission but observation is more difficult here because of the low intensity of the emission. Junctions were also made which displayed both types of emission simultaneously. Junctions with "hard" breakdown characteristics were found to give spotty microplasma emission while those with "soft" characteristics emitted an appreciable amount of uniform radiation. Figure 46 shows schematically the effect of a dislocation on the energy bands as conjectured by Chynoweth and Pearson; calculations show that $\Delta E_g = 0.2$ ev is not unreasonable. Figure 46 may be compared to Fig. 39 as proposed by

Mertz (*300*) for the effect of a stacking fault in ZnS. Chynoweth and Pearson also observed prominent light emission at a region of severe crystallographic misalignment (possibly a grain boundary) cutting across the junction.

Batdorf *et al.* (*518*) studied breakdown and light emission in Si junctions which had been carefully prepared so as to avoid dislocations, field inhomogeneities, and edge effects, and had accurate parallel plane geometry. Many differences in behavior from the junctions described previously were observed. The breakdown voltage was very high, 44 volts, so that internal field emission did not occur; in slightly imperfect junctions microplasmas were seen to form at 23–24 volts. Although the light emission in these uniform junctions still occurred in spots, these were much more diffuse and weaker than typical microplasma spots so that the emission was almost uniform; the designation "macroplasma" was suggested for this type of excitation. The light intensity varied as the 4/3 power of the current over a wide range but some peculiar structure was seen in the characteristic just below the breakdown voltage. For the imperfect junctions the output was a linear function of current and also displayed similar structure but this corresponded to microplasma formation. It was therefore concluded that microplasmas also formed in the uniform junction just before breakdown. No current noise was found in the uniform junction, although it did occur in the imperfect junctions correlated with the microplasma light. Current multiplication (optically injected carriers) was also enhanced in the imperfect junctions in the region of the microplasma singularities. Many features of this light emission (such as the dependence on the 4/3 power of the current) remain unexplained. However, these workers were able to conclude that microplasma formation is not a necessary accompaniment of avalanche breakdown in Si but is induced by a sufficient number of inhomogeneities, probably dislocations.

Goetzberger (*519*) has also observed uniform light emission in Si *n-p-n* or *p-n-p* three-layer diode structures which do not require great care in preparation. In this case interaction of avalanche multiplication and transistor-type current gain leads to a negative current-voltage characteristic. In the negative resistance region self-adjustment occurs to equalize the emission over the area. If the bottom layer was removed by etching, a typical microplasma light emission pattern was obtained and the negative resistance region of the characteristic disappeared.

Kikuchi and Tachikawa (*520*) have also extensively studied light emission, current multiplication, and microplasma noise in Si reverse-biased junctions. They concluded that four different types of "weak spots" exist as shown below:

Type	Microplasma noise	Light emission	Current multiplication
I	Yes	Yes	No
II	Yes	No	No
III	No	Yes	Yes
IV	No	Yes	No

These different kinds of spots were found to occur mixed and at random in the junction. Type I is the usual type of microplasma spot. It is admitted that the existence of type II spots may still be in question. The light emission from Type III and IV spots is higher than from Type I. Type III and IV spots give a soft reverse characteristic and Types I and II a hard characteristic. Type III spots may be produced by scratching the surface. These workers think that deep levels due to oxygen or perhaps other impurities contribute to visible emission in Si junctions, either by the Zener effect or by impact ionization. In support of this view, they were able to observe visible light in Ge junctions only when oxygen was deliberately introduced (507). Shockley and Goetzberger (520a) have also proposed SiO_2 precipitates as responsible for microplasma formation and light emission in Si. Kikuchi and Tachikawa (520) also suggested a p-n-p-n or p-n-n^*-p structure as responsible for the switching action of microplasma spots, with the internal p (or n^*) region serving as a source of holes and arising from impurity clustering.

Davies and Storm (509) found no changes in the emission spectrum of reverse-biased Si junctions in the energy range 1.0–1.4 ev when the temperature was changed from 300°K to 77°K. Contrary to the case of emission at forward bias, it was concluded that exciton decay does not contribute to the reverse-bias emission. It was also concluded that if interband recombination of energetic carriers and intraband transitions both contribute to the emission, as suggested by Chynoweth and McKay (55), then the intraband contribution must extend to energies greater than 1.2 ev.

Gee (521) has reported visible light emission (a faint reddish glow) when p-type Si is anodically oxidized. As the oxide layer thickness increases with time the emission appears and then disappears as the voltage across the layer begins to increase rapidly. No emission was observed for n-type samples.

Electroluminescence in silicon is far from simple. Since the electrical characteristics and breakdown mechanism may vary widely, depending on conditions of sample preparation, many modes of light emission are also possible.

E. Gallium Phosphide

Electroluminescence in GaP was first observed by Wolff *et al.* (*37*). Light was observed when point contacts to single crystals were biased in either direction. The output was proportional to the current (if a "threshold" current was subtracted) but was about 20 times as great for a given current in the reverse direction as for the same current in the forward direction. No out-of-phase output was detected. The output as a function of voltage was found to obey an $\exp\left[-(V_0/V)^{1/2}\right]$ relationship. The light seemed to be emitted predominantly in the vicinity of the cathode. The temperature dependence was stated to be negligible (77 to 433°K). A layer of GaP imbedded in a dielectric also showed ac electroluminescence.

The emission for pure crystals was observed by Wolff *et al.* (*37*) to be orange. The short wavelength limit was at 5650A, near the absorption edge ($E_g = 2.2$ ev), and it was concluded that most of the emission occurred through activator levels, probably excess Ga (self-activation). The efficiency was estimated as about 10^{-7} visible quanta per electron. Orange cathodoluminescence, but no photoluminescence, was also observed. Crystals doped with Zn gave higher efficiency (10^{-5} quanta/electron) with the emission appearing deep red and having a short wavelength limit at about 6800A. Other crystals with Zn gave yellow-green emission (10^{-6} quanta/electron) consisting in addition to the red band of another band in the region of 5300–6300A with peak at 5900A. Doping with C, Si, Ge, Ti, Mn, Cu, S, Se, or Te had no effect on the orange luminescence. The long wavelength (infrared) limit of the emission was not determined. These workers pointed out that GaP:Zn is isoelectronic with ZnS:Cu and has the same crystal structure as cubic ZnS (sphalerite). The excitation near the cathode was ascribed to impact ionization by accelerated electrons. Since in about one out of ten cases the emission did not occur near the cathode, recombination of injected minority carriers was suggested as a second possibility.

Holt *et al.* (*38*) found electroluminescence in polycrystalline GaP specimens to occur at grain boundaries. At low current densities the emission was mainly at the surface but for higher currents sheets of light joining two surfaces were observed. Most boundaries emitted for either polarity of the applied voltage. Probing indicated that most of the applied voltage appeared at the boundaries and that these had nonlinear characteristics. Emission was also observed at point contacts to single grains, but only for current flow in the forward direction; the spectrum observed in this way was the same as that produced at grain boundaries. It was concluded that a high electric field was not sufficient to cause electroluminescence but that minority carrier injection must occur followed by radiative recombination. These workers believe that impurity accumulation produces an *n*-type region between the p-type grains, forming a back-to-back diode arrangement. The forward-biased junction is responsible for the emission and the reverse-biased junction for the voltage drop. These junctions were revealed in a scanning electron microscope; the shift in position upon voltage reversal corresponded to a thickness of 0.25μ for the n-type region.

Loebner and Poor (522) found that reverse-biased GaP rectifiers emitted a broad spectrum with peak at 6200A, exhibiting sharp cutoff at 5200A due to self-absorption, and extending beyond 1.2μ in the infrared region; emission from spots near the surface contained photons with energy greater than the band gap. This emission was ascribed to electron avalanches. The same samples biased in the forward direction emitted a symmetrical band with peak at 9000A (0.9μ) and about 0.5μ wide which was attributed to recombination of holes injected into the n-type material at Cu impurity centers. Both emissions were proportional to the current.

Loebner and Poor (39) also studied other purer GaP crystals (the major impurity was 5–50 ppm of Cu). As grown these contained junctions formed by a highly conductive n-type layer on the surface, and presumably an intermediate nearly intrinsic layer as found in electroluminescent SiC crystals. Current and light were obtained only for forward bias conditions. Microscopic examination showed the light to be emitted uniformly over an area several microns below the surface. The emission intensity was proportional to the square of the current. The emission spectrum was a narrow band with peak at 2.20 ev (5625A); the short-circuit photovoltaic current of the same junction had a peak at 2.4 ev. This good agreement with the known energy gap and the observed square-law dependence on current lead to the conclusion that the emission resulted from bimolecular band-to-band transitions. The emission in these pure crystals was a monotonic function of, and strictly in phase with, the voltage and current. Loebner and Hegyi (447), however, found that crystals of GaP-GaN, but predominantly GaP and which showed striations, showed either one, two, or three peaks per sinusoidal voltage half-cycle depending on the amplitude of the voltage. In this case it was concluded that two different mechanisms of electroluminescence excitation and also quenching of the emission by the field occurred, all instantaneous and in phase with the voltage (see Section III,I). The two mechanisms were not elaborated.

Mandelkorn (523) found that n-p-n or p-n-p GaP structures gave emission for either polarity of an applied voltage but that single diodes emitted only in the reverse direction. In the latter case the emission was white and appeared in the form of small spots and a white line at the surface, i.e., very similar to the avalanche emission in Si. Kikuchi and Iizuka (524) later made similar observations (no emission for forward bias) in undoped crystals and also observed noise pulses similar to those for Si microplasmas.

Allen and Gibbons (525) studied the emission at reverse bias further. The reverse current was found to be small until a critical voltage was exceeded above which the current increased rapidly and orange emission with a broad spectrum appeared at discrete points. These points appeared one at a time as the current was increased and disappeared in reverse order as it was decreased. Both the number and intensity of the spots increased with increasing current and the total light output varied as the 5/4 power of the current. Current multiplication of injected carriers was observed. The rise and fall time of the emission was found to be less than 5×10^{-9} sec. Allen and Gibbons concluded that these observations were all consistent with avalanches formed by "hot" carriers. The difference in emission color between these samples and those of Mandelkorn may be due to different distances of the absorbing material traversed by the radiation. Gorton et al. (526) also studied the reverse-bias emission in GaP point-contact diodes. The emission was found to lie between 1.96 and 2.19 ev, with a peak at 2.12 ev, the value found by these workers for the band gap. Appearance of new light spots was found to be correlated with breaks in the current-voltage characteristic.

Grimmeiss and Koelmans (40) found that undoped polycrystalline GaP samples were mainly n-type. The emission observed when a tungsten contact was biased either negative or positive had a peak at 6250A, but for positive (reverse) bias there was an indication of a second peak at 5650A; in some crystals, particularly at high power input, this second peak was clearly resolved. The emission appeared at various regions in the samples and the position was independent of polarity. Weakly Zn-doped crystals were still n-type and showed the same orange-red emission. Addition of high amounts of Zn produced dark p-type crystals which were nonelectroluminescent. No photoluminescence of the undoped crystals was observed at room temperature, but at low temperatures a deep red emission with peak at about 6300A was obtained. The excitation spectrum for the photovoltaic effect was also measured and found to have peaks at 4200A and 5600A for undoped and at 4200A and 6000A for weakly Zn-doped samples. The light emission in these polycrystalline samples probably occurred at internal p-n junctions, as in the experiments of Holt et al. (38). Recombination of injected minority carriers apparently occurred at levels within the forbidden gap; these were attributed to Ga and P vacancies (acceptors and donors, respectively). The energy level diagram suggested by Grimmeiss and Koelmans (527) is shown in Fig. 47. The activation energies of 0.19 and 0.07 ev shown were confirmed by conductivity measurements on p-type and n-type regions, respectively. Samples prepared at high pressures of P were p-type, also consistent with this model.

Grimmeiss and Koelmans (527) later studied GaP:Zn in more detail.

In agreement with Wolff *et al.* (*37*), they found that the electroluminescence efficiency in this case is higher than that of undoped samples by a factor of 100 to 1000. With large area contacts, light-emission was found only for forward bias. In this case the presence of Zn introduces a new band peaked at 7000A. This is presumably the same emission seen earlier in Zn-doped samples by Wolff *et al.* (*37*) and also by Ullman (*528*). Ullman found that the Zn concentration was critical; above about 0.01% Zn, only nonluminescent crystals were obtained. Grimmeiss and Koelmans found that simultaneously with the introduction of Zn the emission at 6200A for undoped material disappeared but that at 5650A was still observed, although smaller

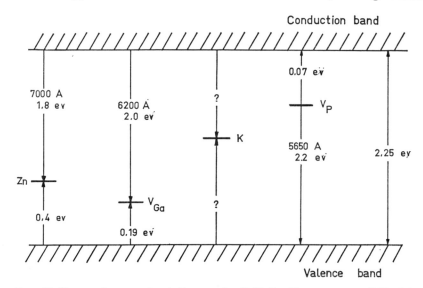

FIG. 47. Proposed energy level diagram for GaP:Zn. K represents a "killer" level resulting in nonradiative transitions. (From Grimmeiss and Koelmans, *527*.)

than the peak due to Zn. Upon cooling to liquid nitrogen temperature both emission bands became narrower and the relative intensity of the 5650A band increased; the longer wavelength band shifted to 6800A but the 5650A band did not shift. The shift in relative intensity is consistent with a Schön-Klasens model. Thermal quenching of the emission was pronounced even at room temperature. The photoluminescence of these samples, also measurable only at low temperature due to thermal quenching, consisted of a major peak at 6800A and a minor peak at 6100A. The photoluminescence intensity was a linear function of the exciting intensity over the entire range. The dependence of each of the three bands seen in electroluminescence (7000, 6200, and 5650A) on current, however, showed a very high slope (about 20) for low currents and approached a linear dependence for high current. The linear part was essentially independent of temperature, while the superlinear portion shifted to higher currents as the temperature was increased.

The assignment for the Zn level in GaP:Zn made by Grimmeiss and Koelmans (527) is also shown in Fig. 47 and is supported by an activation energy of 0.4 ev for p-type conductivity at high temperatures. The absence of edge emission corresponding to the band gap energy was assumed to result from the fact that such a transition would have to be phonon-assisted. Because of the low luminescence efficiency, even in the linear range at high currents, a level responsible for nonradiating transitions was also assumed; its position, however, is uncertain. These workers studied the kinetics to be expected from such a model (14 types of transitions) and conclude that the observed nonlinearity can be explained. In particular, the shift of the nonlinear portion of the characteristic to higher currents for higher temperature was found to be controlled by the donor activation energy, 0.07 ev.

Gershenzon and Mikulyak (41) have recently studied the electroluminescence at both diffused and alloyed p-n junctions in high purity monocrystalline GaP. At forward bias only the diffused junctions emitted light. The electrical characteristics of these junctions also indicated the presence of an intermediate nearly-intrinsic (self-compensated) n^*-layer, similar to that in electroluminescent SiC junctions (62). It therefore appears that an intrinsic region is a necessary condition for efficient electroluminescence of this type.

The forward-bias emission observed by Gershenzon and Mikulyak (41) consisted of two bands. The major one was in the red region, with width (0.02 ev) independent of temperature and peak at an energy 0.40 ev less than the band gap; its peak wavelength was therefore 6750A at 300°K and 6300A at 80°K. No infrared emission was detected in the region 0.85–2.0μ. The peak energy increased by 0.02 ev for high bias voltage. The efficiency at room temperature was 10^{-4} to 10^{-6} quanta/electron and the decay time was 2×10^{-8} sec; the efficiency increased at lower temperatures. The output varied linearly with current at low-temperature and at a faster rate above room temperature; saturation of the output was observed at fairly low currents. Because of its characteristics this emission band obviously arises from centers lying within the forbidden energy band; the density of such centers was calculated to be 10^{13}–10^{14} cm^{-3}. Although the energy difference of 0.4 is the same as that found for Zn by Grimmesis and Koelmans (527), this band appeared in diodes produced by diffusion of either Zn or Cd and could not be identified with photoluminescent peaks characteristic of samples heavily doped with Zn, Cd, or Cu. However, a similar red emission was found in the photoluminescence spectrum of many undoped crystals, where it is enhanced by the presence of excess Ga, suggesting the influence of a vacancy. The relatively great width of this band also seems significant, and Gershenzon and Mikulyak suggest the possibility of clusters. The width, the position, and the intensity were different from sample to sample; the peak position varied as much as 0.05 ev. This emission therefore seems to arise from centers which depend in some way on the stoichiometry or the growth conditions but their precise nature is as yet undetermined.

The second band observed by Gershenzon and Mikulyak (41) for forward bias had a width which was approximately $3kT$ and corresponded to an energy about 0.04 ev less than the band-gap (5400–5600A). This green band decreased in relative intensity as the temperature was decreased and was difficult to resolve at 80°K. The efficiency was 10^{-6} to 10^{-8} quanta per injected carrier (considering only the radiation which escaped from the sample). The intensity varied quadratically with current for low currents but became linear at higher injection levels. This band seems to be identical to that observed by Loebner and Poor (39) and to result from "intrinsic" (phonon-assisted) interband recombination; exciton processes, however, cannot be ruled out. The change to linear kinetics for high currents was ascribed to narrowing of the depletion layer (1000–2000A wide for zero bias) until it becomes comparable to the diffusion length.

Gershenzon and Mikulyak (41) observed light emission for reverse bias in both diffused and alloyed diodes, both above and below breakdown. The spectra were all identical, exhibiting a single broad maximum at photon energies must below the band gap and slowly dropping off in both directions (see Fig. 48). The cutoff at short wavelengths is due to band-edge absorption, while the shoulder is ascribed to a change from indirect to direct transitions. These spectra were independent of current but the output showed a change in slope at a current which was identified as the breakdown point; the characteristic was linear above this point and superlinear below. The reverse-bias emission in the diffused diodes biased above breakdown originated at small spots (less than 1μ in diameter) near the junction. Near breakdown the individual spot intensities appeared to be invariant with current and an increase in current resulted in an increase in the number of emitting spots. The current per spot in this region was about $100\mu a$. For higher currents the intensity of the individual spots also increased but the linear dependence of output on current was maintained. The spot density was greatest near an intersection of the junction with the surface or a grain boundary. The efficiency of the emitted radiation was 10^{-5} to 10^{-7} quanta per carrier and the decay time was less than 1.5×10^{-8} sec (the limit of detectability). The light emission accompanying breakdown in the alloyed junction occurred in small irregular areas, larger than those for diffused junctions; in this case the output always increased faster than the current.

Since the emission spectra for reverse bias was the same in all their specimens, Gershenzon and Mikulyak (*41*) concluded that the emission mechanism was also the same, although the excitation process differed in different types of junctions. If interband recombination were involved,

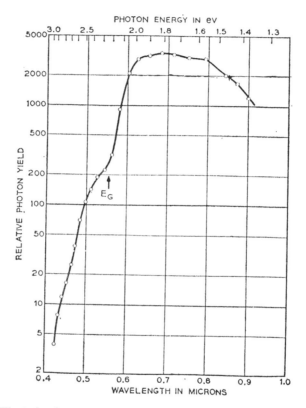

FIG. 48. Electroluminescence spectrum for reverse-biased GaP diode. (From Gershenzon and Mikulyak, *41*.)

even through the assistance of the unidentified centers responsible for the red emission observed for forward bias, then a threshold wavelength should be expected. No forward-biased emission was detected at wavelengths less than 1.45 ev, but the reverse-bias spectrum shows no inflection in this region (Fig. 48). It was therefore concluded that intraband transitions were predominantly responsible for the emission. Because of the large self-absorption it is difficult to say whether other processes producing high-energy photons are also important at shorter wavelengths. In the diffused diodes avalanche breakdown and microplasma formation were responsible for the emission, which was similar in many respects to that for the corresponding emission in silicon (see the preceding section), as also observed by other workers (*523–526*). The alloyed junctions were much narrower (as low as 150A) and hence internal field emission was found to be the predominant mechanism. The carriers accelerated by the field below breakdown were ascribed to thermal generation at deep-lying centers in the depletion layer. By electrical measurements the density of these levels was found to be 10^{15}–10^{18} cm^{-3}. It was not, however, possible to show experimentally that in this case the light is actually emitted uniformly over the junction.

As this review is written there are rumors that electroluminescence efficiencies much higher than those published and discussed above have been obtained in GaP and that the impurities responsible for some of the emission bands which have been observed are being isolated; the details, however, are not yet available.

F. Galvanoluminescence in Al_2O_3 and Other Oxides

The luminescence from aluminum electrodes immersed in an electrolyte has a long history. As long ago as 1898 Braun (*16*) reported that when an alternating voltage was applied they emitted white or yellowish-red light from their entire surface which changed to blue as the current was increased. By use of a rotating disk stroboscope he established that the glow began at a definite phase of the current which resulted in development of H_2 bubbles at the electrode and stopped at a definite phase of the decreasing current; he characterized the emission as "sharply defined intermittent light," i.e., with fast decay. Mg and Zn electrodes were found to give similar but weaker luminescence. This emission was also studied by several other early workers (*529*). Berti (*529*) seems to have been the first to conclude that it was associated with a poorly conducting oxide layer on the anode. Such anodically formed oxide films are used commercially for rectification and in electrolytic capacitors and many of the early observations of the luminescence were made incidentally in this way. As noted in the Introduction (Section I) in some cases, particularly with organic electrolytes, the emission is due to electroytically produced chemiluminescence (*530*); such emission will not be considered further here.

Forrest (*531*) noted that as the current is increased small violet sparks are superimposed on the uniform glow observed at lower currents and finally breakdown occurs. He concluded that the film of gas formed at the anode played an essential role in the mechanism and that the emission occurred simply as the result of a glow discharge in this gas layer between the metal and the electrolyte, a conclusion reached earlier by Güntherschulze (*529*). He subjected the electrolytic cell to pressures from 1/40 to 4 atmospheres but found little or no effect on the performance. Magnetic fields up to 4000 oersteds also produced no effect, in accordance with the view that the discharge is limited to a region about 10^{-6} cm thick at the anode. The spectrum was found to be continuous with a peak at about 5550A. Forrest also studied the emission at the cathode, which is observed only for operation on ac or as a transient following reversal of voltage after a period of anodic operation.

Dufford (*532*) found that 25 different electrolytes could be used to produce galvanoluminescence with Al electrodes. Emission was also obtained from Zn, Mg, Ta, W, Ag, Ce (mischmetal), Sb, and Mg; no emission was obtained with Pb, Mo, Cu, Fe, Ni, Pt, or Sn. In some cases only scintillations were observed, in others a steady glow in addition. The brightness was found to increase rapidly with applied voltage (after stabilization at each voltage) until heating occurred; for higher voltages the output decreased. Dufford commented that higher efficiencies could probably be obtained with watercooled anodes and this was later verified by Sullivan and Dufford (*532*). The efficiency was found to be between 10^{-8} and $5 \times 10^{-6}\%$; the highest value found was for etherated magnesium bromide with platinum electrodes and occurred at the unusually low value of 13 volts. Sullivan and Dufford also commented on the fact that, although the brightnesses are of different orders of magnitude, under certain conditions the brightness of galvanoluminescence increases with applied voltage in the same way as does that of an incandescent tungsten filament. The emission was noted to be bluish white in almost all cases, with very little red emission present. These workers discounted any gaseous source for the uniform glow but agreed that small gas discharges were responsible for the scintillations (which were sometimes found to have a higher luminous efficiency than the glow). Raoult (*533*) later confirmed this observation by finding the scintillation spectrum to consist of lines due to Al and O.

Güntherschulze and Betz (*534*) found that emission could be obtained from Al electrodes in $(NH_4)_2CO_3$ as low as 2.65 volts rms; of this applied voltage not more than one volt was thought to be present at the anode. Higher voltages were required for other metals. No influence of the electrolyte concentration on output was found (Dufford (*532*) earlier had also found only small changes due to concentration). An effect of different electrolytes on the brightness was attributed to their varying solubility for Al_2O_3; citric acid was the best tried for Al. A great influence of impurities in the Al on the light output was noted. They concluded that the continuous spectrum of galvanoluminescence is thermal radiation due to hot electrons, 20 years before similar suggestions were made for electroluminescence in semiconductors. By correlating the dependence of output on voltage with that of a blackbody (compare Sullivan and Dufford's comparison to a tungsten filament), it was concluded that electron temperatures of 27,000°K were attained. The effect of impurities was studied in more detail later by Betz (535), who found that Cu, Mg, Cr, or Fe had little or no effect on the output, Zn depressed it, and Mn caused a large increase. He concluded that the emission was similar to that of normal impurity-activated phosphors. Audubert and Viktorin (536) detected ultraviolet radiation upon anodic oxidation of aluminum and found the wavelength to be longer the higher the voltage, contrary to what might be expected. Gumminski (537) found the emission from Al electrodes to extend from 3705A to 5874A with a maximum near 4590A. The emission at long wavelengths increased when the voltage was raised and the presence of Mn in the Al also caused a shift to the red.

Anderson (538) found greatest output with Al electrodes in oxalic acid. He commented on the fact that although the spectrum depended on impurities in the metal, it was independent of the electrolyte. Figure 49A shows the variation of voltage, current, and light output with time after application of positive voltage following the reverse condition. Decay of the emission from a high initial value to a steady level is shown, in addition to decay when the voltage is removed (there is a change in scale for the light output curve at AB). Figure 49B shows the corresponding conditions when the Al is made the cathode following anodic operation; only a "flash" is obtained. The cathodic flash was brighter than the anodic flash and was redder than the anodic glow, as also observed earlier by Rummel (539). The decay time for the anodic flash was about three times that for the cathodic flash; the decay curves were neither exponential nor hyperbolic. For pure Al the output was lower and the decay slower (20–60 msec) than for commercial Al containing Mn (6–16 msec). The intensity of the cathodic flash decreased if the sample was allowed to rest before the reverse voltage was applied; in a typical case an interval of 10 sec produced only 20% of the output obtained for a one second interval.

Anderson (538) noted that galvanoluminescence is observed only for metals whose oxides are n-type conductors (Al, Zn, Mg, Ta) and not with those whose oxides are p-type conductors (Cu, Fe, Ni). Anderson's model for the excitation assumes that the impurity centers responsible for the conductivity can migrate under the action of a field. The resultant space charge formed at the oxide-electrolyte interface when the Al is positive produces a field of about 10^7 volts/cm. Electrons entering the oxide from the electrolyte produce secondary electrons from the valence band. The positive holes thus formed become trapped at impurity centers and emission occurs upon recombination of electrons with these trapped holes. The emission is thus assumed to be impurity-activated luminescence following an

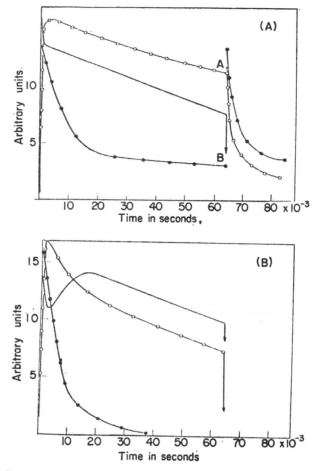

FIG. 49. Curves of voltage, current, and light output for Al electrode in oxalic acid. (A) Al anode after operation as cathode; there is a change in scale for the light curve at the point AB where the applied voltage is removed. (B) Al cathode after operation as anode. (●—●)—luminescent intensity; (○—○)—voltage across cell; (—)—current passing through cell. (From Anderson, *538*).

acceleration-collision excitation mechanism, quite similar to that proposed much later for electroluminescence in ZnS.

The most extensive study of the galvanoluminescence of Al electrodes has been made by van Geel *et al.* (*17*). These workers emphasized that the first layer of oxide formed on the electrode is nonporous which is followed by a porous layer (*540*). The porosity depends on the solubility of the electrolyte for Al_2O_3. These workers found that the luminescence during oxidation occurs only in the nonporous layer, in which the field strength is very high and uniform and conduction is largely (more than 95%) by ionic motion. In a completely formed layer, on the other hand, ionic conductivity is low and space charge formation occurs. During formation the thickness of the oxide and the voltage across it both increase proportionally to the time ($d = 13A/volt$, reference 540), so that the field strength is constant. The luminescence brightness, however, increases faster than the thickness and is related to the current I and the thickness d by the relation

$$L = aI(e^{bd} - 1). \tag{31}$$

The value of b is about 10^5 cm^{-1}. Above a certain film thickness the porous layer begins forming, the capacitance remains constant, and the luminescence decreases. The last fact is attributed to absorption in the porous layer of light generated in the underlying oxide. If the voltage is varied below that used for forming the layer the output is proportional to the current, i.e., to

$$L = p(e^{qV} - 1). \tag{32}$$

With formed oxide layers the small leakage current (reverse direction of the rectifier) produces only a weak luminescence. For alternating voltage light is emitted during both half cycles. Van Geel et al. (17) found that the light peak always led the voltage maximum while the current lagged the voltage. On the other hand, G. Curie and D. Curie (442) found no phase difference between the light and the voltage. Van Geel, Pistorius, and Bouma found that the cathodic flash may be either greater or less than the anodic flash, depending on conditions. The two types of flash are mutually dependent, each requiring that the other have occurred previously. Contrary to Anderson (538), these workers found that anodic operation created a very stable condition and that the cathodic flash could be obtained even after several hours of standing. On the other hand, no anodic flash was observed if more than ten minutes was allowed following cathodic operation. It should be noted that these studies were made with an aqueous solution of boric acid and borax; other electrolytes would presumably have given different results. Additional low-intensity anodic flashes may also be obtained when the anodic system is first short-circuited and then voltage reapplied in the same direction. Simultaneous ultraviolet excitation (2537A) increased the luminescence during formation greatly. The cathodic flash was also much stronger if the film was irradiated during or after the preceding anodic operation; the following anodic flash was also intensified. On the other hand, irradiation after the cathodic flash produced no intensification of the following anodic flash. It was therefore concluded that the anodic flash is a residue of the cathodic flash.

Van Geel *et al.* (*17*) concluded that the small fraction of the current during oxidation which is electronic is responsible for the luminescence by impact ionization (the field is of the order of 10^7 volts/cm). The emission in a formed layer for operation on alternating current was ascribed to trapping of electrons and space-charge formation. The fact that increasing the temperature reduced the permissible time between cathodic and anodic flashes is consistent with trapping. These authors conclude with the statement that "We have given a number of experimental results and are well aware of the fact that our explanation of the phenomena is incomplete. The fact that ionic and electronic processes take place simultaneously . . . constitutes a great difficulty." Smith (*18*) has studied the effect of the surface condition of the electrode on the electrical and luminescent properties and concluded that defects in the film are the controlling factor. Such defects may be responsible for breakdown effects (similar to microplasmas in Si) as well as serving as luminescence activators. Van Geel and his co-workers (*541*), on the basis of electrical measurements on Al rectifiers, have suggested that *p-n* junctions may exist in the oxide layer due to differences in oxygen concentration. Such junctions could obviously play an important role in galvanoluminescence. Sasaki (*542*) has also established the existence of *p-i-n* junctions in the anodic film on Ta electrodes.

It should also be mentioned that Güntherschulze and Gerlach (*67*) in 1934 observed light emission from pulverized ruby (Al_2O_3 : Cr) in high alternating electric fields. High vacuum was used as an insulator to prevent excitation by gas discharges but the experimental conditions were certainly not ideal. Light emission (pale lemon-yellow) has also been observed from Al_2O_3 "cold electron emission" cathodes in vacuum (*32, 68*). Adams and his colleagues (*543*) have recently reported dc electroluminescence from Al_2O_3 activated by Cr, Mn, or rare earth elements; heat treatment in N_2 and Cl_2 was necessary to induce the emission. In each case the spectrum was characteristic of the particular activator and the output was much greater than that excited by ultraviolet, indicating that true electroluminescence occurred. Electroluminescence in other oxides is discussed in Sections IV,*G,1* and IV,*G,4*.

G. *Other Materials*

1. *Other II-VI Compounds.* In addition to ZnS (Section III) and CdS (Section IV,*A*), electroluminescence has also been observed in ZnSe (*25–27, 647*) and CdTe (*28*) but apparently not yet in ZnTe or CdSe. In the case of ZnSe:Cu powders the emission is peaked at about 6500A. Such phosphors, however, do not usually have good output for excitation at low frequency. Their frequency dependence of output indicates that quenching occurs; this may be related to the small distance of the Cu level in this phosphor from the valence band, which is about the same as that for ZnS:Ag (see Table IV). Van Doorn and de Nobel (28) observed weak electroluminescence from CdTe p-n junctions (Au doping was used for the p-type region) at 77°K. This emission was peaked at 8640A while the photo-luminescence was peaked at 8800A (see Table III); this difference was attributed to self-absorption and the difference in origin of the generated light.

Wachtel (35) has prepared electroluminescent CaS:Cu,Eu phosphor powders with red emission arising from Eu centers; the absence of blue Cu emission is attributed to energy transfer from Cu to Eu centers. The output of these phosphors, however, is relatively weak and depends greatly on the physical state of the material. The excitation seems to result from a kind of internal "contact electroluminescence" (217) resulting from agglomeration of particles. CaS does not seem to be as suitable a host for formation of Cu_2S segregations as does ZnS. The fact that CaS is hygroscopic is also a disadvantage. Wachtel also made similar orange-emitting electroluminescent BaS:Cu phosphors; although not actually made, blue-emitting CaS:Cu phosphors should have resulted from omission of the Eu in CaS:Cu,Eu. Lozykowski and Meczynska (36) have also reported electroluminescence in SrS and BaS.

Electroluminescence in zincite (ZnO:Mn) crystals was first observed by Lossew (15), who stated that it was very feeble compared to that for SiC. He later (471) observed galvanoluminescence when the same crystals were immersed in an electrolyte. Krieg and Lange (544) observed light emission during electrolytic polishing of zinc. Destriau (20) also observed emission from ZnO powders activated by Cu. Fischer (29) used sintered samples with low conductivity and observed rectification. Light emission was observed with direct voltages as low as 2.5 volts and occurred only when the barrier was biased in the reverse direction. Fischer assumed that the excitation was due to impact ionization and that the work function (contact potential) of the metal contact accounted for excitation at voltages smaller than the forbidden energy gap (3.2 ev). Vereschchagin (30) observed that the electroluminescence of ZnO is greatly influenced by the state of the surface and is increased by a factor of 2 to 3 when the container is evacuated, similar to the earlier observation of Thorington (211) on ZnS. Pettsol'd (31) studied compacted mixtures of ZnO (n-type) and Bi_2O_3 (p-type). The conductivity obtained was a function of the Bi_2O_3 content, the heating time and temperature, and the cooling rate; samples with high resistivity produced yellow emission while more conducting ones emitted blue. The emission was greatest at the electrodes where most of the voltage drop occurred and was therefore not primarily due to p-n junctions formed in the bulk by the addition of Bi_2O_3. The current-voltage characteristics were highly nonlinear. Time lags of several minutes were observed when the voltage was reversed.

Electroluminescence has been incidentally observed from BeO and MgO (and also Al_2O_3) films used as cold electron emitters (*32–34*). Mizushima *et al.* (*34*) reported a luminous efficiency of 20% for MgO but it is not clear whether this is an energy efficiency (if so, this would be a very impressive figure) or is given in terms of quanta per electron emitted; the latter seems more likely, however. The emission from BeO was described as "brilliant purple" and that from MgO as "bright blue"; no emission was observed from ZnO, BaO, CaO, or SrO (*32*). Woods and Wright (*545*) earlier studied "field-enhanced cathodoluminescence" in MgO. The secondary electron emission and the light output were found to be greatly enhanced when an electric field was applied across the oxide. With some samples the electron and light emission continued for long times (an hour or more) when the bombarding cathode-ray beam was switched off. This electron emission as a result of the high field across the oxide layer is called the "Malter effect" (*546*) and was first observed in Al_2O_3. Analysis of the current-voltage charactristics indicates formation of electron avalanches in the oxide layer (*547*), while the emission is greatest if a porous layer is used. It may be noted that this condition with a majority of the applied voltage across the oxide layer and the remainder across the vacuum space is very similar to that in anodic galvanoluminescence, where most of the voltage is across the oxide layer and the remainder across the electrolyte, but the polarity is reversed. Woods and Wright observed several emission bands in the emission from MgO; there were indications that blue emission was favored by excess Mg and red by excess O.

2. *Other III-V Compounds.* Some of the properties of several Group III-V compounds of interest, as well as those of some related materials, are summarized in Table VII. The electroluminescence of GaP has been discussed in detail in Section IV,E. The other compounds have received much less attention; the emission of most of them lies in the infrared region of the spectrum because of the low band gap. Braunstein (*43*) observed forward-bias electroluminescence from GaAs, GaSb, and InP (and also Ge-Si alloys). The emission spectrum for GaSb was peaked at 0.625 ev, in fair agreement with the band gap, but that for GaAs was peaked at 1.10 ev (compared to $E_g = 1.38$) and was much wider; the discrepancy in the latter case was not explained. In these experiments the output was a linear function of the injected current. Wolff *et al.* (*37*) also observed electroluminescence from GaAs and mixed crystals of GaP-GaAs and GaP-InP but reported that the emission was more difficult to obtain than from GaP. Pankove and Massoulié (*548a*) have recently found in GaAs, in addition to a broad band at 0.95 ev due to deep centers, a narrow emission corre-

sponding to the band gap (1.45 ev at 4°K) and a third peak with energy 0.09 ev less than the band gap.* Loebner and Poor (39) measured the electro-luminescence spectrum of InP and found the peak to be at 1.23 ev, in good

TABLE VII. SOME PROPERTIES OF THE III–V COMPOUNDS AND RELATED MATERIALS[a]

Material	Interatomic distance (A)[b]	Index of refraction	Optical band gap (300°K,ev)	Mobility (cm²/volt-sec)	
				Electron	Hole
C (diamond)	1.54	2.42	5.4–4.6	1800	1550
BN	hexagonal		~5.0		
SiC	1.89 (sphal./wurt.)	2.6	2.2/2.9	100	10
AlN	wurtzite	2.13, 2.20	4.6		
Si	2.35	3.42	1.04	1900	425
AlP	2.36	3.4	2.42(3.0)		
GaN	wurtzite		3.34		
AlAs	2.44		2.4		
GaP	2.36	2.9	2.24	110[c]	70[c]
Ge	2.44	3.99	0.63	3900	1700
AlSb	2.63	3.2	1.49	40	230
GaAs	2.44	3.4	1.38	6000	240
InP	2.54	3.1	1.27	5000	60
GaSb	2.63	3.8	0.68	4000	2000
InAs	2.62	3.5	0.33	27,000	280
Sn (grey)	2.80		0.08	2000	1000
InSb	2.80	3.96	0.162	77,000	1000

[a] Data primarily from references (181, 486, 548).
[b] Cubic sphalerite (zincblende) structure unless indicated otherwise.
[c] See reference (41).

agreement with the band gap. In this case (as for the corresponding experiments for GaP), the recombination was found to be bimolecular. Loebner and Hegyi (447) also studied the electroluminescence of GaP-GaN mixed crystals (see Sections III,I and IV,E).

Considerable interest has been exhibited in InSb because of its extremely high mobility (see Table VII) and the fact that the efficiency for radiative recombination of injected carriers is unusually high. Because of the small band gap, calculations of the recombination must include the effects of

* Note added in proof: Keyes and Quist (649) have recently indicated that the electroluminescence efficiency of GaAs may be as high as 85%. This is the highest value yet reported for any electroluminescent material. Coherent ("LASER") emission has also been observed in GaAs (651).

degeneracy (44, 549); the calculated radiative lifetime for intrinsic material is of the order of 6×10^{-7} sec, of the same order as the measured value of 3.6×10^{-7} sec (550), indicating the predominance of this type of recombination. Moss and Hawkins (45) found that the emission resulting from recombination of optically injected carriers had a peak wavelength of about 7.5μ, as expected, and that the efficiency for radiative recombination was approximately 20%, a significantly higher value than that of 10^{-6} for many other semiconductors. The only observation of electroluminescence in this material, however, seems to be that of Basov et al. (648) who recently reported emission from electron avalanches at low temperatures.

On the other extreme, considerable interest has been devoted to III-V compounds with band-gaps wider than that of GaP which would be expected to exhibit visible electroluminescence. Wolff et al. (47, 551), for example, have studied the electroluminescence of AlN. Emission was obtained either for ac (including insulated electrodes) or dc operation. In the former case the output was in phase with the applied voltage; for dc excitation the emission occurred at the cathode and decayed with time. These workers concluded that the excitation is by means of impact excitation rather than minority carrier injection. The emission spectrum was found to consist of a series of narrow bands in the region 400–500 mμ, corresponding to the spectrum of N_2, plus broad bands in the region 500–700 mμ which depend on the impurity content. Red emission (610 mμ peak) ascribed to Mn^{4+} (low concentration, 10 ppm), green emission (520 mμ peak) ascribed to Mn^{2+} (1%), red emission due to Be^{2+} or Cr^{3+}, and blue emission due to Si or excess Al were reported. The appearance of the N_2 bands is very unusual and suggests that indirect photoluminescent excitation is involved; the fact that no emission was observed in vacuum, and greatly reduced output in gases other than N_2, points to the same conclusion. However, the output was found to have the same dependence on voltage as that for ZnS [Eq. (8)]. Furthermore, irradiation with external radiation (400–500 mμ) did not excite emission and in some cases (high Mn) no photoluminescence was observed at all. These workers therefore believe the emission to be true electroluminescence, although the presence of surface N_2 is necessary for some as yet unexplained transfer process. The luminous efficiency was measured as only 10^{-3} lumens/watt but high brightnesses (50 ft-L) are obtainable. Adams and Au Coin (543) have also studied electroluminescence in mixed crystals of AlN-Al_2O_3.

Wolff et al. (47) also observed weak bluish-white electroluminescence from GaN. The luminescence of this material has been studied by Grimmeiss and his co-workers (42). Several emission bands were observed in the photo- and cathodoluminescence of samples doped with Li, Zn, Cd, or Mg. These results indicate that Zn introduces a level 0.4 ev above the valence band (emission at 4320A), Cd one 0.69 ev above (5080A), and Li one at 0.95 ev (5820A); the complicated short-wavelength emission (peaks at 3810, 3905, and 4010A) was ascribed to levels lying 0.1, 0.21, 0.28, and 0.33(?) ev below the conduction band. The electroluminescence of this material was described only as "very weak"; further work was handicapped by the absence of large single crystals so that p-n junctions could not be prepared. Lorenz and Binkowski (548b) have also recently studied the cathodoluminescence of GaN.

Grimmeiss et al. (48) have studied the electroluminescence of AlP crystals which showed rectification at point contacts. The emission was observed either in the neighborhood of the contact or inside the crystal. The photoluminescence showed a peak at 6100A while the electroluminescence spectrum was found to consist of two bands with peaks at 5550 and 6150A. Conductivity measurements on p-type regions gave two activation energies of 0.15 and 0.37 ev; these energies added to those corresponding to the emission give the band gap (2.42 ev) as determined from reflectivity measurements and thus identify these two acceptor levels (of unknown origin) as the sources of the emission. The emission was therefore ascribed to carrier injection at p-n junctions. It may be noted, however, that earlier workers found a value of 3.0 ev for the band gap of AlP; the reason for this large discrepancy is unexplained.

The electroluminescence of another wide band-gap semiconductor, BN, has been studied by Larach and Shrader (46). The emission spectrum (whether of photo-, cathodo-, or electro-luminescence) consisted of a complex series of as many as 24 narrow bands extending from 2900 to 6500A; the relative intensity of the various bands varied with the current density for cathode-ray excitation or with the wavelength of ultraviolet excitation. The photoluminescence intensity was a maximum at 875°K and declined to 50% of the maximum value at 1375°K; the thermal quenching energy above the maximum corresponded to 1.08 ev. For field excitation the phosphor was suspended in castor oil as often done for ZnS. The output increased with increasing frequency, although appreciably less than linearly, and as the 6.5 power of the voltage. The "brightness wave" consisted of a single peak (but with fine structure at the maximum), leading the applied voltage, with no secondary peak. Strangely enough, no information was given on the effect of variation of frequency or voltage on the emission spectrum. No data are available concerning the efficiency of electroluminescence in this material but experiments by Lehmann indicate that it is quite low.

Multiband photo- and cathodo-luminescence in BN had been observed earlier by Tiede and Tomaschek (478), who attributed it to traces of carbon serving as an activator. Since Larach and Shrader (46) found no change in emission spectrum upon firing in oxygen or other gases, they concluded that the fine structure is an intrinsic property of BN and arises from vibrational effects. Lehmann (552), on the other hand, attributes the luminescence of BN not to the material itself but to adsorbed hydro-boron-nitride compounds (similar to hydrocarbons but with one B and one N atom replacing two C atoms). It is difficult, however, to understand the performance at extremely high temperatures on this basis. The luminescence of BN remains something of an enigma. Since BN has an ultraviolet emission, it has been suggested that the electroluminescence from this material be used to excite normal photoluminescent phosphors and thus achieve emission colors not easily obtained with conventional electroluminescent materials; this does not seem very practical, however, because of the low efficiency. Although normal BN has a hexagonal (graphitic) structure, cubic BN has recently been prepared at very high pressures. The luminescent properties of this modification have apparently not been investigated.

Fischer (553) has considered the requirements for efficient carrier-injection electroluminescence. He emphasizes the necessity for p-i-n, rather than p-n, junctions as also pointed out by Patrick (62) and others. He states further that the diffusion lengths (and hence the mobilities) for electrons and holes should be approximately the same. In most cases, of course, the electron mobility is much greater than that for holes (see Table VII). This will be less true the more homopolar the chemical bonding involved in the compound; this in turn is favored by close spacing in the periodic table of the elements involved and by use of lighter "cations" and heavier "anions." Fischer also states that a crystal structure related to that of diamond (complete homopolar bonding), such as zincblende or wurtzite, is to be preferred. To alleviate problems of self-absorption of light generated by interband transitions both Lehovec (125) and Fischer (553) have suggested use of materials with "tapered band gaps" or "graded-seal junctions" formed by alloying materials with different band gap.

3. Diamond. Another wide band-gap semiconductor of considerable interest, at least from the theoretical viewpoint, is diamond. According to their optical and electrical properties, diamonds are classified into the following types (554):

I. Apparent absorption limit at 3.5–4.0 ev plus infrared absorption at 7.8μ, due to high concentration of defects and dependent on specimen; also absorption lines at 2.99 ev (4150A) and 2.47 ev (5032A).

IIa. Absorption edge at 5.3 ev with tail depending on specimen; 7.8μ absorption absent; resistivity of 10^{14}–10^{16} ohm-cm.

IIb. Absorption similar to IIa except for 7 or 8 additional lines in infrared; p-type semiconductivity with resistivity as low as 100 ohm-cm at room temperature (activation energy about 0.35 ev).

The photo- and cathodoluminescence of diamond has also been investigated (555). A very prominent blue band is observed with peak at 4400–4500A; the width is independent of temperature. It will be noted that the energy corresponding to this emission is equal to half the band-gap. Emission is also observed in the form of lines at 4150, 5030, 5390, and 5755A superimposed on broad bands. These main lines are accompanied by a complicated structure of additional peaks. There is little Franck-Condon shift between the emission lines and those observed in absorption. The emission may extend to wavelengths as long as 7000A. Various defects and impurities have been proposed as the origin of the emission, including substitutional N_2 (4500A band), interstitial N_2 (5755A line) and interstitial C_2 (5030A line). Since the 5030A line can be influenced by particle bombardment and heat treatment it may also be connected with vacancies. Type I diamonds are more strongly luminescent than type IIa. Although Dyer and Matthews (555) reported that type IIb samples were non-luminescent, Austin and Wolfe (554) found that they are distinguished from other types in exhibiting green phosphorescence arising from trapping. Halperin and Nahum (60) found the emission to be low but the spectrum was measurable. Type IIb samples are usually, but not always, blue in appearance.

Electroluminescence was first observed in diamond (Type IIb) by Wolfe and Woods (56). The emission was primarily in the neighborhood of a forward-biased (negative) point contact; in one case light also appeared to come from several internal points. The emission appeared purple-blue and consisted of a single broad band with peak at 4400A. For ac excitation a single output peak was observed, in phase with the negative voltage cycle. The output was found to depend linearly on either current or voltage if a "threshold" was subtracted in each case. This emission was atrributed to minority-carrier injection and subsequent recombination at centers situated near the middle of the band gap. Bell and Leivo (556) also observed blue emission at forward-biased contacts to Type IIb diamonds.

Fischer (58) studied the electroluminescence induced in insulating diamond (of unspecified type) by field strengths of the order of 5×10^4 volts/cm. The specimens were mounted in vacuum in order to avoid spurious results due to gas discharges. The emission was accompanied by an increase in conductivity; at higher field strengths external electron emission was also observed. The light (blue) appeared primarily at the anode and increased as the 1.5–2.5 power of the voltage. At high currents (0.5 ma) heating occurred and the luminescence was quenched. Deposition in vacuum of various metals and subsequent heating or heating in an H_2/BBr_3 atmosphere had no important effect but bombardment with B ions increased the electroluminescence (bluish white) and conductivity if the bombarded region was the anode. The emission was ascribed to impact ionization by avalanching electrons. Logie and Urlau (57) also observed green emission from small points in Type I diamonds. Reversal of polarity did not affect the locality, color, or intensity of the emitting spots; they were also unaffected by temperature variation from room temperature to liquid air.

Krautz and Zollfrank (59) also studied the electroluminescence of Types I and IIa (insulating) diamonds; they state that it had been observed earlier by O. Hermann. Close-spaced (200–250μ) internal hyperboloidal electrodes were used. The field strengths employed were above 10^6 volts/cm and vacuum insulation was used. Microscopic observation revealed that the light distribution was very nonuniform and varied from sample to sample depending on structural defects; lines of emitting points were sometimes observed. The emission from Type I samples was much weaker than that of Type IIa samples and appeared mainly near the electrodes only at very high field strengths and high frequency; in these samples the number of defects is apparently so high that a nearly-uniform field distribution is established. For direct voltage the emission was strongest near the cathode. The emission color from various samples was described as greenish blue, green, or yellowish green; in the latter case additional blue emission was also observed at higher voltage. For ac excitation the light output pulse led the voltage in phase and no secondary peak was present. Emission occurred only for one polarity at low voltage and there was a preferred polarity even for high voltage. If the voltage was very high the emission had the appearance of a gas discharge and small graphite whiskers formed at the electrodes; these enhanced the field strength and therefore the light output.

Male and Prior (59a) studied the emission induced in a diamond, which had blue photoluminescence, when excited by an alternating voltage of 150 volts applied to two graphite electrodes 1.5 mm apart. Emission was observed in the ultraviolet region as far as 5.6 ev (the band gap). The major peak was very narrow, occurred at 5.278 ev (2520A), and was about 0.1% of the peak intensity of the blue band (4400A). A minor peak also occurred at 5.125 ev (2600A). It was suggested that this emission resulted from exciton annihilation, with phonon cooperation.

Type IIb (semiconducting) diamonds have recently been studied further by Halperin and Nahum (60). Electroluminescence was excited by 100 volts applied to electrodes separated by 4 mm. It was stated that the emission appeared blue when the field was first applied but turned greenish-yellow after a short time, after which the spectrum was measured. The spectrum was identical to that for ultraviolet excitation and consisted of a broad band peaked at 4700A. The emission was localized at several bright spots and decreased with decreasing temperature; no light could be detected at 80°K. Austin and Wolfe (554) also earlier found that Type IIb diamonds lost their p-type character at 123°K. By measurements of infrared absorption, dark conductivity and thermoluminescence, Halperin and Nahum identified levels lying 0.21, 0.30, 0.35, 0.52, and 0.67 ev above the valence band.

It thus seems that at least two types of electroluminescence can be observed in diamond. For semiconducting (Type IIb) samples minority-carrier injection may be followed by radiative recombination (via centers or by exciton annihilation). For insulating diamonds application of very high electric fields can result in electron acceleration and impact ionization. None of the literature on this material seems to give a figure for the electroluminescence efficiency, and much remains to be done in identifying the various energy levels involved.

4. Miscellaneous Materials. A number of miscellaneous materials in which electroluminescence has been reported are listed in Table I. In many cases little information is available and they will not be discussed further here. The electroluminescence of organic material such as acridine orange, gonacrin, carbazole, derivatives of 8-hydroxyquinoline, etc. (78, 79) has been relatively little explored outside the group under Bernanose at the University of Nancy; these materials also will not be discussed in detail here.

The photo- or cathodoluminescence of Cu_2O (a p-type conductor with band gap of 2.3 ev) at room temperature consists of infrared emission with a peak near 1.0μ (557). Bloem (557) found that at 20°K this band is resolved into two sub-peaks at 0.9 and 1.4μ while a new band, also a doublet, appears in the visible region at 0.72 and 0.82μ. These emissions have been ascribed to copper and oxygen vacancies, respectively. Copper oxide rectifiers are of course, well known. Frerichs and Handy (69) also observed electroluminescence in reverse-biased rectifiers (Cu positive, Cu_2O negative). Measurements are complicated by the occurrence of current "creep" (current increasing with time for reverse bias and decreasing for forward bias) during many seconds. Even while the current is increasing the light output decreases. When these effects were avoided it was found that the electroluminescence output varied with voltage and current in a complicated manner but was a linear function of the power input (constant efficiency). The efficiency was a maximum near 0°C and decreased for either higher or lower temperatures. The rise and decay times of the emission produced by a voltage pulse were about one msec. Because of the "creep" phenomenon addition of dc pre-bias to an alternating voltage can result in temporarily increased output ("memory").

The current "creep" in Cu_2O has been attributed to electrolytic motion of Cu^+ ions. By using the electroluminescence as a measuring tool, Frerichs and Liberman (69) were able to determine the mobility as about 10^{-11} cm²/volt-sec at room temperature. In these experiments with point contacts it was found that the electroluminescence was favored by a material with low electronic work function such as Zn, that it occurred at the contact rather than in the bulk material, and when the contact was negative, i.e., biased in the forward direction. The observed emission is therefore to be attributed to injection of electrons into the p-type Cu_2O. (In the previous experiments of Frerichs and Handy the emission occurred at the Cu_2O-transparent electrode contact rather than the Cu_2O-Cu contact as at first assumed).

Macinktosh (558) and Baryshev (558a) suggested that in the class of infrared photoconductors including PbS, PbSe, and PbTe the carrier lifetime should be limited by radiative recombination, but electroluminescence has not yet been observed in these materials.

Electroluminescence excited in $BaTiO_3$, $SrTiO_3$ and similar ferroelectric materials by high-frequency electric fields was first observed by Harman (71) and later by Stauer (72). Harman used frequencies above 500 kcps and average field strengths less than 10^3 volts/cm; he stated that there was a different effect at lower frequencies (below 50 kcps) and higher fields but these results have not been published. No luminescence was observed for excitation with ultraviolet or X-rays. The electroluminescence occurred nearly uniformly in a surface layer under the electrode and varied as the 4th or 6th power of the applied voltage. The output was a maximum near the Curie temperature of $BaTiO_3$ because of the impedance of the crystal bulk in series with the low-permittivity surface region; the effective voltage is therefore highest at the Curie point (125°C). The electroluminescence persisted to 300°C, however (although decreasing in intensity), and is thus not a direct result of the ferroelectricity of the material.

Electroluminescence of $BaTiO_3$ and $SrTiO_3$ in the form of small spots was also observed at 300°C by Harman (71) when a direct voltage was applied in the reverse direction to a rectifier formed by electrodes of different area; there was no emission when the voltage was first applied and 20–30 sec were required for equilibrium to be achieved. This reverse-bias emission was attributed to avalanche breakdown. The voltage required and the spectrum of the high-frequency induced emission depended on the electrode material used. The sensitivity was also affected by the surrounding gaseous atmosphere. Emission was measured in the ultraviolet as far as 3000A (beyond the absorption edge of $BaTiO_3$). The efficiency (for radiation below 6500A) was extremely low, of the order of 10^{-6} to $10^{-7}\%$. Field emission from the electrode and avalanche excitation was suggested as the source of the emission. The thickness of the low-permittivity surface layer ($\epsilon \sim 5$) was calculated as about 3×10^{-5} cm. Although emission was observed from $BaTiO_3$, $SrTiO_3$, $CaTiO_3$, TiO_2, $KNbO_3$, and $PbZrO_3$, no electroluminescence was observed for ferroelectric materials containing OH bonds.

$CaWO_4$ (scheelite) is an efficient blue-emitting photoluminescent and cathodoluminescent phosphor not requiring impurity activation; the emission is ascribed to WO_4 groups in the lattice. Güntherschulze and Gerlach (67) observed electroluminescence from this material as early as 1934. Vacuum was employed for insulation and a nonlinear resistor disc was used to prevent breakdown. If the phosphor was positive relative to the resistor, blue emission was observed at many points. If the voltage was increased the number of points and their intensity increased. Individual points varied in position but the light output was steady. Considerable gas was evolved and eventually caused breakdown. For the reverse polarity the current was much higher but the light output was much smaller; no gas evolution was observed. In this case the emission also contained a red component (due to heating?).

Zn_2SiO_4:Mn (corresponding to the mineral willemite) is a very common efficient green-emitting photoluminescent and cathodoluminescent phosphor. Although various attempts have been made to obtain electroluminescence from this material, the output has always been quite low. Destriau (20) mentions electroluminescence from silicates. Bramley and Rosenthal (73) embedded the phosphor in a low melting-point (silicate?) glass and applied alternating fields of the order of 5×10^4 volts/cm. In contrast to ZnS phosphors, the output increased by a factor of less than 5 when the frequency was increased from 120 cps to 16 kcps. The output in these experiments varied as roughly the square of the voltage and was quenched for temperatures above 200°C. Microscopic observation revealed that the emission arose at the electrode interface and it was therefore attributed to field emission from the electrode induced by a nonuniform voltage distribution. Ueta (74) used polystyrene to suspend Zn_2SiO_4:Mn and $(Zn,Be)_2SiO_4$:Mn phosphors; although the latter material shows both a green and a red band for ultraviolet excitation, the green was predominant in electroluminescence.

Fischer (29) placed contacts on single crystals (particles?) of zinc silicate phosphors and obtained emission with direct voltages. Luyckx and Stokkink (75) stated that the brightness peaks for Zn_2SiO_4:Mn sometimes led and sometimes lagged the voltage peak; high frequency oscillations were also observed at the brightness peaks, indicating approach to breakdown (1700 volts were required for Zn_2SiO_4 as compared to 180 for ZnS). Rulon and Butler (559) have claimed that Zn_2SiO_4 may be made electroluminescent by treating the surface with $SnCl_4$ so as to form conductive tin oxide; the material is then incorporated in a dielectric in the normal manner. A brightness of only 0.015 ft-L for operation at 600 volts, 60 cps was obtained, however; ZnS:Cu phosphors normally give 1–4 ft-L at 120 volts, 60 cps. Mizushima *et al.* (*34*) observed both electron and light emission from cold cathodes of $CdWO_4$ and Zn_2SiO_4.

Nicoll and Kazan (*76*) observed electroluminescence in conventional cathode-ray tubes when a direct voltage was applied between the aluminum backing on the phosphor and a transparent coating on the outside of the glass faceplate which was heated to provide sufficient conductivity. The same results were obtained if the tube was destroyed and air admitted. Microscopic examination showed that the light was emitted intermittently, resembling scintillations. In some cases the output was greater with the Al negative but in other cases the reverse was true. Emission was observed with "practically all the common (CRT) phosphors." In the case of zinc silicate a brightness of 1.5 ft-L was obtained when a current of 700 ma was caused to flow through an area of 2 cm² by 2000 volts; the efficiency is obviously very low. The poorly conducting glass plate served to limit destructive breakdown at the individual phosphor particles (similar to the nonlinear resistor disc in the experiment of Güntherschulze and Gerlach (*67*)).

Bowtell and Bate (*560*) observed electroluminescence from a large number of compressed phosphor samples, including ZnS activated by Cu, Ag, Mn, or P; $Ca_3(PO_4)_2$ activated by Dy; Zn_2SiO_4, $(Ca,Mg)SiO_3$, $Cd_2B_2O_5$, $Zn_3(PO_4)_2$, and cadmium chlorophosphate all activated by Mn. The essential feature in this case is the coating of the phosphor particles with an ionizable salt. Potassium silicate ("water glass") was mainly used, but many alkali and alkaline-earth compounds were stated to be effective (Zalm (*2*) also found that alkali or alkaline earth sulfides on the surface will evoke electroluminescence in ZnS). The emission in this case was localized at the electrodes (the anode for dc operation). Following application of the voltage the light output slowly increased to an equilibrium value while the current decreased, implying ionic migration and polarization. Since potassium silicate or similar materials are normally used as binders in cathode-ray-tube screens, Bowtell and Bate suggested that there may be a connection between their observations and those of Nicoll and Kazan. Lehmann has performed similar experiments and found that the material of the electrode has an important effect on the brightness obtained from phosphors treated in this way. The output is often nearly independent of the operating frequency over a wide range and decreases for high frequencies (above about 1000 cps).

Lehmann (*217*) has shown that many (but not all) photoluminescent but nonelectroluminescent phosphors become electroluminescent if they are mechanically mixed with a metallic or semiconducting powder. In the case of metal powders the particle size and shape were more important than the particular material used. Among the phosphors which show such "contact electroluminescence" are ZnS activated by Cu, Ag, or Mn, (Zn,Cd)S activated by Cu or Ag, CaS:Bi, CaWO$_4$, Zn$_2$SiO$_4$:Mn, Zn$_3$GeO$_5$:Mn, Zn$_3$(PO$_4$)$_2$:Mn, CdSiO$_3$:Mn, Cd$_2$B$_2$O$_5$:Mn, Ca$_3$(PO$_4$)$_2$:Tl; UO$_2$(NO$_3$)$_2$ · 6H$_2$O, and anthracene. The voltage dependence of the emission was found to be the same as that of normal electroluminescent ZnS:Cu phosphors. For a further discussion of contact electroluminescence see references [83] and [218].

The situation concerning electroluminescence in the alkali halides is not very clear. Torbin [63] reported luminescence in the form of "streamers" from NaCl crystals in fields approaching breakdown. Vorob'ev and Kuchin [646] also apparently saw emission from the alkali halides at very high fields. On the other hand, Andrianov and Kats [615] stated that electroluminescence had never been observed in these materials so that they apparently considered the emission observed previously not to be pure electroluminescence. Georgobiani [652] has concluded that it should be much more difficult to excite electroluminescence in ionic than in covalent materials. However, by use of films of CsI:Tl only one micron thick so that electron avalanches could not be formed, he and Golubeva [653] have recently succeeded in obtaining uniform emission at field strengths of the order of 2×10^6 volts/cm. It is also of interest to note that in an isolated observation as long ago as 1933 Lehfeldt [64] seems to have observed electroluminescence in AgCl crystals doped with CuCl.

V. FIELD EFFECTS IN EXCITED PHOSPHORS

In addition to pure electroluminescence, the phenomena observed when an electric field and some kind of stimulating radiation are simultaneously or sequentially applied to a luminescent material are also of fundamental and practical interest.* Such effects are often described as electrophotoluminescence (with ultraviolet or X-radiation), electrocathodoluminescence (with cathode-ray excitation), etc. Williams (5) has suggested that in naming these compound effects the first prefix should denote the controlling agency and the second the source of power. Thus he distinguishes between electrophotoluminescence and photoelectroluminescence. It is obvious that to make such a distinction one must believe that the details of the mechanism are understood; unfortunately this is not always the case. Although it is clear that photoelectroluminescence is to be expected only in electroluminescent materials, "electrophotoluminescence" may occur in either non-electroluminescent or electroluminescent materials; in the latter case it may be confused by simultaneous electroluminescence. It is also obvious that the "normal" luminescence may be either depressed ("quenched") or enhanced by the second exciting agent and this is not conveyed by the proposed names. The terminology in this field is therefore not in a very happy state. Many interesting effects have also been observed which involve two different types of excitation (for example, ultraviolet and infrared) in addition to an electric field.

When one considers the number of possible actions of an electric field on phosphors, it is immediately obvious why it is very difficult in some cases to decide which are of importance in practice. The following considerations should be borne in mind in attempting any explanation:

(1) One must differentiate between phosphors which have good electroluminescent properties and those which do not. Presumably the electric field in the former is more strongly distorted and localized than in the latter.

(2) One must differentiate between phosphors with luminescent centers in which the excitation and emission is confined to the centers themselves and those in which transitions to the conduction band are involved.

(3) One must bear in mind that although many well-developed phosphors have very high efficiency, i.e., very few nonradiating transitions at ordinary temperatures, this may not be true for experimental phosphors in general nor even for "good" phosphors at elevated temperatures.

(4) An excited phosphor in the steady-state output condition is never-

* For earlier reviews see references (1, 3, 134, 135).

181

theless in a state of dynamic equilibrium only. Many competing processes occur simultaneously.

(5) In different materials different processes may obviously be of importance. Even in the same material, depending upon conditions of preparation and operation, conditions may vary.

In addition to field effects in conventional phosphors such as ZnS, there also exist materials, mainly organic liquids or solutions, which can be transformed from a nonluminescent to a luminescent condition or from a nonabsorbing to an absorbing condition (or vice versa) by the application of a voltage. Alburger (561) has called these "electroflors." They are essentially pH "indicators," while the action of the voltage is to control the local pH by electrochemical action on a solution of ionizable salt. Examples of such materials are dichlorofluorescein, coumaric acid, or chromotropic acid in a NaCl solution (562).

A. The Gudden-Pohl and Other Transient Effects

1. **The Gudden-Pohl Effect.** The earliest study of an electrophotoluminescent effect was made in 1920 by Gudden and Pohl (115). The effect which is known by their name is a transient increase in emission resulting from the action of an electric field on a phosphor. It can be observed either superimposed on the quenched or enhanced steady-state emission (to be discussed below) for continuous excitation or after the exciting radiation has been removed. In the latter case (that actually used by Gudden and Pohl) it can be observed either during the normal afterglow or phosphorescence or at longer times when the emission has decayed to negligible levels; the amount of light emitted is less the greater the time between cessation of excitation and application of the field. These observations indicate that electron trapping plays an essential role. The Gudden-Pohl effect may be observed in nonelectroluminescent as well as electroluminescent phosphors. The minimum field strength required to produce the effect in ZnS is of the order of 10^3 volts/cm and hence is much less than that required for excitation of electroluminescence. These facts therefore indicate that there is no essential connection between the two phenomena. The changes in electrical properties produced by application of fields to excited phosphors (the electrical analog of the Gudden-Pohl effect) have been studied by Kallmann and Mark (119).

If a static field is applied to a phosphor, polarization charges quickly build up inside the material and reduce the effective field to zero before all the traps can be emptied. Removal of the applied field causes a sudden increase in internal field which again decreases to zero, producing another flash of emission. The same effect is produced by removal of a field which is applied before or during excitation (20, 564, 563). The effects of polarization can obviously be avoided by the use of alternating fields (first used by Hinderer (565)). In this case the emission consists of light pulses at twice the field frequency and decreasing in amplitude. A second light flash is often also observed at removal of an alternating field. The higher the voltage the more rapid is the decrease in output; the decay is thus more rapid than the normal phosphorescence. The quantitative dependence of output on voltage is often quite complicated. Olson and Danielson (566) state that the Gudden-Pohl light sum observed during phosphorescence is independent of the frequency of the alternating field between 80 and 5000 cps.* Matossi and Nudelman (439a), on the other hand, found the light flash at field application (sustained excitation) to decrease with increasing frequency up to about 10,000 cps, above which it either remained constant or slowly increased. These workers also observed the flash at field removal to increase with increasing frequency, with saturation sometimes occurring. Olson and Danielson (566) found the flash at removal of the field to be greater the higher the voltage, the frequency or the temperature; however, the opposite effect of temperature may also be observed (569).

Krautz (564) studied over 250 phosphors of different composition, including nonsulfides. The strongest Gudden-Pohl effect was observed with self-activated ZnS and ZnS:Mn but is to be expected in any phosphor which shows evidence of trapped electrons by thermoluminescence or phosphorescence. Destriau and Mattler (567) studied the "brightness waves" obtained with alternating fields and found many similarities to the corresponding phenomena in electroluminescence. Successive peaks (corresponding to opposite polarity) often differ systematically in size. They found the light peaks to occur earlier in the cycle the lower the frequency and the higher the applied voltage; for very high frequency, the light peaks were found to lag behind the voltage maxima in these experiments. The "lead time" is greater for the first peak and becomes less for successive peaks. Krautz (564) also found that the decay rate decreases for successive applications of a direct voltage for short periods following excitation. These observations are consistent with a model involving the action of the field on trapped electrons. The shallowest traps are emptied first so that the effective trap depth increases and hence the effect of the field decreases with time. The shift with frequency for alternating fields is the same as that observed for the primary peaks of electroluminescence (Section

---

* One must be very careful in interpreting such statements to distinguish between the height of the Gudden-Pohl flash and the area under it (light sum). Olson and Danielson measured the latter and also used the quenched output with field on as a reference point, while Matossi and Nudelman measured the maximum peak height above the output with no field. Interpreted in the latter way the curves of Olson and Danielson also show a decrease with increasing frequency.

III,*I,1*) and explained, for example, by Thornton (*334*) on the basis of field-controlled release of electrons from traps.

Destriau and Mattler (*20, 568*), using X-ray excitation, studied the effect of excitation intensity and time on the total light emitted upon subsequent application of an alternating field (the "light sum"). Surprisingly, it was found that the light sum was a maximum for a certain exposure time, this value becoming smaller the greater the X-ray intensity. This was interpreted as arising from a competing action of the X-rays, perhaps from ionization of lattice atoms in the vicinity of the filled traps; the luminescence centers themselves appear unaffected as the luminescence during excitation shows no decline with time. The optimum exposure time was independent of the applied voltage. A similar effect was also observed for excitation with ultraviolet radiation or alpha particles (*569*). Destriau and Mattler (*569*) studied the effect of temperature in this case and found that the amount of excitation required for this optimum decreased linearly as the temperature was increased and that the maximum light sum was obtained for intermediate temperatures, 35–50°C. A similar optimum temperature was observed by Olson and Danielson (*566*) and also by Destriau and Mattler (*569*) for the Gudden-Pohl peaks (at least for the peak for field application) superimposed on the quenching effect (discussed in the next section). Since the cause of an optimum exposure time is yet uncertain, the explanation of the temperature effect is also not definite. It would seem, however, that an optimum temperature could result from competition between the action of temperature before the field is applied in reducing the number of filled traps on which the field can act and an action of temperature in aiding the field-emptying process.

Since in the Gudden-Pohl effect the field acts on electrons in traps, it is of interest to compare the effect with that of other agents which affect trapped electrons, namely, temperature and infrared radiation. If this is done it is found that fields are less effective. Thus, no Gudden-Pohl flash is obtained after thermoluminescence or infrared irradiation, which empty all traps if sufficiently intense (*20*). On the other hand, the intensity of thermoluminescence is little effected by previous application of a field which produces a strong Gudden-Pohl effect (*20, 564*).* This apparently results from the fact that a field strong enough to empty all filled traps cannot be applied without dielectric breakdown, that the applied field is concentrated in localized regions due to electrical inhomogeneity, that the field has a very directional effect, or a combination of these factors. A directional effect was indeed observed by Destriau (*20*). After excitation the phosphor

---

* Destriau (*1*) has observed cases in which the thermoluminescence curve following application of a field starts out below the normal curve but later crosses it. Strangely enough, Kotera and Naraoka (*570*) show the opposite effect.

was subjected to a field until the emission ceased; since an alternating voltage was applied, polarization should not be involved. If the sample was rotated and the field reapplied a new flash of emission was observed; this could be repeated several times without re-exciting the phosphor. The second flash was zero for a rotation of 180° and a maximum for 90°. Destriau (20) states that the intensity of infrared required to produce a significant decrease in the Gudden-Pohl flash is much less than that for a noticeable effect on normal phosphorescence. Visible radiation also has a quenching action on the Gudden-Pohl effect. Vigean (571) found that yellow light produced maximum quenching, even greater than infrared, at least in the sample studied.

Destriau (20) found that if the normal emission (phosphorescence, L) at a time t after cessation of excitation and the Gudden-Pohl light sum (S_1) obtained if a field is applied at a time t after excitation are measured, then L decreases more rapidly with t than does S_1. (If this were not so then a Gudden-Pohl flash could not be achieved at times long after detectable phosphorescence has ceased.) He also found that a second flash could be obtained if the same alternating field was reapplied, in the same direction, at a time t' after the first application. The amplitude of this second flash (S_2) was found to increase at first with increasing t', then pass through a maximum (which may require several hours) and then decrease again. He attributed this effect to transfer of excitation from traps unaffected by the first field application to those which were affected. This effect was also studied later by Mattler and Curie (434). The thermal redistribution can be between traps of different depth, since the field acts selectively on shallow traps, or between traps of the same depth but responding to fields in different directions as discussed earlier.

Alexander et al. (572) studied the Gudden-Pohl flash produced when a static field is applied to a continuously excited (Zn,Cd)S:Cu phosphor. The flash emitted when the voltage was applied was greater than that when it was removed if the illuminated electrode was positive but the situation was reversed for the opposite polarity. This behavior may be the result of nonuniform absorption in the phosphor. Nakamura (573) also found that the results were markedly different depending upon whether the exciting radiation was strongly absorbed (fundamental absorption region) or weakly absorbed (edge absorption region), as shown in Fig. 50. This worker also found that the rate of decay is greater for the first peak (voltage applied) than the second (voltage removed). Destriau and Mattler (569) found that the relative height of these two peaks was also a function of temperature. With single crystals of ZnS, Steinberger and Bar (574) found a flash only when the voltage was applied and none at its removal. It is difficult, however, to generalize about such effects as almost every conceivable

combination of transient effects seems to have been reported in the literature (see Fig. 51). Thus, depending upon the phosphor and the conditions,
Matossi and Nudelman (*439a*) and Kotera and Naroka (*570*) observed at
removal of the field an increase in output, a decrease, or neither.

Kotera and Naraoka (*570*) studied 44 different materials but the correlation with composition is not straightforward. In the case of hexagonal
ZnS:Cu the phosphorescence intensity (measured one minute after cessation of ultraviolet excitation) was found to be a maximum for a Cu content
of 3×10^{-3} mole % while the infrared stimulability and Gudden-Pohl

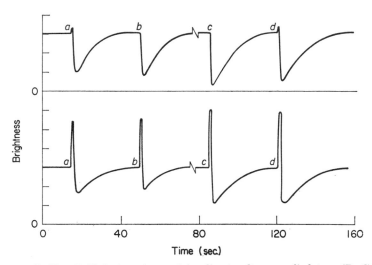

Fig. 50. Gudden-Pohl flashes observed for direct voltage applied to a (Zn,Cd)S:Cu
phosphor excited in the fundamental absorption region (upper curve) or the edge absorption region (lower curve). A positive potential is applied to the transparent electrode at
point *a* and removed at *b*; at point *c* a previously applied positive potential is changed
to negative and at *d* back to positive. (From Nakamura, *573*.)

effect were a maximum for 1×10^{-3} mole % Cu. Essentially the same
dependence on composition was found for corresponding cubic phosphors
but the Gudden-Pohl effect in this case was much stronger while the phosphorescence and thermoluminescence were weaker and the infrared stimulation was not measurable. These observations obviously indicate an important difference between the traps involved in the different phenomena.
The Gudden-Pohl effect of the cubic materials decreased continuously as
the temperature was increased above room temperature while that of the
hexagonal phosphors had a maximum at 70°C (thermoluminescence peak
at 55°C).

If the only action of the field in the Gudden-Pohl effect is that of lifting trapped electrons to the conduction band, from which they can recombine with excited luminescence centers, then the light sum should be comparable to that obtained with other means of trap emptying such as temperature or infrared radiation. Since in normal phosphorescence at room temperature

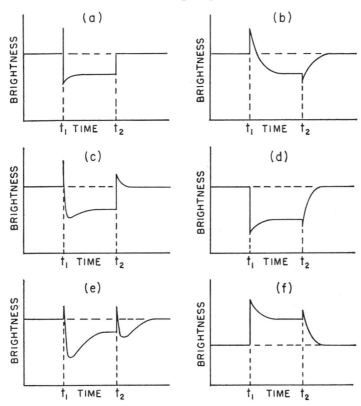

FIG. 51. Schematic representation of the various effects which may be observed when an alternating electric field is applied to a continuously excited phosphor (at time t_1) and then removed (at time t_2). (a) and (b) are taken from Kotera and Naraoka (570); (c) and (d) show observations of Destriau and Mattler (569) for quenching effect in phosphors with strong and weak persistence, respectively; (e) is taken from Nakamura (573); (f) shows enhancement effect observed by Destriau and his colleagues (440).

all traps are not always emptied, then some cases where the Gudden-Pohl light sum is greater than that normally observed might be expected. On the other hand, if field-induced nonradiating transitions occur (see Section V,B), a reduction in light sum should be expected if a field is applied during phosphorescence (20). An example of this as observed by Olson and Danielson (566) for a (Zn,Cd)S:Cu phosphor with long persistence (the yellow component of the standard P7 cathode-ray-tube phosphor)

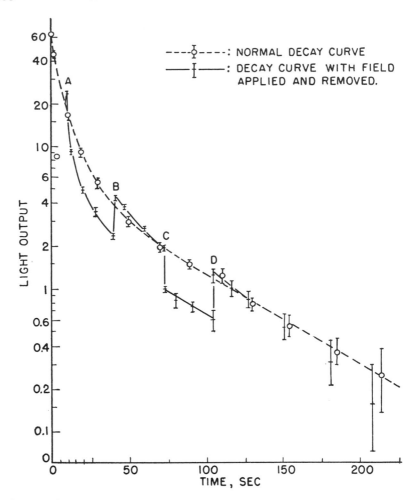

FIG. 52. Phosphoresce decay curve for (87Zn,13Cd)S:0.006Cu phosphor with and without applied field of 4.3×10^4 volt/cm alternating at 5000 cps (field applied at A and C; removed at B and D). The curve shows Gudden-Pohl pulses for field application and removal plus field-quenching of luminescence. (From Olson and Danielson, *566*.)

is shown in Fig. 52. It may be noted that at long times the curve for which a field was applied and removed seems to be falling below the normal curve.

The most obvious mechanism for the Gudden-Pohl effect is that the field liberates trapped electrons by a tunneling process or by thermal liberation over a potential barrier lowered by the field. The case of tunneling with a linearly rising field (i.e., the case of "electrically excited glow curves" rather than the Gudden-Pohl effect) has been studied by Haering (*114*). Curie (*157, 434*), however, believes that the traps are emptied by the impact of electrons accelerated in the conduction band by the field. The effect is then similar to his model for excitation of electroluminescence except that much lower field strengths are required because of the much smaller depth of traps compared to luminescence centers. If the Gudden-Pohl flash observed at application of an alternating field is due to release of trapped electrons, it is difficult to ascribe the flash observed at removal of the field to the same effect.* Matossi and Nudelman (439, 439a) suggest that the latter results from recombination of excess charge carriers accumulated in the conduction band by the action of the field. Such excess charge may arise either from a smaller recombination coefficient for electrons with greater than thermal velocity or from release of polarization charges stored up (probably near the surface) by the field. Actually, much more work must be done before the mechanism of the Gudden-Pohl effect, its relation to phosphorescence, thermoluminescence, and infrared stimulation, and its dependence on phosphor composition will be fully understood.

2. Effect of Fields on Infrared Stimulation of Luminescence. SrS: Eu,Sm (the so-called "Standard VI" phosphor) is an example of an infrared-stimulable phosphor (13). The luminescence emission, which is excited by blue light, is characteristic of the Eu activator. If the phosphor is irradiated with infrared long after all phosphorescence has ceased, even hours later, a burst of emission is observed. This stimulation arises from the presence of Sm; the infrared stimulation spectra is determined by the Sm but the emission is that due to Eu. Low et al. (575) found that application of an alternating electric field to this phosphor during excitation could increase the emission upon subsequent infrared irradiation by as much as 45%. Concurrently the effect of an electric field applied during stimulation (and hence analogous to the Gudden-Pohl effect) was much reduced (to as little as 7% of its value without a field during excitation). The effect of the "sensitizing" field was observable even if several hours elapsed before the infrared stimulation but could be removed by irradiation with blue light. In a later paper Steinberger et al. (576) studied the Gudden-Pohl effect in this phosphor during excitation, during phosphorescence, and during stimulation. The observed differences include the longer persistence of the Gudden-Pohl peak during stimulation (several seconds) as compared to that during excitation of phosphorescence (a few tenths of a second) and some differences in voltage dependence. During excitation the ratio of the Gudden-Pohl peak at field removal to that at field application is greater the shorter the interval in which the field is off.

Figure 53 shows some of the other results obtained by Steinberger et al.

* To call two effects with different mechanism by the same name is to invite confusion but is commonly done. Matossi and Nudelman refer to them as the "first stimulation" and the "second or cutoff stimulation."

(*576*) on SrS:Eu,Sm. The enhancement of infrared stimulability is greater if the field is maintained during phosphorescence as well as during excitation (Fig. 53c); application of a field during phosphorescence only, however, has little effect on the stimulability (Fig. 53d). Application of a field during stimulation also produced a large increase in stimulated output

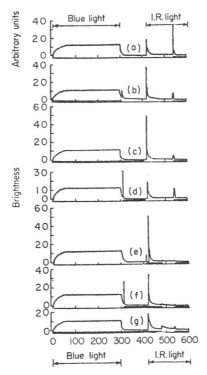

Fɪɢ. 53. Schematic representation of the effect of an alternating electric field on the infrared stimulability and the Gudden-Pohl effect during stimulation of a SrS:Eu,Sm phosphor. The heavy lines indicate the duration of the field. (From Steinberger *et al.*, *576*.)

(Fig. 53e) but this is reduced (although not to the level for no field action) if the field was applied during phosphorescence as well (Fig. 53f). Finally, continuous application of a field (during excitation, phosphorescence, and stimulation) had essentially no effect on the stimulated output (Fig. 53g). Figure 53 also shows that the Gudden-Pohl effect during stimulation is always reduced by previous field action. Field action during stimulation is most effective in this respect and action during phosphorescence least effective. Again it is seen that no simple correlation exists between the Gudden-Pohl effect and infrared stimulability. Application of the field during stimulation did not increase the total amount of light emitted; the greater peak height was compensated by a faster decay. Application of the field prior to stimulation, on the other hand, increased the total output as well as the initial brightness. It may be noted that application of a field during excitation produced quenching of the fluorescence; infrared radiation has no quenching effect in this case. The phenomena involved in this phosphor are obviously quite complicated. The infrared stimulation is ascribed to deep traps introduced by Sm; the field, on the other hand, apparently is effective only on shallower traps and probably only on a fraction of these.

In the quenching of luminescence by electric fields a transient quenching effect is often observed in addition to the steady-state quenching and the transient Gudden-Pohl enhancement of output (see Fig. 51). The kinetics of such effects are very complicated and are not understood in detail. Some comments concerning these transient regions will be made in the next section which is concerned with the steady-state quenching.

B. Quenching of Luminescence by Fields

1. The Phenomena of Quenching. Many of the early experiments on electrophotoluminescence were, unfortunately, not carried out under very simple conditions and are often very difficult to interpret. For example, in 1934 Coustal (577) subjected a previously excited ZnS:Cu or ZnS:Mn phosphor layer to an electrical glow discharge in air. Depending upon circumstances, he obtained either quenching (presumably due to the field of the discharge) or enhancement (presumably due to ultraviolet radiation generated in the discharge) of the phosphorescence.

In 1935 Déchêne (578) performed an electrophotoluminescent experiment under slightly better conditions. He wet a sulfide phosphor powder with water and placed it between electrodes to which was applied a high direct voltage. Under these conditions the ionic conductivity of the water was sufficient to maintain a current of the order of microamperes per square centimeter, sufficient to counteract the polarization of the phosphor particles and maintain a field across them so that Déchêne was able to observe field effects on phosphors with sustained fields and not simply during the short interval before polarization built up. Actually the field in his experiments was strongest near the electrodes and the effects he observed were also greatest there. Déchêne made his observations both during the phosphorescence and with simultaneous excitation. At the moment of field application a momentary increase in emission (the Gudden-Pohl effect) was observed. This, however, was followed by a sustained quenching of the emission. This quenched emission in the afterglow might be only 24% of the normal value; for simultaneous excitation and field action, however, the quenching observed was fairly small (only to 82% of normal). Upon removal of the applied voltage a second Gudden-Pohl stimulation was observed. Because of these observations the sustained quenching of luminescence by an electric field has sometimes been called the Déchêne effect.

In 1943 Destriau (*579*) reported on field quenching experiments on phosphors using powders imbedded in an insulator and alternating fields, i.e., the arrangement used by him in electroluminescence. This method of avoiding polarization effects has obvious advantages over that used by Déchêne in that higher and uniform fields may be obtained. In this way the luminescence may be quenched almost to zero. Destriau (*20, 580*) found that sulfide phosphors with persistent phosphorescence gave large Gudden-Pohl peaks but only a small quenching effect (Fig. 51c). On the other hand, samples with little phosphorescence gave little or no Gudden-Pohl peaks and a large degree of quenching (Fig. 51d). There thus seems to be no essential connection between these two effects nor is the presence of deep traps necessary for quenching. Quenching is observed in a variety of phosphors, both electroluminescent and nonelectroluminescent, and for various types of excitation (ultraviolet, X-rays, cathode rays, etc.). Quenching is much more common than enhancement of luminescence by fields; it will be shown in Section V,*C*,*1*, however, that quenching and enhancement can occur as distinct competing processes.

The simplest way of quantitatively expressing the simultaneous effect of an electric field and of radiation on a phosphor is the ratio

$$R = \frac{L_B}{L_R + L_E}, \qquad (33)$$

where

L_B = output with both field and radiation acting,
L_R = output with radiation only acting (photoluminescence, etc.),
L_E = output with field only acting (electroluminescence).

It will be noted that L_R and L_E enter in this definition in exactly the same way, so that there is no inherent prior assumption as to whether one is dealing with an effect of the field on the luminescence excited by the radiation or an effect of the irradiation on the electroluminescence. If R is greater than unity, enhancement of the output has occurred and if R is less than unity, quenching has occurred. For nonelectroluminescent materials R is simply L_B/L_R.[*]

Destriau and Mattler (*580*) found that the results obtained for both the quenching and Gudden-Pohl effects depended markedly on the wavelength

---

[*] Destriau often used the quantity $t = (L_R - L_B)/L_R = (1 - R)$ in quenching phenomena. The ratio $(L_B - L_E)/L_R = R + (L_E/L_R)(R - 1)$ has also been employed.

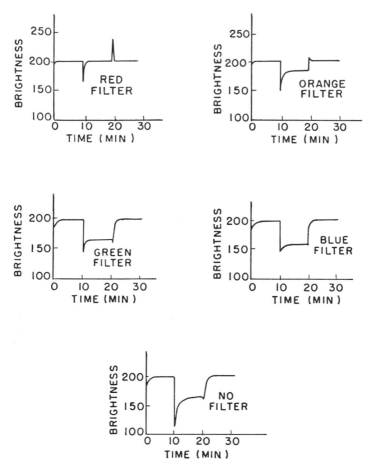

FIG. 54. Effect of alternating field on brightness of Levy-West fluoroscopic screen as observed through various filters. X-rays applied at $t = 0$, field applied at $t = 10$ min and removed at $t = 20$ min. For convenience the curves have been adjusted to give the same value of output without field. (From Destriau and Mattler, *580*.)

of observation. Figure 54 shows the behavior of a Levy-West fluoroscopic screen (ZnS:Ag,Ni) when measurements were made through different optical filters. Here it is seen that Gudden-Pohl peaks are seen only for long wavelength emission* (and then only at field removal), whereas quenching is more pronounced for short wavelengths. It is obvious that the quenching ratio is a function of the wavelength of observation in this case. Destriau (*581*) also found that application and removal of a field prior to

---

* It is possible that Ni, which emits in the near infrared (*250*), is responsible for the long wavelength emission rather than Ag in this case.

excitation produces a transient quenching effect when the phosphor is irradiated, that is, the phosphor has a "memory" of the previous field action.

The magnitude of the quenching effect increases (i.e., the value of R decreases) with increasing field strength. The quantitative dependence may differ from sample to sample. In many cases R seems to be a linear function of the voltage over a wide range. Destriau and Mattler (569) have proposed that

$$R = [1 + e^{+\alpha V} - e^{-\beta V}]^{-1}, \tag{34}$$

where α and β are two constants, with $\beta/\alpha = 9$ for one phosphor studied. Both Matossi and Nudelman (439a) and Olson and Danielson (566) found that the quenching is greater the higher the frequency of the alternating field; the former found that $(1 - R)$ is often a linear function of f while the latter reported it to vary as the logarithm of f. It may be noted that Olson and Danielson made their observations not for continuous excitation but during the phosphorescence of an extremely persistent phosphor (see Fig. 52). Miller (582) studied quenching at frequencies as high as 4×10^7 cps but in most cases the maximum effect was achieved in the region 10^5–10^6 cps. At very high frequencies maxima and minima in output were found which were attributed to resonance of trapped electrons; this, however, probably requires further verification. In general the amount of quenching decreased as the ultraviolet excitation intensity was increased. Of the materials studied, $(Zn,Cd)S:Cu$ was found to give the greatest quenching and $ZnS:Ag$ least. When the radio-frequency field was modulated with an audio signal, the modulated light output component was found to decrease above 100 cps.

Destriau and Mattler (569) have studied the effect of temperature on the quenching effect. For most materials the normal fluorescence intensity decreases as the temperature is increased above room temperature (thermal quenching), but the output with field applied decreases even more rapidly so that the quenching ratio R also decreases (Fig. 55). The dependence of R on temperature is also affected by the applied field strength in a complicated way. The magnitude of the transient quenching effects at application and removal of the field were found to be decreased at higher temperatures (also shown in Fig. 55) although the steady-state quenching was increased.

Daniel et al. (583) found that a high degree of steady-state quenching of luminescence can be achieved with quite low direct voltages in a large number of phosphors, including CdS, CdSe, $(Zn,Cd)S$, and ZnO. The major requirements are strong absorption of the exciting radiation, good electrode contact, and reasonable conductivity; in particular, a finite hole mobility is necessary. Polycrystalline or sintered samples, or even powders with a small amount of binder, are effective in addition to single crystals. Almost complete quenching was claimed for only a few volts applied, although no curves of output as a function of voltage were given. The quenching is obtained when the illuminated electrode is negative. It is assumed that in this case positive holes produced by the radiation are "extracted" at this electrode and electrons leave the phosphor at the other so that the number of radiating recombinations is drastically reduced. The flow of a small

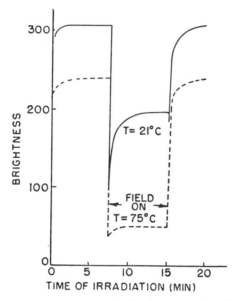

FIG. 55. The effect of temperature on the luminescence of a (Zn,Cd)S:Ag phosphor with and without alternating electric field. (From Destriau and Mattler, 569.)

photocurrent even with no applied voltage indicates the presence of some extraction even in this case; slight enhancement of the output was sometimes observed when the illuminated electrode was made positive to prevent this loss of carriers. Quenching was also observed when alternating voltages were applied. An increase in voltage above the value (about 15 volts) required to give 80% modulation in output had little further effect. The modulation decreased with increasing frequency; the time constant was of the same order as that for the normal phosphorescence. The requirements of good electrical contact and nonuniform absorption, as well as the observed voltage-current characteristics, are in accord with the proposed mechanism. The effect depends on a large difference in electron and hole lifetime; in CdS these may be of the order of 10^{-3} and 10^{-11} sec, respectively.

Bleil and Snyder (584) observed the luminescence of unactivated non-electroluminescent CdS crystals excited by ultraviolet radiation or by electrons. The cathodoluminescence was composed of red emission consisting of two peaks at 6930 and 7420A and green emission in the region 5070–5400A consisting of from two to five subpeaks in various samples. The fine structure was not observed in photoluminescence (3650A excitation). Application of low static fields (up to 10^3 volts/cm) caused all the green peaks to shift in the same manner to longer wavelengths by about 0.1A/volt/cm (the curve given is actually nonlinear) and to decrease slightly in amplitude. The two red peaks showed the same shift but were strongly quenched. This quenching was the same for both red peaks and linear with field strength up to 600 volts/cm but above this value the shorter wavelength peak was more strongly affected. The field effects with ultraviolet excitation were about half the magnitude of those for cathode-ray excitation. When the field was removed, an appreciable time was required for the crystal to return to the original state. The green emission recovered quickly (that is, within the 10-min spectrographic exposure time employed) but the red peak required more than two hours for complete recovery. The crystal contacts were ohmic but the dependence of photocurrent on voltage was found to be less than linear. In this experiment the field was perpendicular to the incident radiation rather than parallel as in most electrophotoluminescent experiments. Many details of this experiment are unexplained, including the different behavior of the green, the 6930A, and the 7420A peaks (it should be noted that the cause of the complicated structure in the emission seems to be uncertain in the first place). The shift in emission wavelength is much greater than that observed for the absorption edge in CdS by Williams (130). Bleil and Snyder believe that "self-trapping" of electrons in the lattice is induced by the field, together with a nonradiative process, but this must for the time being be considered only as a hypothesis (no thermoluminescence data were given).

It may be noted that Destriau (585) could find no quenching by fields of the scintillations excited by alpha particles, even in phosphors which did show quenching when excited by ultraviolet or X-rays. On the contrary, following excitation by alpha particles the Gudden-Pohl effect was very strong, even in samples which showed little effect after X-irradiation; in this case the emission was quenched by infrared radiation. These differences are probably connected with the very high local density of excitation with alpha particles. Alfrey and Taylor (313a) later did observe quenching of alpha particle scintillations in single crystals of ZnS:Cu. The bombardment occurred through a thin aluminum electrode. When a positive voltage was applied to this electrode, the scintillations were not affected. However, with a negative voltage the mean height of the scintillation was reduced by as much as a factor of 10 before detectable electroluminescence was observed. Quenching was also observed for alternating fields but was less the higher the frequency. ZnS crystals which did not exhibit electroluminesence also showed no quenching. A field produced no effect on other common scintillators such as KI:Tl or naphthalene. The fact that quenching occurred only in electroluminescent crystals apparently indicates the necessity for a cathodic barrier and the attendant high fields, as suggested by Alfrey and Taylor, rather than to carrier extraction as in the experiments of Daniel and his colleagues (583). The effect of frequency with alternating fields was interpreted in terms of variation of the barrier thickness.

Jaffe (586) and Halsted (587) have observed quenching of cathodoluminescence by electric fields. Halsted found that for ZnS:Mn films the quenching could be as much as 60% ($R = 0.4$) and was greater the higher the ratio of the field frequency to the electron beam current density and the higher the applied voltage. The former effect was ascribed to neutralization of the internal field by charges introduced by the electron bombardment. Gobrecht et al. (623) also observed quenching of the cathodoluminescence of an electroluminescent ZnS:Cu,Al phosphor when it was subjected to an alternating electric field. The amount of quenching was greater the higher the frequency of the field and the lower the excitation intensity (beam current density). The "threshold" for detectable electroluminescence was the same with or without cathode-ray excitation.

Most studies of the quenching effect of electric fields have been restricted to sulfide-type phosphors, although Hershinger and Lasser (583) also studied ZnO. Vorob'ev et al. (588) have recently observed quenching of the infrared luminescence of Cu_2O in contact with an electrolyte to which voltage is applied; the quenching was ascribed to formation of a potential barrier at the surface.

2. Output Waveform in Quenching of Photoluminescence. The waveform of the light output which results when an alternating voltage is applied to an excited phosphor is of interest and should aid in explaining the mechanisms involved. In this case the observations are obviously different depending upon whether the excitation is continuous or intermittent (X-ray generator or ultraviolet lamp operated on dc or ac). The influence of irradiation on the "brightness waves" of electroluminescent phosphors is a related effect which is discussed in the next section.

Destriau (426, 438) studied the waveforms for a phosphor excited by an X-ray generator operating as a half-wave rectifier (50 cps). A summary of his results, which are typical of ZnS and (Zn,Cd)S phosphors activated by Cu or Ag, is given in Fig. 56. In the absence of the field the X-ray intensity, and therefore the light output, consists of one pulse per cycle. When the field is applied to the phosphor, the average light output and the normal light peak are reduced and the output waveform is modified by the appearance of a second peak when the field passes through zero (the voltage applied to the phosphor and that applied to the X-ray tube were in phase in these experiments). During the transitory region following the field application this second peak may be very large; the waveform changes continuously and finally reaches a constant shape, still in general with two peaks, when the average output becomes constant. When the field is removed the second peak disappears immediately while the in-phase peak

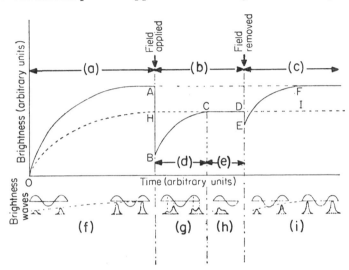

FIG. 56. Variation with time of the average brightness stimulated by X-rays. Curve OAF for no applied electric field; curve OHCDI for field applied and maintained during irradiation; curve OABCDEF for case where field is applied at A and removed at D. The shapes of the brightness waves at various times for the last case are shown below. (a) X-rays with no field; (b) period during which the field acts; (c) after the field is removed; (d) transitory period; (e) permanent quenching; (f) normal shape of the brightness wave—the amplitude increases progressively; (g) a secondary maximum appears when the field passes through zero in each cycle—the amplitude of this sharp peak varies with time; (h) permanent deformation of the brightness wave; (i) when the field is removed the brightness wave assumes its natural form and the amplitude increases progressively. (From Destriau, 438.)

increases in size continuously during the transient recovery period. The exact shape of the brightness waves in the presence of the field may differ depending upon the wavelength of observation. Destriau (441, 589, 603) has also shown that the relative phase between the field and the exciting radiation is important. Using a half-wave X-ray generator operating at 100 cps and a field of 50 cps, so that the phosphor received one pulse of X-rays for each reversal of field, the quenching was a maximum for zero phase difference but almost disappeared for a phase difference of 90° (irradiation a maximum when field was zero). If a constant rather than an alternating field is employed there is no deformation of the brightness waves, which are simply reduced in magnitude and then slowly return to their original height as polarization builds up (438).

For continuous ultraviolet excitation of ZnS phosphors Matossi (439) found that the output with field applied is modulated at twice the frequency of the field. Matossi and Nudelman (439a) found the magnitude of this component to be a maximum at about 100–200 cps and to decrease slightly at lower frequencies and much more rapidly for higher frequencies. The alternating component during the transient region following field application was much greater than that in the steady-state.

Steinberger et al. (590) studied quenching by alternating fields (50 cps) in phosphors continuously excited by ultraviolet radiation. In the transitory period all phosphors showed two light pulses per voltage cycle. In the steady-state region two pulses per cycle were also observed if the voltage was high enough but at low voltages peaks were observed only if the illuminated electrode was positive (denoted as "A" peaks). The situation, however, is far from simple. As the voltage was increased the "A" peaks at first increased, passed through a maximum and then decreased. The "B" peaks (illuminated electrode negative) appeared at higher voltages and usually increased to a saturation value so that at high voltage the two types of peaks were nearly equal. In some cases for very high voltages the height of both peaks decreased and "B" peaks might be larger than "A" peaks. There was no clear-cut relationship between the height of the peaks and the amount of steady-state quenching. The behavior of the "A" peaks was the same for different phosphors but the "B" peaks varied from sample to sample. During the transitory region the "B" peaks decayed faster than the "A" peaks; although usually smaller in the steady-state they were often larger in the transient region. The "A" peaks became more peaked and narrow at the base as the voltage was increased; for Cu-activated phosphors the "B" peaks behaved similarly but for Ag-activated phosphors they were broader at high voltage. The "B" peaks occurred earlier in the cycle at high voltage; their phase relationship with the "A" peaks is different for Cu and for Ag activation.

Because of this multitude of differences between the two types of peaks they observed, Steinberger et al. (590) concluded that they arise from different effects. Their observation is connected with the fact that the exciting radiation is strongly absorbed in the cell; the polarity of the illuminated electrode is important rather than that of the electrode used for observation. Surface effects were also suggested as a factor. The "B" peaks (illuminated electrode negative) are greatly influenced by the phosphor composition and are more variable. The details of these observations still await explanation.

Halsted (455, 587) also made independent observations of the effect of nonuniform ultraviolet excitation in phosphors; 2537A was used for excitation of ZnS:Ag,Al or ZnS:Cu,Al and 3650A for (Zn,Cd)S:Ag,Cl or Zn(S,Se):Cu,Cl phosphors. Application of a field as low as 10 volts/cm produced detectable modulation of the output at the field frequency; fields of 10^3 volts/cm were required to change the average emission level (i.e., produce quenching in the usual sense). The maximum output was obtained when the irradiated electrode was becoming positive or was at its positive maximum. Irradiation at longer wavelengths or application of a field perpendicular to the incident radiation resulted in modulation at a frequency twice that of the applied field as reported earlier by Matossi (439) and a higher voltage threshold for detection. The degree of modulation was found to decrease slightly with increasing excitation intensity and to increase slightly with increased frequency (up to 2×10^4 cps). This modulation was interpreted as resulting from the movement of electrons (the mobile charge carriers in this case) away from and into the region of excitation. Since the alternating component of the light output may represent more energy than that absorbed from the electric field, Halsted pointed out that such a cell is a type of signal amplifier with the irradiation source serving as the power supply. Other effects of nonuniform excitation have been observed by Nakamura (573) and by Daniel and his co-workers (583) and discussed above (see also Fig. 50).

Gumlich (591) performed experiments on a (Zn,Cd)S:Mn phosphor, which showed quenching for ultraviolet excitation but enhancement of output for X-ray excitation, with an ac-operated ultraviolet lamp. A field of 300 volts/cm was sufficient to introduce a noticeable difference in height of successive light peaks; the peak for the illuminated electrode negative was always smaller than that for opposite polarity. With increasing voltage the difference in peak height increased. At 16,000 volts/cm a small secondary peak appeared on the ascending side of the highest peak (illuminated electrode positive). With one sample the smallest peak was almost completely suppressed at a field strength of 1000 volts/cm. Identical results were obtained with symmetrical cells, i.e., with two transparent electrodes. Nonuniform excitation probably also played a role in these experiments. When an ultraviolet lamp operated on dc was used, an output peak was observed when the viewing (and illuminated) electrode was negative (the opposite polarity to that observed by Steinberger et al. (590)). This peak was ahead of the voltage maximum in phase. At higher voltages a second peak appeared. Gumlich also studied the transient behavior of the secondary peaks when a voltage was suddenly applied to an ultraviolet-excited phosphor.

Gutjahr and Matossi (*592*) have recently studied the influence of excitation wavelength and pulse duration on the effect of pulsed continuous fields on a (Zn,Cd)S:Ag phosphor. Some of their results are shown in Fig. 57. The Zn/Cd ratio for this sample is not given but the optical reflection spectrum begins to rise rapidly at 410 mμ (the excitation efficiency is a

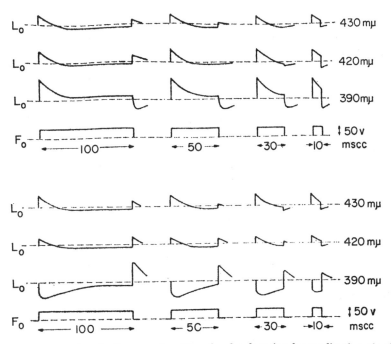

FIG. 57. Effect of excitation wavelength and pulse duration for application of voltage pulses to a (Zn,Cd)S:Ag phosphor. The upper curves are for illumination of the anode and the lower for illumination of the cathode. L_0 is the output without field and F_0 the voltage zero. (From Gutjahr and Matossi, *592*.)

maximum at the same wavelength) so that 390 mμ is in the region of very strong absorption while the other two wavelengths employed are much less strongly absorbed. When repeated 10-msec pulses were applied they observed changes in waveform suggestive of the reversal of predominance of "A" and "B" peaks as seen by Steinberger, Low, and Alexander.

3. Effect of Radiation on Electroluminescent Waveforms. The effect of ultraviolet radiation on electroluminescence brightness waves was first studied by Matossi and Nudelman (*418, 439a*). For low alternating voltages applied to the ultraviolet-excited phosphor only the usual two peaks in phase with the voltage (or actually lagging slightly, according to Matossi and Nudelman) were observed, together with suppression of the average light output. At a voltage just sufficient to produce detectable electroluminescence in the same cell without irradiation new peaks were observed in each half cycle, in advance of the voltage maximum. These peaks became larger, while the peaks associated with the quenching phenomena became smaller, as the voltage was increased and the average light output increased. The primary electroluminescence peaks and the quenching peaks are thus seen to be unrelated, although they occur simultaneously. On the other hand, the usual secondary peaks of electroluminescence (see Section III,I,2) are absent when the phosphor is irradiated. If the ultraviolet excitation is removed, several minutes may be required for the secondary peak to acquire its normal amplitude; on the other hand, if the radiation is reapplied the secondary peak disappears immediately. One phosphor, Zn(S,Se):Cu, also showed a much larger difference between the heights of successive primary peaks, corresponding to opposite field polarity, in the presence of radiation. It may be noted that in this case the exciting wavelength was further removed from the absorption edge than for ZnS:Cu so that this is probably another effect of non-uniform absorption in the phosphor. In the case of some phosphors emitting both the blue and the green band due to Cu, only the green emission was quenched.

Nakamura and Kobayashi (593), Oranovskii and Khmelinin (266), and Patek (437) have also studied the effects of ultraviolet radiation on electroluminescent waveforms. The former stated that ultraviolet radiation caused the secondary peak to shift toward the subsequent primary peak and seem to imply that it becomes "lost" in the larger primary rather than really disappearing. The effect of ultraviolet was reduced by simultaneous infrared irradiation or by high temperature. A polarity effect was observed for irradiation in the fundamental absorption but not for edge absorption. Nakamura and Kobayashi also studied these effects with half-wave rectified fields.

Patek (437) observed that the primary peak could also be increased by simultaneous ultraviolet irradiation.* In Fig. 58 ΔB_1 indicates this increase, while ΔB_2 is the decrease in height of the secondary peak. The increase in the base line L_0 was independent of the applied field and is thus simply the photoluminescence of the phosphor. The increase in primary peak was observed to be large only in green-emitting samples of ZnS:Cu (which contained Cl) and quite small in blue-emitting samples (which contained O). In phosphors with both green and blue emission the value of ΔB_1 was independent of wavelength. As the ultraviolet intensity was increased ΔB_1 at first increased, then decreased, and finally became negative as the

* Other cases of enhancement of output in electroluminescent phosphors are described in Section V,D.

quenching region was entered (high ultraviolet intensity for a constant field strength is obviously analogous to low field strength for constant ultraviolet intensity). The maximum value of ΔB_1 was essentially independent of the field frequency but the greater the irradiation the higher was the frequency (and hence the electroluminescence brightness) required to obtain this maximum value. On the other hand, the decrease in height of the secondary peak, ΔB_2, which was always greater at higher irradiation intensity, was only slightly affected by the frequency. It was therefore concluded that the mechanisms involved are quite different.

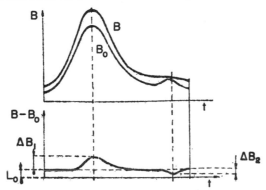

FIG. 58. Electroluminescence brightness waves with (B) and without (B_0) simultaneous ultraviolet irradiation. At the bottom the difference (B-B_0) is plotted. (From Patek, *437*.)

Contrary to Nakamura and Kobayashi (*593*), Patek (*437*) found that the position of the secondary peak was uninfluenced by irradiation but rather that the primary peak shifted slightly (maximum of 6°) and occurred earlier in the presence of irradiation. Also contrary to Nudelman and Matossi (*439a*), Patek found that the time constants for appearance or disappearance of the secondary peak at removal or application of the irradiation were equal, and also increased with decreasing temperature. Since there is still some controversy concerning the exact origin of the secondary peak, the effect on it of irradiation is also difficult to interpret.

4. The Mechanisms of Quenching. It has been concluded above that although quenching of photoluminescence by electric fields may occur simultaneously with electroluminescence, they are not related processes. Indeed, this is quite obvious as quenching also occurs in non-electroluminescent materials. In the following section (V,C) it will also be shown that quenching and enhancing effects due to an electric field may occur simultaneously but are basically unrelated other than the fact that they compete with each other.

It is obvious that the quenching effect must involve the introduction of new nonradiating transitions or a change in the balance between radiating and existing nonradiating transitions favoring the latter. Several possible mechanisms suggest themselves:

(a) filling of empty centers, under the action of the field, by electrons from the valence band as is customarily assumed for thermal or infrared quenching;

(b) a direct effect by the field on the energy levels of the luminescence centers so that non-radiating transitions are introduced or increased;

(c) since nonradiating transitions are often assumed to occur at traps, the field may increase this tendency, i.e., make the traps more "leaky";

(d) the increased velocity of carriers in the presence of the field may change the relative cross sections of luminescence centers and of non-radiative centers;

(e) carriers may be transported through the phosphor by the field to other regions of the crystal such as surfaces, where they become deeply trapped or nonradiating transitions occur.

In connection with the last effect it may be noted that Newman (51) observed that application of a magnetic field to germanium crystals so as to deflect carriers to the surface depressed the electroluminescence output due to the increased number of surface recombinations. The effect of surfaces in field quenching of photoluminescence is supported by unpublished results of W. Lehmann in which it was found that quenching is greater the smaller the particle size of phosphor powders. In these experiments the particle size was often more important than the chemical composition of the sample. Steinberger and Bar (574) also reported that no quenching was observed in single crystals of ZnS. The effect of deep traps is also shown by the "memory" and long time lags observed by Destriau (581) and later by Low et al. (575), Matossi and Nudelman (439a), and Bleil and Snyder (584). That such traps may remain filled for an extremely long time is shown by the "persistent internal polarization" experiments of Kallmann and Rosenberg (594).

In his early papers Déchêne (578) reported that thermoluminescence experiments on phosphors after quenching indicated a more intense emission persisting at higher temperatures (indicating the presence of electrons in deeper traps) but also a smaller total emission or light sum, i.e., a smaller total number of filled traps, indicating that nonradiating transitions had occurred. Unfortunately such experimental correlations have not been looked for by the majority of later workers. Destriau also entertained similar ideas. Thus he and Mattler (569) showed that their results on the effect of temperature on quenching by fields was not consistent with a reduction of the thermal quenching energy, q in Eq. (17), but could be fitted by an additive term representing field-induced nonradiative transitions.

The most extensive attempt to study the quenching effect analytically is due to Matossi (*418, 439*). He introduced into the kinetic equations terms representing field-induced nonradiating transitions, filling of empty luminescence centers by the field, emptying of filled luminescence centers (responsible for electroluminescence), and emptying of filled traps (responsible for the Gudden-Pohl effect). He considered the transient case and the alternating component of the output as well as the steady-state quenching. His results include the fact that the alternating component should be a maximum for some intermediate frequency, as observed (*439a*).

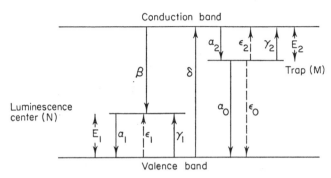

FIG. 59. Simplified model of a nonelectroluminescent photoconducting phosphor. The various electron transitions are identified in the text. (From Ivey, *135*.)

A complete kinetic description of the effects of electric fields on phosphors would become hopelessly complicated. A simplified steady-state treatment, however, can yield results of interest (*135*). Consider the simple model of a nonelectroluminescent photoconducting phosphor shown in Fig. 59. This is basically the model of Schön and others to which has been added three types of field induced transitions (the same types of transitions introduced by Matossi). The symbols utilized denote the following quantities:

α_0 nonradiating recombination,
α_1 production of empty luminescence center by hole in valence band,
α_2 trapping of electron from conduction band,
β radiating recombination,
γ_1 thermal filling of empty luminescence center,
γ_2 thermal release of trapped electron,
δ exciting transition due to absorption of radiation,
ϵ_0 field-induced nonradiating recombination,*

* Here, for convenience the field-induced nonradiating transitions have been shown as arising from the same traps responsible for the nonradiating transitions which exist in the absence of the field. It may be in reality that the field brings into action other sites for nonradiating recombinations (surfaces or other types of trap), but the essential effect will be the same in either case.

ϵ_1 field-induced filling of empty luminescence center,
ϵ_2 field-induced release of trapped electrons,*
E_1 energy difference between luminescence center and valance band,
E_2 energy difference between electron trap and conduction band,
I intensity of incident radiation (number of quanta/sec),
L luminescence output (number of quanta/sec),
M number of traps,
N number of luminescence centers.

Schön (149) has shown that the output in the absence of a field and for low levels of excitation is given by

$$L_R = I\left[1 + \frac{M}{N}\frac{\alpha_0}{\beta}\exp\left(\frac{E_2 - E_1}{kT}\right)\right]^{-1} = I\left[1 + \frac{M}{N}\frac{\alpha_0\alpha_2\gamma_1}{\beta\alpha_1\gamma_2}\right]^{-1}. \quad (35)$$

In this case the luminescence efficiency will obviously be high only if $M \ll N$ and $E_1 > E_2$ (i.e., the traps should be shallow and few in number). From inspection of the figure it can be seen that in the presence of the field the corresponding result is

$$L_B = I\left[1 + \frac{M}{N}\frac{(\alpha_0 + \epsilon_0)\alpha_2(\gamma_1 + \epsilon_1)}{\beta\alpha_1(\gamma_2 + \epsilon_2)}\right]^{-1}. \quad (36)$$

Quenching of luminescence by the field will result ($R = L_B/L_R < 1$) if

$$\frac{\epsilon_2}{\gamma_2} < \frac{\epsilon_0}{\alpha_0} + \frac{\epsilon_1}{\gamma_1} + \left(\frac{\epsilon_0}{\alpha_0}\right)\left(\frac{\epsilon_1}{\gamma_1}\right), \quad (37)$$

while enhancement will occur if the reverse is true.

The exact nature of the field-induced nonradiating transitions is not certain and may be different in different phosphors. The extent to which filling of empty centers by the field (ϵ_1) is important is also not clear. One might expect high temperature to favor the nonradiating transitions and thus to increase the quenching as observed experimentally. Also from competition of radiating processes (assumed to be bimolecular) with nonradiating processes (assumed to be monomolecular) one would expect quenching to be favored at low excitation levels. This conclusion also seems to be in accord with experiment (582, 595). As we have seen, field-emptying of traps (ϵ_2) can act as a process competitive to either ϵ_0 or ϵ_1. One could thus explain Destriau's observations that a phosphor which exhibits a good Gudden-Pohl effect shows only a small amount of quenching, and vice versa.

* Assumed here to arise from a direct action of the field on trapped electrons and not from the action of accelerated electrons.

Studies of the quenching effect in the past have been incomplete and not very systematic. Several experiments which might clarify the situation are listed below. In all cases the quenching characteristics should be correlated with other properties which are known to depend on electron traps, such as phosphorescence, thermoluminescence, infrared stimulation and the Gudden-Pohl effect.

(1) Study of phosphors with different activators (such as ZnS with Cu, Ag, Au, or self-activation) but otherwise identical. This should indicate something concerning the importance of the ϵ_1 process.

(2) Study of phosphors with different depth electron trapping sites (such as those due to O, Cl, Br, I, Al, Sc, Ga, In, or Co) but otherwise identical.

(3) Study of phosphors with common activator and co-activator but variable base material; Hoogenstraaten (254) has shown that introduction of increasing amounts of CdS into ZnS results in continuous reduction of trap depth.

(4) Study of phosphors identical in composition but of different particle size.

(5) Study of the action of thermal or surface treatment on various phosphors; milling, thermal quenching, and surface oxidation or etching come to mind.

5. Effects of Fields on Infrared Quenching of Luminescence. The quenching of luminescence by infrared radiation is a well-known phenomena and is usually ascribed to filling of empty luminescence centers from the valence band (similar to the thermal transition γ_1 in Fig. 59). The holes left in the valence band are then available for a nonradiating transition (α_0 in Fig. 59). Since electric fields also exert a quenching action it seemed of interest to Destriau to combine the two effects. The observations (596) were actually made during phosphorescence rather than for sustained excitation of the phosphor (although the infrared was applied during excitation). This is unfortunate as the results would seem much easier to interpret in the latter case; no work, however, seems to have been done on this effect since 1943.

Destriau interpreted his results as indicating a greater than additive effect, i.e., he concluded that the field had an intensifying action on the infrared quenching. This conclusion, however, was based on the observation that

$$\frac{L_{E+IR}}{L_0} < \frac{L_E}{L_0} \cdot \frac{L_{IR}}{L_0}. \tag{38}$$

Simple calculation on the basis of the model shown in Fig. 59 and Eqs. (35) and (36), however, shows that this is just what is to be expected if, for example, the field is responsible for transition ϵ_0 while the infrared radiation increases γ_1 (similar to ϵ_1) and the two effects are unrelated; in essence this is already shown by the right side of Eq. (37). On the other hand, if both field and radiation affect the same type of transition (ϵ_0 or ϵ_1) then the sign in this inequality should be reversed. Destriau's conclusions concerning this effect are, therefore, not necessarily correct. In view of this and the paucity of experimental data, further experiments seem to be needed. The simultaneous action of fields and infrared radiation on phosphors showing enhancement rather than quenching will be discussed in Section V,C,3.

Kitamura et al. (644) have recently observed that infrared quenching of photoconductivity may be reversed by an electric field so that sitmulation results. This has been interpreted by Diemer (645) in terms of a process in which the field acts to fill quenching centers which are normally active.

C. Enhancement of Luminescence in Nonelectroluminescent Phosphors

1. *Excitation by Ultraviolet or X-Rays.* As stated previously, if an electric field is applied to a phosphor which is simultaneously excited by ultraviolet, X-rays, or some other source, in most cases the result is quenching of the output. Enhancement, on the other hand, was first observed, as recently as 1954, in X-ray excited phosphors by Destriau and his son (597).* Since then it has been studied by a large number of workers. The effect observed by Destriau, as will be shown below, seems not to be related to electroluminescence (although other enhancement effects discussed in Section D below are), and thus far (with a single exception, reference 615) has been observed only in manganese-activated sulfides. In the first observations ultraviolet excitation of the same materials produced only quenching rather than enhancement. This was later found not to be necessarily true (595); the relationship between these two effects will also be discussed below.

This enhancement effect can be detected for very low field strengths, 50–200 volts/cm (440, 597). These values are lower by factors of 100 or 10 than those normal for electroluminescence or the quenching effect, respectively. Although very good electroluminescent ZnS:Mn phosphors may be prepared, these require the presence of Cu in addition; this is not the case for enhancement. On the other hand, Mn is not a requirement for electroluminescence while it is for enhancement. As the field increases the

---

* Schmidt (563) in his 1923 paper mentions the existence of an enhancement effect: "It is a remarkable fact that phosphors excited while in an electric field sometimes luminesce noticeably brighter than during normal excitation. This can be easily demonstrated if one makes two cells of the same phosphor and applies to one a high voltage while both are irradiated with the 365 mμ Hg line and the brightness observed." No further information is given. It may be that with the field applied, ultraviolet radiation generated in the powder provided the additional excitation. In any case, it was 33 years before anyone else observed enhancement in ultraviolet-excited phosphors (595), despite the fact that many people studied field effects in phosphors in the interim.

enhancement ratio quickly reaches a saturation value and sometimes decreases slightly (*440*). This is also in strong contrast to both the quenching effect and electroluminescence. Even if electroluminescence is detectable,

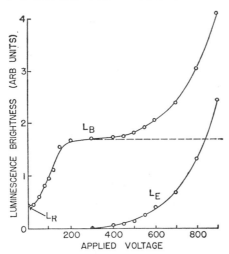

FIG. 60. Light output of a ZnS:Mn,Cl phosphor which shows field enhancement of X-ray excited luminescence and electroluminescence, L_E. L_R is the output with X-rays only and L_B that with both X-rays and field. The dashed curve indicates the expected output in the absence of electroluminescence. (From Destriau, *598*.)

its voltage dependence is distinctly different (see Fig. 60). Destriau (*599*) found that the variation of the enhancement ratio R with voltage (or field strength) is given by

$$\frac{R-1}{R_m - R} = \left(\frac{V}{V_0}\right)^{3/2}, \tag{39}$$

where R_m and V_0 are constants. R_m is the maximum value of R and increases with, but much more slowly than, the X-ray intensity while V_0 is dependent on the phosphor and the cell construction but not on the excitation intensity. There is sometimes a visible change in emission color when the field is applied so that the value of R also depends on the wavelength of observation (discussed more fully below) or on the spectral sensitivity of the detector if a wide wavelength region is observed (*600*). This last effect presumably accounts for the apparent decrease in R for high voltages in the early experiments (*440*).

   It was at first reported (*440*) that the frequency of the alternating field had little effect on the enhancement ratio. Later, with (Zn,Cd)S:Mn,Au,Cl phosphors showing much higher values of R, Mattler (*601*) found that R decreased, rapidly at first and then more slowly, as the frequency was increased from 20 to 4000 cps. Since only a transient effect is found for static fields (440), the enhancement was found to be a maximum at about 5 to 25 cps. This behavior is also in strong contrast to that of electroluminescence and of the quenching effect, both of which increase with increasing frequency. Again, contrary to the first reports (440) that temperature had little influence on the enhancement effect, Mattler (602) found an increase in R for increasing temperature (from 1.2 at $-140°C$ to 2.4 at 100°C for one sample). This is also opposite to the effect of temperature on the quenching effect (569). The electroluminescence of this same sample was a maximum at $-10°C$ for low voltages and at $-70°C$ for high voltages, again showing no correlation with the enhancement.

The "brightness waves" in the enhancement effect are also much simpler than those in electroluminescence or the quenching effect (440, 591, 597). In the steady-state no secondary peaks are observed;* only the amplitude of the output peaks due to the half-wave X-ray generator are amplified. The same phosphors show more complicated waveforms in the quenching effect for ultraviolet excitation or even if observed at short wavelengths (blue emission) for X-ray excitation (600). During the transient period following application of the field, however, additional complications in waveform are observed (440, 591). Temperature also has no effect on the shape of the brightness waves (602). If the frequency of the alternating field is greater than that of the excitation, a small ripple may be seen superimposed on the output (601); this alternating component was a maximum at about 500 cps and disappeared for high frequencies. Although the quenching effect (in ZnS:Ag, for example) is very sensitive to the phase difference between the field on the phosphor and the intermittent excitation, when these two frequencies are equal, and disappears when the difference is 90°, the influence of phase on the enhancement effect is very small (441, 589, 601, 603). Thus Pingault (603) found the enhancement for 90° phase difference to be 60–75%, depending on the sample, of that for no phase shift.

Destriau (441) also observed a very long "memory" in the enhancement effect (Fig. 61). The phosphor may be "pre-sensitized" by applying a field and radiation simultaneously; after the excitation is stopped the field is removed. If the same, or a different, intensity of radiation is applied at a later time, the output will at first be greater than its normal value, to which it decays. The increase in output is less the longer the time between the action of the field and the second irradiation, but the decline is slow so that several hours may intervene. The memory, however, can be erased by visible or infrared radiation. The presence of the memory effect may have

---

* Secondary peaks are normally not observed in electroluminescent ZnS:Cu,Mn phosphors either.

an influence on the small effect of phase difference between field and
excitation in the enhancement effect; on the other hand, a long memory is
also observed in the quenching effect (581), which is greatly affected by
such a phase difference. Pingault (603) also observed that the enhancement
does not immediately attain its steady-state value when a phosphor already
under the action of a field is irradiated, a time of the order of half a second
being required.* On the other hand, the effect is instantaneous if the irradia-

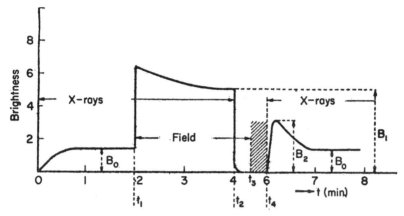

FIG. 61. The "memory effect" in the enhancement of luminescence by electric fields.
X-rays are applied at $t = 0$ and the alternating field at t_1. The steady-state enhancement
ratio is $R_1 = B_1/B_0$. The irradiation is stopped at time t_2 and the field removed at t_3.
The radiation is then reapplied at time t_4. The output is temporarily increased over its
normal value; the "memory enhancement ratio" is $R_2 = B_2/B_0$. The rest time $T = (t_4 - t_2)$ may be many hours. (From Destriau, 441.)

tion is applied before the field. If the X-ray intensity at the second irradiation is made greater, the magnitude of the "memory enhancement ratio"
($R_2 = B_2/B_0$ in Fig. 61) is normally greater and the normal output level is
reached quicker. However, as in the case of the Gudden-Pohl effect (568,
569), an optimum presensitization exposure is sometimes observed, as
shown in Fig. 62.

As stated previously, Destriau and his colleagues (440) found that the
same phosphors which showed enhancement by electric fields of X-ray
excited luminescence showed only quenching for ultraviolet excitation. In
the usual range the value of the enhancement ratio usually increases with
increasing X-ray energy. Destriau therefore suggested that there should
exist an intermediate region of energy for which neither enhancement or
quenching would be observed. He made observations with very low-energy

* Since, however, the X-ray excited luminescence requires some time to reach its
equilibrium value, and since the enhancement ratio is known to increase with the exciting
intensity, this effect is probably not very profound.

X-rays (as low as 7000 volts on the anode). Experiments with such soft X-rays are very difficult because they are absorbed in air and only in the surface of the phosphor. He concluded, however, that for (Zn,Cd)S:Mn 5000 volts (or a minimum wavelength of about 2.4A) should correspond to

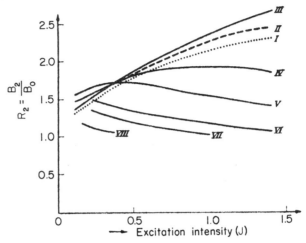

FIG. 62. Effect of excitation intensity at second irradiation (J) and of previous X-ray exposure ($Q = It$) on the enhancement ratio in the "memory effect" ($R_2 = B_2/B_0$, see Fig. 61). Q is expressed in terms of product of current in the X-ray tube (I) at the first irradiation and the exposure time. Q decreases from curve I (640 μa-min) to curve VIII (5 μa-min), the value for each successive curve being lower by a factor of 2. Note that the highest ratio is obtained not for the greatest "presensitization" (curve I) but at intermediate values (curves III or V). (From Destriau, *441*.)

this limit (*604*). Gobrecht and Gumlich (*595*), however, had already shown that depending upon phosphor composition and operating conditions a small degree of enhancement could be obtained in ZnS:Mn even with normal ultraviolet excitation. They found that enhancement in this case is favored by (see, however, the further discussion below):

(1) optimum activator concentration;
(2) high frequency field;
(3) high excitation intensity;
(4) excitation at short wavelengths;
(5) observation at long wavelengths.

Destriau (*600*) and Gobrecht and Gumlich (*595*) both observed that enhancement is observed, even with X-ray excitation, only for the yellow Mn emission; the blue emission, ascribed to lattice defects or "self-activation" (all these samples apparently contained large amounts of Cl, although this is not explicitly stated), was simultaneously quenched. Some results of Gobrecht and Gumlich for both types of excitation are shown in Fig. 63. In no case was the blue emission enhanced by the field. It is seen that R is greatest for a Mn content of 10^{-3}. Increasing the Mn content to 10^{-2} (not shown in this figure) resulted in $R = 1$ in the blue region and only a small enhancement ($R = 1.1$) for X-ray excitation and observation near 590 mμ. For 10^{-1} Mn the field had no effect on the luminescence. Not only

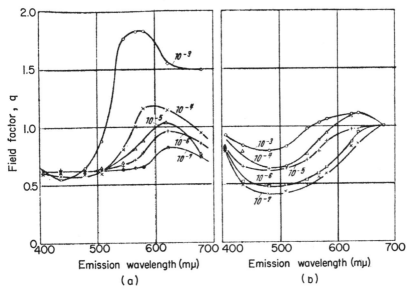

FIG. 63. Influence of Mn concentration and of wavelength of observation on effect of electric field on luminescence of ZnS:Mn excited by X-rays (a) and by ultraviolet radiation (b). Quenching ($R < 1$) is always observed for blue ("self-activated") emission; enhancement ($R > 1$) only for yellow Mn emission and for high Mn content. (From Gobrecht and Gumlich, 595.)

do quenching of the blue emission and enhancement of the yellow exist simultaneously but it was found that concurrent excitation by X-rays and by ultraviolet, under conditions where the latter resulted in quenching, produced an output in the yellow region which was that expected by simple addition of the results with separate excitation. Thus the quenching and enhancement effects occur simultaneously and independently.

Gobrecht and Gumlich (595) found that increasing the excitation intensity, for either X-ray or ultraviolet irradiation, increased the value of R, i.e., decreased the amount of quenching or increased the amount of enhancement, in agreement with other observations (582, 599). They also found that in this case increasing the frequency of the alternating field increased the value of R. It should be noted, however, that for X-irradiation

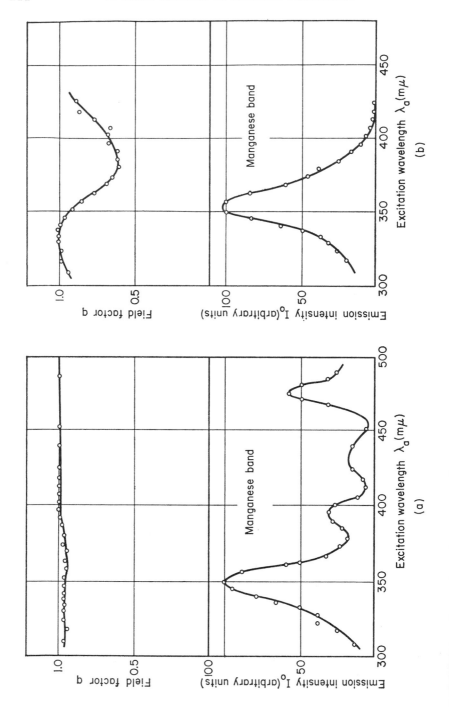

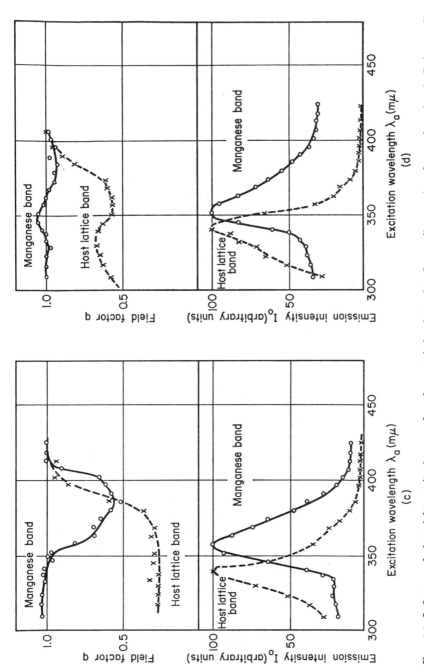

Fig. 64. Influence of ultraviolet excitation wavelength on emission intensity (lower diagrams) and on value of ratio R (upper diagrams) of ZnS:Mn for different Mn content: (a) 10^{-2}, (b) 10^{-3}, (c) 10^{-4}, (d) 10^{-5}. (From Gobrecht and Gumlich, 605.)

the opposite effect of frequency was observed, in agreement with the results of Mattler (601). The effect of ultraviolet wavelength is shown in Fig. 64 for various concentrations of Mn. The three* excitation peaks at 395, 430, and 475 mμ for high Mn content are ascribed to internal transitions in Mn centers; note that there is no effect of the field in this case. The value of R for the Mn emission is a minimum (quenching) for excitation at 380 mμ; in this case the excitation is assumed to involve transitions between Mn centers and the valence or conduction bands. Enhancement is observed only at shorter wavelengths ($\lambda < 340$ mμ) where excitation is presumed to be across the forbidden energy gap of ZnS. These effects are even clearer if plotted for conditions of constant luminescence intensity rather than constant excitation intensity as done in Fig. 64. The results for 10^{-5} Mn in Fig. 64, however, seem to represent an exception to the conclusion drawn since here the enhancement is a maximum at 350 mμ. These results confirm the statement made in connection with electroluminescence that ZnS:Mn represents a complicated phosphor system.

Experiments on the field enhancement effect have also recently been performed by Wendel and his colleagues Winkler and Röppischer (606–608), with some differences from earlier observations. The samples used were (50Zn,50Cd)S:Mn,Cl. With X-ray excitation no quenching was observed for any wavelength of observation (607). This difference from the results of Gobrecht and Gumlich (595) could be due to the fact that the latter employed ZnS:Mn phosphors while in (50Zn,50Cd)S the band edge is much closer to the transition energy of the Mn centers. On the other hand, Destriau (600) also observed quenching of blue emission in (Zn,Cd)S. The materials used by Destriau in these early experiments, however, gave much smaller maximum values of R than those used by Winkler, Röppischer, and Wendel; it is not clear whether Destriau's later and better phosphors also show quenching of emission in the blue region. With X-ray excitation these workers found that the value of R decreased as the field frequency was decreased. With samples containing In, however, Wendel (608) later found that the enhancement was a maximum at 100 cps. Winkler et al. (607) also observed the "memory effect" in their materials. In contrast to Destriau's published results (441), however, they reported that application of a field alone, without concurrent irradiation, also pronounced essentially the same storage. As a matter of fact, this effect had also been observed some time earlier by Destriau (609), but not published; Fridkin (631) also made similar observations.

Wendel (608) has discussed the enhancement effect for ultraviolet excitation in more detail. Although for X-ray excitation the value of R was found to saturate for fields as low as 200 volts/cm, the dependence on

* A fourth peak at 505 mμ is also usually observed (239c, 630).

field strength was more complicated for ultraviolet excitation. For high excitation intensities the value of R always increased or reached a saturation value as the voltage was increased. For intermediate intensities it showed a maximum and then decreased for higher voltages. For low ultraviolet intensities R could even become less than unity, i.e., quenching of the luminescence occurred, if the voltage was great enough. These results seem clearly to indicate the presence of two competing processes: (1) enhancement, which tends to saturation as the voltage is increased and is favored by high excitation intensity, and (2) quenching, which continues to increase as the voltage is increased.* The voltage dependence of these two

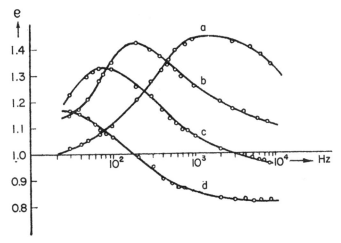

Fig. 65. Influence of ultraviolet excitation intensity and of frequency of an applied alternating electric field on the luminescence of $(50Zn,50Cd)S:Mn,Cl$. Intensity (arbitrary units): (a) 100, (b) 16, (c) 8, (d) 3. (From Wendel, *608*.)

separate processes are the same as those seen for X-ray excitation in appropriate materials ($ZnS:Mn$ and $ZnS:Ag$, for example). The effect of these two competing processes is also shown in the influence of field frequency on the enhancement ratio (Fig. 65) which shows an optimum frequency for each different exciting intensity, the frequency being higher the greater the intensity. It was also found that the optimum frequency was higher the lower the applied voltage. Apparently the ultraviolet intensity in the experiments of Gobrecht and Gumlich (*595*) was great enough so that only the ascending portions of the curves of Fig. 65 were revealed. Wendel found maximum enhancement for excitation in these materials at 425 mμ, which is close to the estimated position of the band gap (428 mμ).

* Obviously quenching cannot continue to increase without limit, however, as R cannot be negative!

It was observed almost from the earliest discovery of this enhancement effect by Destriau and his colleagues that (Zn,Cd)S:Mn phosphors give higher values of R than did ZnS:Mn (440). It was at first reported that additions of Ag decreased the enhancement effect (600) but Destriau (610, 611) discovered that very small amounts of Au (about 5×10^{-6} by weight) caused R to increase. The optimum Zn:Cd ratio was found to be 50/50 by weight (or 40:60 on a molar basis) (610), the optimum firing temperature 1000–1050°C, and the optimum Mn content 2×10^{-3} by weight (611) (see also Fig. 63). Later it was found that Ag (contrary to the earlier report) and also Co increased the value of R, at least for 2×10^{-3} Mn (261). Fe, Ni, and Cr, on the other hand, caused R to decrease; 10^{-6} Ni caused quenching. The effects of such additives, however, is quite critical as it was found, for example, that for 1×10^{-3} Mn, Ag produced only a small effect and Co none. The best of these materials gave values of R between 5 and 6 compared to 3 for no additive. Mattler and Destriau (612) also later found improvements for additions of Cu and Ba. Destriau published values of R as high as 11 (599) and in unpublished work obtained values of 14–20.* More recently Wendel (607) obtained $R = 6$ without the use of such additives and $R = 20$ ($R = 2$ for ultraviolet excitation) with additions of In. Gumlich (628) also obtained improvement in the enhancement ratio for ZnS:Mn phosphors by additions of small amounts of Co ($R = 18$ for 10^{-6} Co, $R = 9$ without Co) but found that such additions were effective in increasing the enhancement only for low values of field frequency (below about 1000 cps).

Although the value of the enhancement ratio is of scientific interest, from the practical viewpoint it is the output with field applied ($L_B = RL_0$) which is important. This was found by Destriau (261) to be a maximum for 1×10^{-3} Mn, 1.2×10^{-6} Au and 1.2×10^{-6} Co (Fig. 66). The combination of Au and Co was better in this respect (but not for maximum value of R) than either Au or Co alone, a fact as yet unexplained. Despite impressive ratios as high as 20, however, the phosphors showing the enhancement effect do not appear to give appreciably more output than conventional fluoroscopic screens (606). Thus, for example the level indicated as 100 in Fig. 66 represents the output of a standard Patterson B2 screen. In general these phosphors are very inefficient in the absence of a field and also exhibit luminescence fatigue (even under irradiation only) and pronounced nonlinearity of output as a function of X-ray intensity (613, 625).

Since the electric field strengths F employed in the enhancement effect are 10–100 times smaller than those for electroluminescence (even neglecting the localization of the field in the latter case), and since the effect of a

* The value of R obtained is, of course, a function of the field strength, the X-ray intensity, etc.

magnetic field H on charge carriers should be determined by the ratio $H/F(1)$, the effect of a magnetic field should be much easier to observe in the former case. However, Destriau found no effect upon applying a field of 10,000 oersteds (*261*). Mattler later repeated this experiment with a field of 35,000 oersteds, but also with no effect (*614*).

Aside from ZnS:Mn and (Zn,CdS):Mn, the only nonelectroluminescent material in which enhancement of photoluminescence by an electric field has been observed is unactivated KBr. Andrianov and Kats (*615*) have

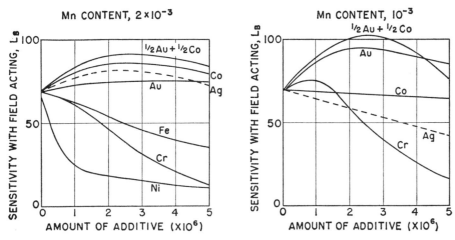

FIG. 66. Influence of additives on output of (40Zn,60Cd)S:Mn,Cl phosphors subjected to X-radiation and to an alternating electric field. (From Destriau, *261*.)

recently reported that if powders of this material are embedded in a plastic dielectric and subjected simultaneously to X-rays and a field of 8×10^4 volts/cm, 50 cps, the output is 1.8 times that with no field. In this case, as for (Zn,Cd)S, there is no change in output waveform due to the field, only an increase in amplitude. Addition of Sn increased the photoluminescence intensity but had no effect on the enhancement ratio.

2. Excitation by Cathode Rays or Alpha Particles. It is of historical interest to note that Destriau (*19*) discovered electroluminescence in ZnS while searching for an effect of electric fields on alpha particle scintillations, reasoning that fields induced by these charged particles contributed to the luminescence process. However, neither quenching nor enhancement of the scintillations by fields was observed (*585*). In 1955, after the discovery of field enhancement of X-ray excited luminescence, Low (*616*) suggested that a similar effect should exist for nuclear particles and proposed it as a possible radiation detector. He apparently had in mind a process involving electron avalanche formation similar to the commonly assumed electroluminescence mechanism; however, he performed no experiments and had no suggestions for specific materials.

The first observation of luminescence enhancement by fields with alpha particle excitation was made by Mattler (617), using the same (Zn,Cd)S:Mn,Cl phosphors used by Destriau for enhancement with X-ray excitation. The effect on the enhancement ratio of varying the applied voltage was much greater than when the same sample was irradiated by X-rays. Although saturation of output was observed in the latter case, this was not so with alpha particles; for low voltages R was lower for alpha excitation but the situation was reversed for high voltages. R was found to decrease with increasing frequency of the alternating voltage (601), as also observed for X-ray excitation. Although the output, either with field on or off, decreases with increasing temperature, Mattler (613) found the value of R to be a maximum near 0°C, although the variation was not very great. Oscillographic studies (613, 618) have shown that neither the height or the width of the individual scintillations is increased by the field. The increase in output results from an increase in the background radiation, which is ascribed to secondary electrons diffusing from the intense ionization region produced in the alpha particle track, and is modulated at twice the field frequency. Since the time constant associated with Mn centers is of the order of 0.5 msec, it is not to be expected that they could respond during the very fast scintillations, which occur on a microsecond scale.

Henck and Coche (619–622) have also studied the enhancement of alpha particle scintillations in (88Zn,12Cd)S:Mn phosphors. In their first paper (619) it is indicated that the enhancement is greater for 10^{-2} Mn than for 10^{-3} Mn; only the output in the yellow region was enhanced while that in the blue was quenched (at least for 10^{-3} Mn), as observed earlier by Destriau (600) and Gobrecht and Gumlich (595) for X-ray excitation. Only quenching was observed for 10^{-4} Mn. Later (621) it was found that the enhancement in the yellow region was a maximum at 10^{-3} Mn. For 5×10^{-3} Mn (and presumably also 10^{-2} Mn) the enhancement was less at 6000A than for 10^{-3} Mn, but enhancement rather than quenching was observed in the blue region as well; the earlier result that 10^{-2} Mn gave maximum enhancement may have resulted from use of a blue-sensitive photomultiplier. The effect of frequency was studied over the range 0.005–50,000 cps and maximum enhancement was achieved at 4 cps, independent of Mn content (621). Transient enhancement was also observed for direct fields (619). The decay in this case was very slow, however; R decreased from 2 to 1.5 in 10 min and continued to decrease (after a Gudden-Pohl flash) at essentially the same rate after the field was removed.

Figure 67 shows the "brightness waves" obtained by Henck and Coche (620) as observed through orange and blue filters. In the former case the output is modulated at twice the field frequency and maximum output occurs slightly after the voltage maximum. The output is greater than that without field at all parts of the cycle. The peak which corresponds to negative voltage on the irradiated elctrode is considerably larger than that for the opposite polarity, in opposition to the results of Halsted (455) for ultraviolet excitation (which, however, resulted in quenching, not enhancement). For observation through the blue filter (quenching) the point of minimum

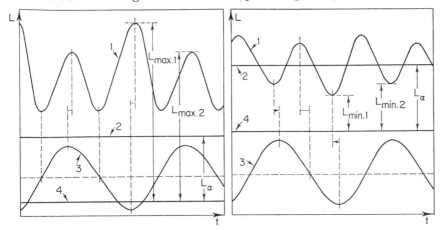

Fig. 67. Light output waveform (curve 1) when alternating voltage (curve 3) is applied to (Zn,Cd)S:5 × 10⁻⁴Mn phosphor excited by alpha particles from Po²¹⁰. (2) is the output level with alpha excitation only and (4) the zero level of the output. Observations at left through an orange interference filter (5804A) and those at right through a blue filter (4790A). Field frequency = 50 cps. (From Henck and Coche, 620.)

output occurs slightly in advance of the voltage maximum while maximum output (which is greater than that with no field applied) occurs slightly before the time when the voltage passes through zero. The two minima per cycle are not equal; maximum quenching occurs for the irradiated electrode negative. Half-wave rectified fields were also employed. A memory effect, similar to that for X-ray excitation, resulting from simultaneous application of radiation and field was also observed (619). For the case of direct voltage a memory effect for field only was also obtained.

Jaffe (586) also found enhancement of luminescence by fields in Destriau's (Zn,Cd)S:Mn phosphors when they were excited by cathode-rays. Introduction of small amounts of Au, in contrast to the case of X-ray excitation, reduced the value of R and sometimes resulted in quenching. As in the experiments of Mattler (617) with alpha particles, but contrary to X-ray excitation, no saturation of R with increasing field strength was observed; Jaffe found R to increase linearly with the field up to 2×10^4 volts/cm. Both cathode-rays and alpha particles are, of course, much less penetrating than X-rays. R was a maximum for a field of about 30 cps and decreased for higher frequencies. The degree of enhancement always decreased with increasing electron beam current density but the dependence on the electron accelerating voltage (4–12 kv) was complex; for low current density R increased with increasing anode voltage but for high current density the reverse was true. The two light peaks for each cycle of applied voltage were not equal and that for the irradiated electrode negative was higher, in agreement with the later result of Henck and Coche (620) for excitation by alpha particles. The light peaks occurred slightly after the

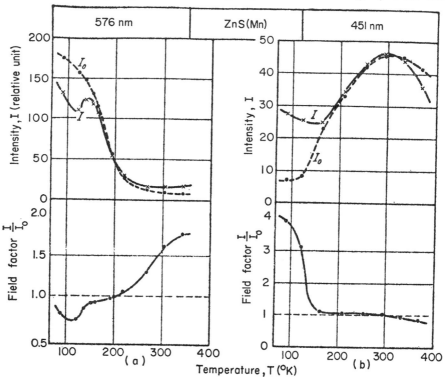

Fig. 68. Effect of temperature on cathodoluminescent output of ZnS:10⁻³Mn phosphor with (I) and without (I_0) electric field (4 × 10⁴ volt/cm, 500 cps). Accelerating potential = 10 kv. Results for yellow emission on left and for blue on right. (From Gobrecht et al., 624.)

voltage maxima, in agreement with Fig. 67; the shift was greater the higher the frequency of the field. The alternating component became larger relative to the continuous component of output at low frequency and high field strength. Although values of R as high as 4 were observed, the cathodoluminescence of these phosphors, even with field applied, was lower by a factor of 5–35 than that of a standard white television phosphor [P4, ZnS:Ag + (Zn,Cd)S:Ag] under the same conditions.

Both Jaffe (*586*) and Gobrecht *et al.* (*623*) found field enhancement of cathodoluminescence only with Mn-activated phosphors. The latter workers used ZnS:Mn (presumably with Cl) and found that only the yellow emission is enhanced at room temperature, in agreement with results with other types of excitation. In this case the value of R was independent of the accelerating voltage (7–21 kv). The simultaneous quenching of the blue (self-activated) emission was greater the lower the accelerating voltage. Later, however, Gobrecht *et al.* (*624*) found that at low temperature this situation is reversed, i.e., the yellow emission is quenched and the blue enhanced (see Fig. 68). This will be discussed further in a following section (V,*C*,*4*). Unfortunately, similar low-temperature studies do not seem to have been made with monochromatic ultraviolet excitation. The value of R for the yellow emission of this phosphor was higher the lower the field frequency (minimum value used, 50 cps), independent of temperature (except for very high beam current density). On the other hand, for the low temperature region where enhancement of the blue emission was observed, the value of R was greater the higher the frequency.

Wendel (*606*) studied the effect of fields on the output of the same (Zn,Cd)S:Mn,Cl phosphor for various kinds of excitation. He obtained $R = 6$ for X-rays, $R = 4$ for cathode rays, $R = 3$ for alpha particles, and $R = 1.4$ for ultraviolet radiation. Henck (*622*) found that the same phosphors which yielded enhancement of output when excited by alpha particles (Po^{210}, 5.3 Mev) gave only quenching when excited by beta rays (P^{32}, 1.7 Mev). It is of interest in this connection to note that he found the output without field to decrease with increasing Mn content for alpha particle excitation but to increase for excitation by beta rays.

3. Effect of Infrared Radiation on the Enhancement Effect. Pingault and Destriau (*625*) observed that the same (Zn,Cd)S:Mn,Cl phosphors which showed enhancement of the X-ray excited luminescence by electric fields also show enhancement if irradiated with infrared. Both effects may also be observed simultaneously (Fig. 69). It may be noted that the phosphor shows fatigue following application of X-rays (peak A) or field (peak M), but not when infrared is applied (PM′N′P′). If a similar experiment is performed with ultraviolet excitation, quenching is observed for either field or infrared. Application of infrared and X-rays simultaneously also produces a transient enhancement ("memory") upon a second excitation by X-rays, as for the case of a field. The action of a field and of infrared radiation is thus seen to be very similar. The enhancement produced by infrared was also found to be a maximum at 580 mμ (*626*), corresponding to the peak of the Mn emission band. Pingault also found the variation of R with infrared intensity (I) to follow the same law, Eq. (39), observed by Destriau (*599*) for the field effect if the voltage V is replaced by I. In both

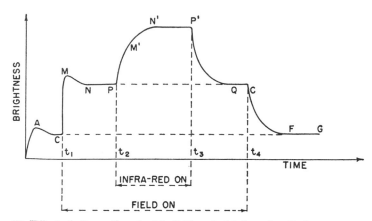

FIG. 69. Effect of alternating electric field and of infrared radiation on X-ray excited luminescence of (Zn,Cd)S:Mn,Cl phosphor. (From Pingault and Destriau, *625*.)

cases the maximum value of R (R_m) increases with increasing X-ray intensity, but I_0 also increases (see Fig. 70), while V_0 is independent of excitation intensity. Mattler (*627*) also found similar infrared enhancement and memory effects when these phosphors were excited by alpha particles rather than X-rays.

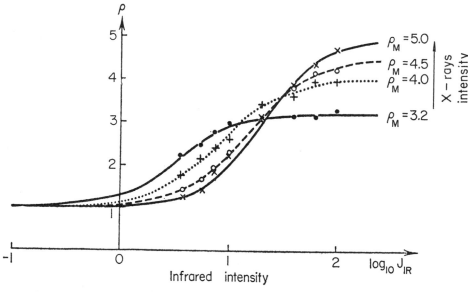

FIG. 70. Variation of enhancement ratio for effect of infrared radiation on X-ray excited (Zn,Cd)S:Mn,Cl phosphor with intensities of infrared and X-rays. (From Pingault, *626*.)

Gumlich (628) has recently examined the effect of infrared on (50Zn, 50Cd)S:Mn,Cl phosphors in more detail. For low field frequencies he finds that

$$R = \frac{I_F}{I_0} > \frac{I_{FR}}{I_R} = R', \qquad (40)$$

where I_0 is the output with X-rays only, I_F that with X-rays and field, I_R that with X-rays and infrared, and I_{FR} the output with all three acting simultaneously. The maximum values of R and R' were obtained for 30 cps. For values of frequency above about 600 cps the inequality in Eq. (40) was reversed. R and R' passed through a minimum at about 5000 cps and then increased, with R and R' apparently approaching each other. Gumlich also found that the influence of the infrared radiation decreased with increasing X-ray intensity, a fact shown in Fig. 70.

4. *The Mechanism of Enhancement in Nonelectroluminescent Phosphors.* Williams (5, 237) suggested that the enhanced output resulting from application of electric fields to these phosphors was "radiation-controlled electroluminescence" resulting from acceleration of electrons introduced into the conduction band by the radiation as proposed for the enhancement effects observed by Cusano and discussed in the next section. Practically all other workers in this field (4, 134, 135, 441, 589, 595, 598, 602, 622), however, agree that there is no connection between the enhancement effect in the materials discussed here and electroluminescence. As pointed out previously, the effects of field strength, frequency, and temperature are quite different (indeed, opposite) in the two effects. The occurrence of "memory" or storage effects is also a marked feature of the enhancement effects while they do not occur in electroluminescence; indeed, deep traps are assumed harmful in the latter case. The influence of phosphor composition is also quite different in the two cases. Destriau found that introduction of CdS into ZnS improved the enhancement ratio while Cd has an adverse effect on electroluminescence. The enhancement effect under discussion here is observed only when Mn is present (with the sole recent exception of KBr), while Mn is not essential for electroluminescence. Finally, with cathode-ray excitation, Gobrecht et al. (623) found enhancement in a nonelectroluminescent ZnS:Mn,Cl phosphor but only quenching in an electroluminescent ZnS:Cu,Al sample.

It has been shown by Schön (149) and others that many phenomena in phosphors may be explained on the basis of a simple kinetic model in which the radiating transitions are assumed to be bimolecular and the nonradiating transitions monomolecular. It is obvious that in this case high electron concentration in the conduction band will favor the bimolecular radiating combinations. This is in agreement with the observation that "impurity quenching" is less pronounced at high excitation intensity. It can also be shown (135) that in this case the application of an electric field which sweeps electrons away from the excitation region for a part of the time and allows them to return and recombine with excited luminescence centers only for a fraction of the period of the applied field will lead to increased output, i.e., to enhancement. The field in this case acts to increase artificially the excitation intensity. It should be noted, however, that this "modulation enhancement" should occur only for nonuniform excitation. If all regions of the phosphor are uniformly excited, transport of carriers from one region to another should have no effect; one region would then be as good as another. In this connection it may be significant that excitation with alpha particles or cathode rays (excitation limited to the particle track in the former case and to the penetration depth in the latter) is usually found to give greater enhancement than ultraviolet excitation, where indeed only quenching may be observed. However, maximum enhancement is observed for X-ray excitation, which should give quite general excitation of the lattice.* Enhancement arising from such an effect should also be greatest at low excitation intensity. This seems contrary to the experimental observations for ultraviolet or X-ray excitation.†

Curie (4) has suggested a somewhat opposite mechanism for enhancement in which the field increases the output by drawing off electrons and holes created in the region of intense excitation, in which the luminescence centers may be saturated, to other regions of the crystal where they excite luminescence centers. The fact that no saturation of the enhancement ratio with increasing field strength is seen for excitation with alpha particles or cathode rays (586, 617), as opposed to excitation with X-rays or ultraviolet radiation, appears to be in agreement with such a model in view of the localization of excitation in the former case. However, as opposed to the modulation mechanism discussed above, Curie's model requires motion of both electrons and holes. It therefore seems unlikely in ZnS because of the low hole mobility unless perhaps some kind of ambipolar diffusion is involved. Neither of these effects seems to explain the fact that enhancement depends upon the presence of Mn centers.

Destriau (599) attributed this type of enhancement effect to creation of new luminescence centers by the exciting X-radiation in the presence of the field and concluded that the saturation of the enhancement ratio with

---

* The effects of different types of excitation on phosphors have been discussed by Kallmann and his colleagues (629).

† The fact that Jaffe (586) found the enhancement to decrease with increasing cathode-ray beam density may be explained, as suggested by Halsted (587), by the fact that the carriers introduced into the sample in this case cause neutralization of the internal field.

increasing field strength and the form of Eq. (39) resulted from equilibrium between the various types of centers. However, he also emphasized the similarity of the effects of fields and of infrared radiation on these phosphors. It will be shown below that a consistent model for most of the observed effects can be constructed on the basis of competing nonradiating transitions and of transitions between the conduction or valence bands and centers in the forbidden band which may be affected by temperature, fields, or infrared radiation.

The occurrence of the quenching effect in conjunction with the enhancement effect as a competing process, so that either one or the other may

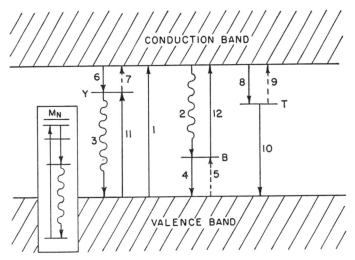

FIG. 71. Simplified energy level diagram for a ZnS:Mn phosphor. Mn represents internal transitions in an Mn ion; these levels lie underneath the valence band. Y represents a disturbed level of the lattice due to Mn incorporation while B represents a disturbance due to a lattice vacancy. T represents a trapping site or level for nonradiating transitions. For further discussion see the text. (From Gobrecht *et al.*, *605, 624*.)

prevail depending on the experimental conditions or that both may occur simultaneously in different spectral regions, has been pointed out above. The occurrence of simultaneous enhancing and quenching effects due to fields (or to temperature or infrared radiation, since the same transitions are involved) has already been discussed in conjunction with the simple kinetic model of Fig. 59 and Eq. (37). This model was drawn only for the case of a photoconducting phosphor such as ZnS:Cu or ZnS:Ag and must be modified for the case of Mn-activated materials. This has been done by Gobrecht *et al.* (*605, 624*), resulting in the energy level diagram of Fig. 71. The experimental results of these workers on the effect of ultraviolet wavelength (Fig. 64) and of temperature (for cathode-ray excitation, Fig. 68) aid greatly in interpreting the mechanism of enhancement.

Excitation in the three peaks at 395 mμ and longer wavelengths in Fig. 64 is ascribed to internal transitions in the Mn centers (shown as Mn in Fig. 71). In this case neither quenching nor enhancement is observed, indicating that the field has no effect on Mn centers themselves. In addition to these centers there also exist levels produced by disturbance of the lattice levels by Mn atoms (indicated by Y in Fig. 71). At shorter wavelengths (340 $< \lambda <$ 395 mμ) such centers may be excited directly* (transition 11, with emitting transition 3). Excitation may also occur in blue-emitting centers (B) arising from zinc vacancies (transition 12, with emitting transition 2). Since transitions to the valence or conduction bands are involved in this case, nonradiating transitions (10) may occur through traps (T) or other impurity levels. If these transitions are favored by the presence of the field, quenching of the emission from both types of centers will result. It is only in the case of excitation at wavelengths less than 340 mμ, which results in excitation across the forbidden band gap (transition 1), that enhancement is observed. In this case enhancement of one kind of emission is always accompanied by quenching of the other (Fig. 64). The total number of recombinations with and without field is the same; what differs is the type of center at which recombination occurs. With high-energy excitation such as cathode rays (Fig. 68) only excitation in the lattice is important.

Gobrecht et al. (624) have pointed out that from Fig. 68 it is seen that application of a field generally has the same effect as increasing the temperature. Thus for the emission at 451 mμ, increasing either the temperature or the field below room temperature results in increased output ($I > I_0$), while above room temperature the reverse is true, i.e., the output decreases with increasing temperature and $I < I_0$. The situation for the yellow emission is roughly (although not exactly) the same. As long as I_0 decreases rapidly with temperature, $I < I_0$; only when the effect of temperature on I_0 becomes smaller is $I > I_0$. At room temperature the yellow emission is strongly thermally quenched (by about a factor of 18 according to Fig. 68). This is interpreted as indicating that the thermal transition 7 in Fig. 71 is strong enough that the occupancy of the excited Y levels is low. Since the blue emission is not thermally quenched at room temperature, it is assumed that the energy separating the B levels from the valence band is greater than that between the Y levels and the conduction band. In this case the effect of the field on transition 7 (ϵ_1 in Fig. 59) will have a

---

* Fig. 71 is a very simplified model which is assumed to be valid for excitation in the lattice; the actual transitions in the Y centers are undoubtedly much more complicated (239c, 605).

small effect while that in aiding transition 5 (ϵ_2 in Fig. 59) can be large. Since the population of the B levels is increased, transitions 2 are impeded and the blue emission quenched. At the same time readjustment of transition rates from the conduction band will lead to an increase in transition 3 and hence to enhancement of the yellow emission. With constant excitation intensity, if one escape route is "plugged up," the rate through those remaining must increase.

At low temperature, however, the situation is quite different. Here thermal transitions are negligible. The effect of the field is much more important for transition 7 than for transition 5 because of the smaller energy separation in the former case. The result is therefore to reduce the number of yellow-emitting transitions and increase those responsible for blue emission, as shown in Fig. 68.

The total number of recombinations in these cases is apparently a constant, with the field changing the internal kinetics and favoring one type of recombination over another. If enhancement of output is to occur, then nonradiative transitions must exist which can be depressed in favor of radiating ones. The competition of enhancement and quenching processes is clearly seen in the results of Wendel (Fig. 65). The occurrence of high enhancement ratios with intense localized excitation such as alpha particles may be ascribed to saturation of luminescence centers with a resulting increase in nonradiating transitions as compared to more uniform excitation by ultraviolet radiation. Figure 68 shows that in the temperature region where enhancement occurs the emission is strongly thermally quenched. The Mn concentration (10^{-3}) which is found to give maximum enhancement ratio in these phosphors is also that at which Thornton (239b) found minimum quantum output as Mn is introduced into $ZnS:Cl$ or $ZnS:Cu,Cl$; in this case the total output was lower than that for no Mn (blue or green emission) or high amounts of Mn (yellow emission) by a factor of 10–20. This is also roughly the same factor shown for thermal quenching in Fig. 68 and the maximum values of R which have been observed. Co is a well-known "killer" in these phosphors (630) and it also leads to increases in the enhancement ratio. It is significant that even after enhancement by the field the output of these materials is little, if any, greater than that of the best phosphors. It therefore appears that all the materials which show this enhancement effect are intrinsically poor phosphors and that the field acts only to counteract their deficiencies by upsetting the internal kinetics in favor of radiating recombinations, as proposed by Ivey (135) and extended by Gobrecht and Gumlich (605, 624).

The observed nonlinearity, fatigue, and memory effects, as well as the fact that infrared radiation in many cases produce the same effect as an electric field, all point to the role of deep electron traps in these phosphors.

There is also presumably a connection between these traps and the presence of the nonradiating transitions which seem to be a prerequisite for enhancement.

D. Enhancement of Luminescence in Electroluminescent Phosphors

1. **The Experimental Observations.** Woods and Wright (545), as discussed in Section IV,G,1, observed increased emission from cathode-ray excited MgO when it was subjected to static electric fields. Since, however, the enhanced light emission could be maintained for several hours after the bombarding beam was turned off, it seems that this emission should be considered as electroluminescence rather than as "field-enhanced cathodoluminescence" as proposed by Woods and Wright. It is similar to the sustained light emission from cold electron-emitting cathodes of MgO and other materials, which also require "starting" by electron bombardment or irradiation with light.

Cusano (237, 445) in 1955 observed another enhancement effect in thin ZnS:Mn,Cl films which he and Williams (237, 446) have described as "radiation-controlled electroluminescence." If these films are provided with ohmic or low-resistivity contacts, no electroluminescence nor transient or steady-state effects on the luminescence of irradiated samples for application or removal of voltage are observed (632). If, however, at least one of the contacts is rectifying or highly resistive, weak electroluminescence is observed if that electrode is negative, similar to the observations of Alfrey and Cooke (310, 311) for ZnS single crystals. This emission may be greatly enhanced if the film is irradiated with ultraviolet, X-rays (237, 445), or cathode rays (632). In this case enhancement also occurs only for one polarity of applied voltage (see Fig. 72). Above a field strength of about 1×10^4 volts/cm the output continues to increase with increasing field strength and no saturation is observed as for the effect discussed in Section V,C.

An enhancement ratio as high as 90 was observed by Cusano. Of even more fundamental interest is the fact that as many as ten visible photons were obtained for each incident ultraviolet (365 mμ) photon. The energy in the emitted radiation was thus at least five times that incident; thus, true energy gain existed, in contrast to the type of enhancement observed by Destriau in nonelectroluminescent materials. The difference in energy obviously was supplied by the electric field. Despite this gain the over-all luminous efficiency was only about 0.2 lumens/watt. The enhancement ratio was found to increase inversely as the square root of the exciting intensity; that is, the output varied directly as the square root of the exciting intensity. The output responded within a few milliseconds to changes in the applied voltage. Transient quenching of luminescence was observed at field application and transient stimulation at field removal; both transient effects were slower for low irradiation intensity. Much longer time lags were observed if the excitation level was changed; these also became longer (as long as several seconds) the lower the exciting intensity. The rise time was greater than the decay time.

Cusano's first experiments were performed with films of ZnS:Mn,Cl, which required excitation by ultraviolet or more energetic radiation. Later it was found that films of ZnS:P,Cl, ZnS:As,Cl (633), and ZnS:Sb,Cl (632) showed similar, but less efficient enhancement with a response in

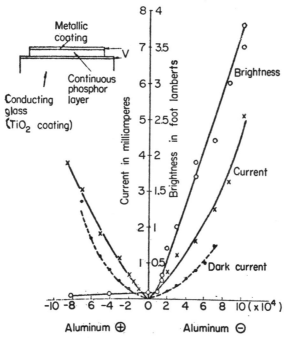

FIG. 72. Dependence on field strength of light output and current for ZnS:Mn,Cl film excited by 3650A ultraviolet radiation. (From Cusano, 445.)

the blue region of the visible spectrum. The response spectra were identical to those for photoconductivity. Introduction of Ni into ZnS:Mn,Cl was also found to produce a weak response throughout the visible region and into the infrared without reduction of the ultraviolet sensitivity (632). Materials such as ZnS:Mn,P,Cl and ZnS:Mn,As,Cl and (Zn,Cd)S films were also studied. ZnS:Ag,Cl showed essentially no enhancement. ZnS:Cu, Cl showed either no or only very small (20–30%) enhancement; enhancement was observed only if both blue and green bands were present in the emission. The presence of a co-activator seems important; Halsted (587) observed only quenching for ZnS:Mn films. Although X-rays are only weakly absorbed in films of the normal thickness (10 μ), with thicker films it was possible to obtain an output five times that of a standard Patterson B2 fluoroscopic screen. However, it was stated that "The improvement has been gained at the expense of increasing the dc electroluminescent background to such a value that the intensifier is not useful in the very low fluoroscopic region." For low cathode-ray beam current densities (5×10^{-10} amp/cm²) the output (with field) was about 20 times that of a standard P20 phosphor screen but because of the slow increase in output with higher excitation intensity no benefit was achieved for current densities greater than 10^{-8} amp/cm².

In most of Cusano's samples a short wavelength (blue) emission band was observed in addition to that due to Mn, P, As, or Sb when the phosphors were excited to cathodoluminescence or photoluminescence. However, in the case of samples containing Mn only the yellow emission of Mn (peak at 590 mμ) was observed when the field was applied simultaneously with radiation. Cusano believes that the excitation of Mn centers is confined to internal transitions and could find no evidence of the trapping states associated with Mn first proposed by Kröger (*239c*) and assumed by Gobrecht and Gumlich (see Fig. 71). With P, As, or Sb, on the other hand, the blue emission was stronger relative to the long wavelength emission (peak at 545, 595, or 665 mμ, respectively) in the presence of the field (*632*).

Cusano's enhancement is essentially a dc effect. Although it can also be observed with alternating voltages, the emission is always in phase with the voltage and decreases with increasing frequency. Figure 73 shows that in this case the enhancement peak occurs during that half-cycle of voltage during which, at lower voltages and for ultraviolet excitation, the emission is actually depressed rather than enhanced. This quenching was not observed for excitation in the lattice* (for example, with cathode rays) while the increase in output for the opposite polarity (called "stimulation" rather than "enhancement" by Cusano) was still present and was generally greater. Cusano (*632*) identified this increase with enhancement of the type studied by Destriau and therefore considers the two enhancement effects to be distinctly different, despite an earlier suggestion by Williams (*237*) that they may be identical. However, Cusano's nomenclature seems confusing and his identification incorrect. He refers to the "stimulation" peaks as being out of phase; however, as shown by Fig. 73, these peaks are also essentially in phase with the voltage. The distinguishing feature is really one of polarity; the opposite definition of polarity for the voltage in Fig. 73 would make these peaks nearly in phase. What Cusano apparently

---

* Since the curves of Fig. 73 are for (Zn,Cd)S (of unspecified Cd content) it would seem that 3650A excitation might also occur in the lattice.

overlooked is that the output in the Destriau-type enhancement effect is normally modulated at twice the field frequency (*586, 613, 620*), as shown in Fig. 67, not at the field frequency as he observed. The waveforms at low field strength in Fig. 73 correspond to the modulation effect observed by Halsted (*455*) rather than to Destriau's enhancement effect. Cusano's conclusion that the two enhancement effects are different, however, is still correct for other reasons; one involves an electroluminescence process, while the other does not (compare the voltage dependence in Fig. 72 with that in Fig. 60).

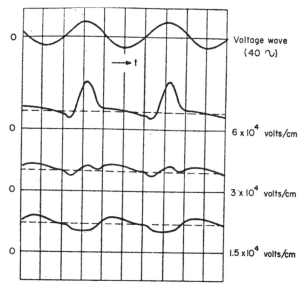

FIG. 73. Output waveforms for (Zn,Cd)S:Mn,Cl films excited by 3650A ultraviolet radiation for different field strengths (field frequency = 40 cps). The dashed horizontal lines represent the photoluminescence for no field. (From Cusano, *632*.)

Woods (*634*) has commented briefly on the enhancement of the ultraviolet-excited luminescence of presumably unactivated but electroluminescent ZnS single crystals following heat treatment in a vacuum. An enhancement ratio of 3–4 was obtained for a field strength (constant or alternating) of 10^3 volts/cm (apparently calculated on the basis of uniform field in the sample). This was the first observation of enhancement of blue and green emission as opposed to yellow (Mn) emission. The phosphorescence was also enhanced in a permanent way, not simply in a transient manner as in the Gudden-Pohl effect. The thermoluminescence was also increased. Crystals activated with Cu did not show enhancement; in this case constant fields had no effect or caused quenching.

Thornton (*338*) observed enhancement of the electroluminescence of a large number of normal phosphor powders when irradiated. For alternating fields normal electroluminescent cells with the phosphor embedded in a plastic dielectric were used. Enhancement was observed for electroluminescent blue or green emitting ZnS:Cu,Cl, yellow ZnS:Cu,Mn,Cl or Zn(S,Se):Cu,Cl, and red ZnSe:Cu,Cl but only quenching for electroluminescent blue ZnS:Cu or for nonelectroluminescent green ZnS:Cu,Cl or blue ZnS:Ag,Cl phosphors. The sensitivity spectrum for enhancement appeared to be identical to that for photoconductivity (extending to about 440 mμ for ZnS:Cu,Cl). The electroluminescent ZnS:Cu phosphor which showed no enhancement also displayed no appreciable photoconductivity. Experiments performed with a double-band ZnS:Cu,Cl phosphor which exhibited green photoluminescence but greenish-blue electroluminescence showed that the additional light during simultaneous action of field and ultraviolet was predominantly blue. A more quantitative spectral study showed that the "combined" emission consisted of the unaltered photoluminescence plus increased electroluminescence output. In this case quenching (discussed below) was also observed only at long wavelengths and not in the blue region. Identification of this enhancement effect with electroluminescence therefore seems quite conclusive.

As the applied alternating voltage was increased, quenching was generally first observed by Thornton, followed by enhancement for higher voltages as shown in Fig. 74, which also includes results for the electroluminescent phosphor discussed above which displayed only quenching. For very high voltages a second region of quenching was sometimes observed although usually the enhancement ratio approached unity asymptotically. From the way in which this ratio is defined [Eq. (33)] it is to be expected that it should approach unity under conditions where either the photoluminescence (L_R) or the electroluminescence (L_E) is negligible compared to the other. The maximum value of R (R_{max}) is usually achieved when L_R and L_E are nearly equal, as shown by the arrows in Fig. 74. As the irradiation intensity was increased, R_{max} at first increased and then decreased and also occurred at higher field strength. In general R_{max} occurred for equal values of $L_E/L_R^{1/2}$, where L_E is obviously a function of both the voltage and the frequency. With alternating fields the highest value of R_{max} observed was only about 1.3.

With some phosphor powders which showed good dc electroluminescence and photoconductivity, Thornton (338) was able to observe strong enhancement effects with radiation and direct voltages. In this case the phosphor powder was embedded in a very small amount of plastic binder so that the cells consisted essentially of a single layer of phosphor particles (about 10μ thick) in intimate contact with both electrodes (365). Enhancement was achieved with the following phosphors (the color given is that of photoluminescence and ac electroluminescence); blue ZnS:Cu,Cl, green ZnS:Cu,Cl, and yellow Zn(S,Se):Cu,Cl. The color of the dc electroluminescence of these samples was blue, blue, and green, respectively. The short wavelength dc electroluminescence and not the longer wavelength photoluminescence was enhanced when both kinds of excitation were applied. The voltage and polarity dependence of the output was very similar to that observed by Cusano for ZnS:Mn,Cl films (Fig. 72) except that the high currents (unaccompanied by luminescence) for the metal electrode positive observed by the latter did not occur. Electroluminescence became detectable at about the same field strength at which L_B began to increase rapidly.

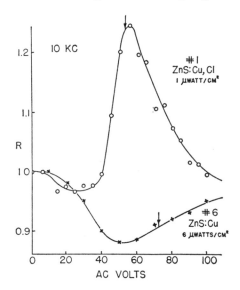

Fig. 74. Effect of simultaneous application of alternating voltage and 3650A ultraviolet radiation to two electroluminescent powders embedded in plastic (layer thickness, 2 mils). One sample (ZnS:Cu) displays only quenching, the other (ZnS:Cu,Cl) quenching followed by enhancement for higher voltages. The arrows indicate the points where the electroluminescence and photoluminescence were equal. (From Thornton, 338.)

The enhancement observed with constant voltage was much higher than that with alternating fields; values of R as high as seven were observed at room temperature. As in Cusano's experiments the radiant power gain exceeded unity for a wide range of excitation intensity. The value of R increased with decreasing temperature and $R = 40$ was obtained at 90°K. The variation of enhancement ratio with field strength and radiation intensity observed by Thornton for dc was essentially the same as that for ac operation. At high radiation intensity (greater than that corresponding to $R_{\max}$ for a given voltage) the combined output L_B increased as the square root of the excitation intensity, as also observed by Cusano. Time lags which increased with decreasing excitation intensity were also observed.

It will be seen that there are many similarities between the enhancement effects observed by Cusano with phosphor films and those observed by Thornton with powders. There is one important difference, however. Cusano obtained only very small enhancement (maximum $R = 1.3$) with ZnS:Cu,Cl and achieved his best results with ZnS:Mn,Cl. Thornton, on on the other hand, obtained his best results with ZnS:Cu,Cl and only quenching or low enhancement with ZnS:Cu,Mn,Cl. This situation, however, may not be as contradictory as it at first appears. Thornton observed not only small enhancement with ZnS:Cu,Mn,Cl phosphors but also low photoconductivity; it appears that Mn in these phosphors quenches photoconductivity as well as photoluminescence (239b). It will be seen below that according to one model the presence of photoconductivity is necessary for this type of enhancement to occur. Cusano's films, although exhibiting dc electroluminescence, did so only weakly; for good output it was necessary to apply additional Cu to the surface, presumably to form Cu_2S (632). Thornton, on the other hand, used commercial phosphors with good electroluminescent properties. Thornton (338) was the first to observe an enhancement effect in copper-activated ZnS. Similar enhancement was later observed by several other workers (437, 635, 636). Since these latter workers all used alternating fields and no direct contact to the phosphor, only a small degree of enhancement was achieved; see, for example, the results of Patek (437) shown in Fig. 58.

2. The Mechanism of Enhancement in Electroluminescent Phosphors. Williams (237, 446) proposed that the enhancement observed by Cusano (237, 445) resulted from "radiation-controlled electroluminescence." The normal acceleration-collision mechanism (Fig. 2) was assumed. The initial electrons for the acceleration however, were presumed to result from the radiation rather than from the sole effects of field and/or temperature as for pure electroluminescence. The specific mechanism (237, 446, 632) assumed that the radiation not only releases free electrons which are accelerated but also positive holes which are trapped in and cause enhancement of the potential barrier at the cathode. The distribution of potential within the phosphor is thus controlled by an action of the radiation on the barrier. If the barrier field becomes high enough, additional electrons may enter from the electrode by tunneling as in the experiments of von Hippel and his colleagues (100, 101) with alkali halide crystals. According to Cusano (632) there is no need to assume carrier multiplication or avalanche formation. The observed high photoelectroluminescent gains (ratio of radiant power output to radiant power input or ratio of quanta out to quanta in) can be explained, despite the poor electroluminescent energy efficiency (even in ZnS:Mn,Cl) of 3×10^{-4} or about one output quantum for 300 electrons traversing the cell, on the basis of high photoconductive gain (ratio of electrons flowing through the cell to quanta absorbed).* Experimentally determined values of the photoconductive gain (632) were 10^3–10^4 for ZnS:Mn,Cl and 10^6 for ZnS:As,Cl; this last figure is offset by the lower electroluminescence efficiency of 7×10^{-6} in this material.

It was at first suggested (237, 446) that Mn was important for enhancement because the transitions are confined to the deep-lying internal levels without ionization being involved. In this case, as discussed above, only Mn emission was observed in the presence of the field although shorter wavelength emission occurred for excitation by ultraviolet or cathode rays. The self-activation centers, on the other hand, were assumed necessary to supply electrons under the action of the radiation and to serve as hole traps for barrier enhancement; in ZnS:Mn only quenching was observed (587). With the later observation of enhancement with P, As, Sb, and even Cu, the necessity for "field-stable" centers of the Mn type had to be abandoned. In this case two types of ionizable centers are involved and the distinguishing feature was ascribed to a large difference in electron capture cross-section, particularly in the presence of high fields. Both Thornton and Cusano found that short wavelength emission is favored for dc electroluminescence, indicating greater cross-section for these centers. The longer wavelength centers are assumed to remain preferentially ionized and to be responsible for the barrier enhancement. The time lags observed by Cusano could conceivably be ascribed to changes in this positive space charge.

Thornton (338) emphasized the similarity of many of his observations to those of Cusano, although the materials and experimental conditions used were quite different, and therefore suggested that the same mechanism is involved. He at first assumed that electrons introduced into the conduction band by the radiation are accelerated by the field in the same way as are the electrons in normal electroluminescence and thus augment the output. This is similar to Williams' "radiation-controlled electroluminescence" mechanism discussed above except that in the case of phosphor powders embedded in fairly large amounts of dielectric (alternating field case) the possibility of electron ejection from the electrodes does not exist.

Attempts to apply the kinetic models to this situation seem attractive. Thus Lehmann (135, 637) considered the equation

$$\frac{dn}{dt} = c(N - n)I + \epsilon n(N - n) - bn^2, \tag{41}$$

* The photoconductive gain is equal to the ratio of the carrier lifetime to the transit time (181).

where n is the number of electrons in the conduction band, N the number of activator centers, I the excitation intensity, c the photoexcitation coefficient, ϵ the electroluminescence excitation coefficient, and b the recombination coefficient ($L = bn^2$). Then if $n \ll N$ it can be shown that

$$R = \frac{1 + 2x + \sqrt{1 + 4x}}{2(1 + x)}, \qquad (42)$$

where $x = bcI/N\epsilon^2 = L_R/L_E$. Obviously R approaches unity for very large and very small values of x, is always greater than unity, and has a maximum value of $4/3$ at $x = 2$. Except for quenching, which was not "built into" Eq. (41), these results are in reasonable agreement with Thornton's results for alternating fields (Fig. 74). This agreement, however, is probably fortuitous as the absence of enhancement in the case of a good electroluminescent ZnS:Cu phosphor cited above is unexplained.

Ivey (135) has also discussed a more complicated kinetic model including nonradiating transitions and shown that many of the features observed by Thornton (including much higher values of R) may be qualitatively explained in this way. Matossi (638) had also shown earlier that under certain conditions the observation by Cusano, and later by Thornton, that the ratio R varies inversely as the square root of the excitation intensity can be explained on the basis of somewhat similar kinetics (without nonradiating transitions). Unfortunately, however, although many things can be explained or made plausible by kinetic considerations, "proofs" on this basis are very difficult as the identification of the terms in the equations selected is often not unique and the results obtained depend upon the particular assumptions and simplifications made.

The radiation-controlled electroluminescence model of Williams discussed above involves a photosensitive potential barrier. Loebner (454) also suggested the importance of photosensitive barriers in electroluminescence and photoelectroluminescence. Thornton (338) concluded from his experiments that photoconductivity is a prerequisite for enhancement while Cusano (632) invokes photoconductive gain to explain the magnitude of the observed enhancement. Both Thornton and Cusano found that the sensitivity spectrum for the enhancement effect is the same as that for photoconductivity. Ivey (135) has shown that photoconductivity of the phosphor bulk, rather than a photoeffect on the barrier only, can explain many of the observations of enhancement.

The theory of radiation converters or amplifiers consisting of separate photoconductive and electroluminescent elements, electrically connected in series so that the photoconductor controls the voltage on the electroluminescent cell, has been treated by a number of workers (639–643). The analysis, however, is very complicated, particularly if the calculation is made for ac, because of the nonlinear properties of both electroluminescent and photoconductive materials. In the photoconductive-control model for enhancement effects (135) the thin phosphor film or powder particle is visualized as consisting of a potential barrier, responsible for the electroluminescent emission and occupying only a small fraction of the total volume, in series with the bulk of the material which is photoconductive and photoluminescent. The situation is thus identical to that for two-element amplifiers. One is still concerned with "radiation-controlled electroluminescence" but the control is not a direct influence on the excitation process but an indirect process of external voltage control. The major differences from Williams' model is that the phosphor bulk plays an active, and not merely a passive, role in the process. The result of irradiation in both cases is a redistribution of potential in the phosphor, which obviously affects the electroluminescence. That the effective voltage for electroluminescence is greater in the presence of radiation than its absence is shown by studies of the output waveform made by Thornton (338); such observations, however, do not indicate the mechanism responsible for the increased barrier potential.

It can be shown (135) that this photoconductive-control model, with arbitrary but reasonable assumptions concerning the photoconductor behavior, can explain the fact that as the radiation intensity is increased the value of applied voltage required for the maximum enhancement ratio also increases, that this maximum value of R simultaneously first increases and then decreases, and that R_{max} occurs at constant values of $L_E/L_R^{1/2}$. These observations have apparently not been explained on the basis of Williams' model. The time lags in photoconductors are well-known and thus those observed in the enhancement could be similarly explained. No particular kind of centers are necessary and hence the existence of the effect in a large number of electroluminescent phosphors, as observed, is to be expected. In the case of phosphors in contact with the electrodes, the current flowing in the dark will establish a voltage across the phosphor bulk higher than in the case of insulated samples and the enhancement ratio should therefore be greater (due to a greater degree of control) with dc than for ac, as observed; the observation of Cusano that the enhancement ratio decreases with increasing field frequency may also be explained in this way. The voltage across the phosphor bulk will also be greater the lower the temperature, in agreement with the greater enhancement at low temperature found by Thornton.

It seems generally concluded that in these electroluminescent phosphors one is dealing with "radiation-controlled electroluminescence." There is, however, no universal agreement as to the exact nature of the control mechanism. Although Cusano (632) agrees that the enhancement observed by Thornton and Patek probably results from photoconductivity of the phosphor bulk, he believes that in his experiments the control occurs in the potential barrier itself. On the other hand, Thornton has emphasized the many similarities between his experiments and those of Cusano.

E. Summary

As stated earlier, it is not yet always possible to make positive identification of the mechanisms responsible for the wide variety of effects observed when electric fields are applied to phosphors which are simultaneously irradiated.

The Gudden-Pohl light flashes upon application of a field are attributed to the effect of the field on electrons in traps. The flashes observed at removal of an alternating field seem to be connected with changes in capture cross-section in the presence of the field and their influence on the kinetics of the luminescence process. Other transient effects of a complicated nature also occur and are largely unexplained.

Quenching of luminescence by fields may occur in electroluminescent or nonelectroluminescent phosphors and is presumably due to field-induced nonradiating transitions whose exact nature is not yet clearly understood. The quenching mechanism can exist simultaneously with enhancing mechanisms.

The type of enhancement observed by Destriau does not seem to be connected with the mechanism of electroluminescence excitation. It apparently occurs only in materials which for some reason (impurity or thermal quenching) are normally inefficient phosphors. This effect is greatly influenced by the intense localized excitation produced by high-energy excitation but can also occur to a lesser extent for low-energy ultraviolet excitation. It is essentially a kinetic effect resulting from competition of several simultaneous processes.

The enhancement observed by Cusano and Thornton are considered to be essentially identical, although the particular experimental arrangement greatly affects the results obtained. These effects are considered to be "radiation-controlled electroluminescence," but the exact nature of the control process is still open to discussion.

REFERENCES

1. Destriau, G., and Ivey, H. F., *Proc. IRE* **43**, 1911 (1955).
2. Zalm, P., *Philips Research Repts.* **11**, 353, 417 (1956).
3. Matossi, F., "Elektrolumineszenz und Elektrophotolumineszenz." Vieweg, Braunschweig, Germany, 1956.
4. Curie, D., *in* "Progress in Semiconductors" (A. F. Gibson, P. Aigrain, and R. E. Burgess, eds.), Vol. 2, p. 249. Wiley, New York, 1957.
5. Piper, W. W., and Williams, F. E., *Solid State Phys.* **6**, 96 (1958).
6. Hahn, D., *Ergeb. exakt. Naturwiss.* **31**, 1 (1959).
7. Henisch, H. K., "Electroluminescence." Pergamon, New York, 1962.
8. Ivey, H. F., Part I in *IRE Trans. Electron Devices* **ED6**, 203 (1959); Part II in *J. Electrochem. Soc.* **108**, 590 (1961); Part III in *Electrochem. Technol.* **1** (1963).
9. Garlick, G. F. J., "Luminescent Materials." Oxford Univ. Press, London and New York, 1949.
10. Williams, F. E., *Advances in Electronics* **5**, 137 (1953).
11. Kröger, F. A., *Ergeb. exakt. Naturwiss.* **29**, 61 (1956).
12. Klick, C. C., and Schulman, J. H., *Solid State Phys.* **5**, 97 (1957).
13. Garlick, G. F. J., *in* "Handbuch der Physik" (S. Flügge, ed.), Vol. 26, p. 1. Springer, Berlin, 1958.
14. Curie, D., "Luminescence Crystalline." Dunod, Paris, 1960.
15. Lossew, O. W., *Telegrafia i Telefonia No.* **18**, 61 (1923); *Wireless World* **15**, 93 (1924); *Phil. Mag.* [7], **6**, 1024 (1928); *Physik. Z.* **30**, 920 (1929).
16. Braun, F., *Ann. physik. Chem.* **65**, 361 (1898).
17. van Geel, W. C., *J. phys. radium* **17**, 714 (1956); van Geel, W. C., Pistorius, C. A., and Bouma, B. C., *Philips Research Repts.* **12**, 465 (1957).
18. Smith, A. W., *Can. J. Phys.* **37**, 591 (1959).
19. Destriau, G., *J. chim. phys.* **33**, 587 (1936); *Trans. Faraday Soc.* **35**, 227 (1939).
20. Destriau, G., *Phil. Mag.* [7], **38**, 700, 774, 800, 885 (1947).
21. Böer, K. W., and Kümmel, U., *Z. physik. Chem. (Leipzig)* **200**, 193 (1952).
22. Diemer, G., *Philips Research Repts.* **9**, 109 (1954).
23. Smith, R. W., *Phys. Rev.* **93**, 347 (1954); **105**, 900 (1957).
24. Woods, J., *Proc. Phys. Soc. (London)* **B69**, 975 (1956).
25. Hegyi, I. J., Larach, S., and Shrader, R. E., *J. Electrochem. Soc.* **104**, 717 (1957).
26. Larach, S., and Shrader, R. E., *RCA Rev.* **20**, 532 (1959).
27. Lozykowski, H., *Bull. acad. polon. sci., Ser. Sci. Math. Ascron. Phys.* **8**, 719 (1960).
28. van Doorn, C. Z., and de Nobel, D., *Physica* **22**, 338 (1956); de Nobel, D., *Philips Research Repts.* **14**, 361, 430 (1959).
29. Fischer, A., *Z. Naturforsch.* **8a**, 756 (1953).
30. Vereshchagin, I. K., *Optics and Spectroscopy (U.S.S.R.)* **8**, 219 (1960).
31. Pettsol'd, E. G., *Izvest. Akad. Nauk S.S.S.R. Ser. Fiz.* **24**, 104 (1960).
32. Mayer, D. W., *in* "Proceedings of the 5th U.S. National Conference on Tube Techniques" (D. Slater, ed.). Pergamon, New York, 1961.
33. Skellett, A. M., Firth, B. G., and Mayer, D. W., *Proc. IRE* **47**, 1704 (1959).
34. Imai, T., Miyushima, Y., and Igarashi, Y., *J. Phys. Soc. Japan* **14**, 979 (1959); Mizushima, Y., Igarashi, Y., and Imai, T., *ibid.* **15**, 729 (1960).
35. Wachtel, A., *J. Electrochem. Soc.* **107**, 199 (1960).
36. Lozykowski, H., and Meczynska, H., *Bull. acad. polon. sci., Ser. Sci. Math. Astron. Phys.* **8**, 725 (1960).

37. Wolff, G. A., Hebert, R. A., and Broder, J. D., *Phys. Rev.* **100,** 1144 (1955); also article *in* "Semiconductors and Phosphors" (M. Schön and H. Welker, eds.), p. 547. Wiley (Interscience), New York, 1958.

38. Holt, P. A., Alfrey, G. F., and Wiggins, C. S., *Nature* **181,** 109 (1958); also article *in* "Solid-State Physics in Electronics and Telecommunications" (M. Désirant and J. L. Michiels, eds.), Vol. 2, p. 747. Academic Press, New York, 1960.

39. Loebner, E. E., and Poor, E. W., Jr., *Phys. Rev. Letters* **3,** 23 (1959).

40. Grimmeiss, H. G., and Koelmans, H., *Philips Research Repts.* **15,** 290 (1960).

41. Gershenzon, M., and Mikulyak, R. M., *J. Appl. Phys.* **32,** 1338 (1961).

42. Grimmeiss, H. G., and Koelmans, H., *Z. Naturforsch.* **14a,** 264 (1959); Grimmeiss, H. G., Groth, G., and Maak, J., *ibid.* **15a,** 799 (1960).

43. Braunstein, R., *Phys. Rev.* **99,** 1892 (1955).

44. Allen, J. W., and Mackintosh, I. M., *J. Electronics* **1,** 138 (1955); *Proc. Phys. Soc. (London)* **B68,** 985 (1955).

45. Moss, T. S., and Hawkins, T. H., *Phys. Rev.* **101,** 1609 (1956); Moss, T. S., *Proc. Phys. Soc. (London)* **B70,** 247 (1957).

46. Larach, S., and Shrader, R. E., *Phys. Rev.* **102,** 582 (1956); **104,** 88 (1956).

47. Wolff, G. A., Adams, I., and Mellichamp, J. W., *Phys. Rev.* **114,** 1262 (1959); Meeting Electrochem. Soc., Chicago, May 1–5, 1960 (Abstr. No. 53).

48. Grimmeiss, H. G., Kischio, W., and Rabenau, A., *Phys. and Chem. Solids* **16,** 302 (1960).

49. Haynes, J. R., and Briggs, H. B., *Phys. Rev.* **86,** 647 (1952).

50. Haynes, J. R., *Phys. Rev.* **98,** 1866 (1955).

51. Newman, R., *Phys. Rev.* **91,** 1313 (1953).

52. Aigrain, P., *Physica* **20,** 1010 (1954); Aigrain, P., and Benoit à la Guillaume, C., *J. phys. radium* **17,** 709 (1957).

53. Newman, R., *Phys. Rev.* **100,** 700 (1955).

54. Haynes, J. R., and Westphal, W. C., *Phys. Rev.* **101,** 1676 (1956).

55. Chynoweth, A. G., and McKay, K. G., *Phys. Rev.* **102,** 369 (1956).

56. Wolfe, R., and Woods, J., *Phys. Rev.* **105,** 921 (1957).

57. Logie, H. J., and Urlau, R. C., *Nature* **180,** 1254 (1957).

58. Fischer, A., *Z. Physik.* **149,** 107 (1957).

59. Krautz, E., and Zollfrank, G., *Optik* **14,** 446 (1957).

59a. Male, J. C., and Prior, J. R., *Nature* **186,** 1037 (1960).

60. Halperin, A., and Nahum, J., *Phys. and Chem. Solids* **18,** 297 (1961).

61. Lehovec, K., Accardo, C. A., and Jamgochian, E., *Phys. Rev.* **83,** 603 (1951); **89,** 20 (1953).

62. Patrick, L., *J. Appl. Phys.* **28,** 765 (1957); Patrick, L., and Choyke, W. J., *ibid.* **30,** 236 (1959).

63. Torbin, N. M., *Fiz. Tverdogo Tela* **2,** 2493 (1960).

64. Lehfeldt, W., *Nachr. Ges. Wiss. Göttingen Math.-physik. Kl.,* p. 270 (1933).

65. Piper, W. W., and Johnson, P. D., U.S. Patent 2,721,950 (1955).

66. Scharf, K., *J. phys. radium* **17,** 723 (1956).

67. Güntherschulze, A., and Gerlach, M., *Z. Physik* **88,** 355 (1934).

68. Elinson, M. I., Vasil'ev, G. F., and Zhdan, A. G., *Radiotekh. i Elektron.* **4,** 1718 (1959).

69. Frerichs, R., and Handy, R., *Phys. Rev.* **113,** 1191 (1959); Frerichs, R., and Liberman, I., *Phys. Rev. Letters* **3,** 214 (1959); *Phys. Rev.* **121,** 991 (1961).

70. Jeges, K., U.S. Patent 2,809,316 (1957).

71. Harman, G. G., *Phys. Rev.* **111,** 27 (1958).

72. Stauer, E. V., *Izvest. Akad. Nauk S.S.S.R. Ser. Fiz.* **24,** 1350 (1960).

73. Bramley, A., and Rosenthal, J. E., *Phys. Rev.* **87,** 1125 (1952); Mass. Inst. Technol. Physical Electronics Conf., Cambridge, Massachusetts, 1952.

74. Ueta, M., *J. Phys. Soc. Japan* **8,** 429 (1953).

75. Luyckx, A., and Stokkink, A. J., *Brit. J. Appl. Phys. Suppl. No.* **4,** 57 (1955).

76. Nicoll, F. H., and Kazan, B., *Proc. IRE* **43,** 1012 (1955).

77. Astafurov, A. V., *Optika i Spektroskopiya* **2,** 540 (1957); *Izvest. Akad. Nauk S.S.S.R. Ser. Fiz.* **22,** 419 (1958).

78. Bernanose, A., *Brit. J. Appl. Phys. Suppl. No.* **4,** 54 (1955).

79. Namba, S., Yoshizawa, M. and Tamura, H., *Oyo Butsuri* **28,** 439 (1959).

80. Herwelly, A., *Acta Phys. Austriaca* **5,** 30 (1951).

81. Destriau, G., *J. phys. radium* **14,** 307 (1953).

82. Gobrecht, H., Hahn, D., and Gumlich, H. E., *Z. Physik* **136,** 612 (1954).

83. Lehmann, W., *J. Electrochem. Soc.* **109,** 540 (1962).

84. Frölich, H., and Simpson, J. H., *Advances in Electronics* **2,** 185 (1950).

85. Whitehead, S., "Dielectric Breakdown of Solids." Oxford Univ. Press, London and New York, 1951.

86. Franz, W., *in* "Handbuch der Physik" (S. Flügge, ed.), Vol. 17, p. 155. Springer, Berlin, 1956.

87. Zener, C., *Proc. Roy. Soc.* **A145,** 523 (1934).

88. Frenkl, J., *Phys. Rev.* **54,** 647 (1938); *J. Tech. Phys. (U.S.S.R.)* **5,** 685 (1938).

89. Vol'kenstein, F. F., *J. Tech. Phys. (U.S.S.R.)* **9,** 171 (1939).

90. Joffe, A. V., and Joffe, A. F., *J. Exptl. Theoret. Phys. (U.S.S.R.)* **9,** 1428 (1939); *J. Phys. U.S.S.R.* **2,** 283 (1940).

91. von Hippel, A., *Z. Physik* **67,** 707 (1931); **75,** 145 (1932); **88,** 358 (1934); *Phys. Rev.* **54,** 1096 (1938).

92. Seitz, F., *Phys. Rev.* **76,** 1376 (1949).

93. Frölich, H., and Seitz, F., *Phys. Rev.* **79,** 526 (1950).

94. Frölich, H., *Proc. Roy. Soc.* **A160,** 230 (1937); **A171,** 496 (1939); **A172,** 94 (1939); **A178,** 493 (1941); **A188,** 532 (1947).

95. Frölich, H., *Proc. Roy. Soc.* **A188,** 521 (1947).

96. Esaki, L., *Phys. Rev.* **109,** 603 (1958).

97. Chynoweth, A. G., *in* "Progress in Semiconductors" (A. F. Gibson, F. A. Kröger, and R. E. Burgess, eds.), Vol. 4, p. 95. Wiley, New York, 1960.

98. Dexter, D. L., *Phys. Rev.* **93,** 985 (1954).

99. Markham, J. J., *in* "Defects in Crystalline Solids" (N. F. Mott, ed.), p. 304. Physical Society, London, 1955.

100. von Hippel, A., Gross, E. P., Jelatis, E. P., and Geller, M., *Phys. Rev.* **91,** 568 (1953).

101. Geller, M., *Phys. Rev.* **101,** 1685 (1956).

102. McKay, K. G., *Phys. Rev.* **94,** 877 (1954); McKay, K. G., and McAfee, K. B., *ibid.* **91,** 1079 (1953); Chynoweth, A. G., and McKay, K. G., *ibid.* **108,** 29 (1957); Chynoweth, A. G., *ibid.* **109,** 1537 (1958).

103. Miller, S. L., *Phys. Rev.* **99,** 1234 (1955); **105,** 1246 (1957); Wolff, P. A., *ibid.* **95,** 1415 (1954).

104. Shockley, W., *Bell System Tech. J.* **30,** 990 (1951).

105. Burton, J. A., *Phys. Rev.* **108,** 1342 (1957).

106. Tauc, J., *Nature* **181,** 38 (1958).

107. Patrick, L., and Choyke, W. J., *Phys. Rev. Letters* **2,** 48 (1959).

108. Senitzky, B., *Phys. Rev.* **116,** 874 (1959).

109. Simon, R. E., and Spicer, W. E., *Phys. Rev.* **119,** 621 (1960); *J. Appl. Phys.* **31,** 1505 (1960).

110. Goffaux, R., *J. phys. radium* **21**, 94 (1960).
111. Gunn, J. B., *in* "Progress in Semiconductors" (A. F. Gibson, P. Aigrain, and R. E. Burgess, eds.), Vol. 2, p. 211. Wiley, New York, 1957.
112. Yamashita, J., *in* "Progress in Semiconductors" (A. F. Gibson, F. A. Kröger, and R. E. Burgess, eds.), Vol. 4, p. 63. Wiley, New York, 1960.
113. Böer, K. W., and Kümmel, U., *Z. Naturforsch.* **9a**, 177 (1954); also article *in* "Arbeitstagung Festkörperphysik," Vol. 2, p. 167 (K. W. Böer, ed.). Barth, Leipzig, 1955.
114. Haering, R. R., *Can. J. Phys.* **37**, 1374 (1959).
115. Gudden, B., and Pohl, R. W., *Z. Physik* **2**, 192 (1920).
116. Dutton, D., and Maurer, R., *Phys. Rev.* **84**, 363 (1951); **90**, 126 (1953).
117. Böer, K. W., Oberlander, S., and Voigt, J., *Ann. Physik* [6] **2**, 130 (1958).
118. Haering, R. R., and Adams, E. N., *Phys. Rev.* **117**, 451 (1960).
119. Kallmann, H., and Mark, P., *Phys. Rev.* **105**, 1445 (1957); Kallmann, H., Kramer, B., and Mark, P., *Phys. Rev.* **109**, 731 (1958).
120. Oppenheimer, J. R., *Phys. Rev.* **31**, 166 (1928); *Proc. Natl. Acad. Sci. U.S.* **14**, 363 (1928).
121. Lanczos, C., *Z. Physik* **62**, 518 (1930); **65**, 431 (1930); **68**, 204 (1931).
122. Gross, E. F., and Zakharchenia, B. P., *Doklady Akad. Nauk S.S.S.R.* **97**, 57 (1954); *Zhur. Tekh. Fiz.* **28**, 231 (1958); *Soviet Phys.-Tech. Phys.* **3**, 206 (1958).
123. Petrov, A. N., Talyts, G. G., and Giterman, M. S., *Fiz. Metal. i Metalloved. Akad. Nauk S.S.S.R.* **9**, 327 (1960).
124. Allen, J. W., *Nature* **187**, 51 (1960).
125. Lehovec, K., *Proc. IRE* **40**, 1407 (1952).
126. Gibson, A. F., *J. Sci. Instr.* **35**, 273 (1958).
127. Franz, W., *Z. Naturforsch.* **13a**, 484 (1958).
128. Keldysh, L. V., *Zhur. Eksptl. i Theoret. Fiz.* **34**, 1138 (1958); *Soviet Phys. JETP* **7**, 788 (1958).
129. Böer, K. W., Hänsch, H. J., and Kümmel, U., *Naturwissenschaften* **45**, 460 (1958); *Z. Physik* **155**, 170 (1959).
130. Williams R., *Phys. Rev.* **117**, 1487 (1960).
131. Bulyanitsa, D. S., *Zhur. Eksptl. i Theoret. Fiz.* **38**, 1201 (1960).
132. Vavilov, V. S., and Britzin, K. I., *Fiz. Tverdogo Tela* **2**, 1937 (1960).
132a. Damaskova, S., and Patek, K., *Z. Physik* **164**, 428 (1961).
133. Snitko, O. V., *Fiz. Tverdogo Tela* **1**, 980 (1959).
134. Ivey, H. F., *J. Electrochem. Soc.* **104**, 740 (1957).
135. Ivey, H. F., *in* "Solid-State Physics in Electronics and Telecommunications" (M. Désirant and J. L. Michiels, eds.), Vol. 4, p. 611. Academic Press, New York, 1960.
136. Lossew, O. W., *Compt. Rend. Acad. sci. U.R.S.S.* **29**, 360, 363 (1940); *Bull. Acad. Sci. U.S.S.R.* **5**, 494 (1941).
137. Many, A., and Bray, R., *in* "Progress in Semiconductors" (A. F. Gibson, P. Aigrain, and R. E. Burgess, eds.), Vol. 3, p. 117. Wiley, New York, 1958.
138. Bess, L., *Phys. Rev.* **105**, 1469 (1957).
139. Lambe, J. J., Klick, C. C., and Dexter, D. L., *Phys. Rev.* **103**, 1715 (1956).
140. Hopfield, J. J., *Phys. and Chem. Solids* **10**, 110 (1959).
141. Collins, R. J., *J. Appl. Phys.* **30**, 1135 (1959).
142. Pedrotti, L. S., and Reynolds, D. C., *Phys. Rev.* **120**, 1664 (1960).
143. Van Roosbroeck, W., and Shockley, W., *Phys. Rev.* **94**, 1558 (1954).
144. Dumke, W. P., *Phys. Rev.* **105**, 139 (1957).
145. Bowlden, H. J., *Phys. Rev.* **106**, 427 (1957).

146. Shockley, W., and Read, W. T., Jr., *Phys. Rev.* **87**, 835 (1952).

147. Hall, R. N., *Phys. Rev.* **87**, 387 (1952).

148. Eagles, D. M., *Phys. and Chem. Solids* **16**, 76 (1960).

149. Schön, M., *Tech. Wiss. Abhandl. Osram-Ges.* **6**, 49 (1953); *Physica* **20**, 430 (1954).

150. Broser, I., and Broser-Warminsky, R., *Brit. J. Appl. Phys. Suppl. No.* **4**, 90 (1955); *Ann. Physik* [6] **16**, 361 (1955).

151. Duboc, C. A., *Brit. J. Appl. Phys. Suppl. No.* **4**, 107 (1955).

152. Klasens, H. A., *Phys. and Chem. Solids* **7**, 175 (1958); **9**, 185 (1959).

153. Zener, C., Internal Westinghouse Report, 1952.

154. Tauc, J., *Czechoslov. J. Phys.* **7**, 275 (1957).

155. Weinstein, M. A., *J. Opt. Soc. Am.* **50**, 597 (1960).

156. Williams, F. E., *Bull. Am. Phys. Soc.* [2], **5**, 70 (1960); Meeting Electrochem. Soc., Chicago, May 1–5, 1960 (Abstr. 41).

157. Curie, D., *J. phys. radium.* **13**, 317 (1952); **14**, 135, 510, 672 (1953).

158. Piper, W. W., and Williams, F. E., *Phys. Rev.* **87**, 151 (1952).

159. Piper, W. W., and Williams, F. E., *Phys. Rev.* **98**, 1809 (1955).

160. Piper, W. W., and Williams, F. E., *Brit. J. Appl. Phys. Suppl. No.* **4**, 39 (1955).

161. Zalm, P., *J. phys. radium* **17**, 777 (1956).

162. Goffaux, R., *Bull. acad. roy. Belg. Classe Sci.* **40**, 508 (1954); *J. phys. radium* **17**, 763 (1956); **18**, 1 (1957).

163. Goffaux, R., *J. phys. radium* **20**, 18A (1959).

164. Nagy, E., *J. phys. radium* **17**, 773 (1956); *Acta Phys. Acad. Sci. Hung.* **6**, 153 (1956).

165. Chynoweth, A. G., and Gummel, H. K., *Phys. and Chem. Solids* **16**, 191 (1960).

166. Rose, D. J., *Phys. Rev.* **105**, 413 (1957).

167. Wolff, P. A., *Phys. and Chem. Solids* **16**, 184 (1960).

168. Henisch, H. K., and Marathe, B. R., *Proc. Phys. Soc.* (*London*) **76**, 782 (1960).

169. Low, G. G. E., *Proc. Phys. Soc.* (*London*) **B68**, 310 (1955).

170. Strock, L. W., and Brophy, V. A., *Am. Mineralogist* **40**, 94 (1955); Buck, D. C., and Strock, L. W., *Am. Mineralogist* **40**, 192 (1955).

171. Smith, F. G., *Am. Mineralogist* **40**, 658 (1955).

172. S. Rothschild, *in* "Solid-State Physics in Electronics and Telecommunications" (M. Désirant and J. L. Michiels, eds.), Vol. 4, p. 705. Academic Press, New York, 1960.

173. Kröger, F. A., and Hellingman, J. E., *J. Electrochem. Soc.* **93**, 156 (1948); **95**, 68 (1949).

174. Kröger, F. A., and Vink, H. J., *J. Chem. Phys.* **22**, 250 (1954).

175. Prener, J. S., and Williams, F. E., *J. Chem. Phys.* **25**, 361 (1956).

176. Prener, J. S., and Weil, D. J., *J. Electrochem. Soc.* **106**, 409 (1959).

177. Kröger, F. A., Hellingman, J. E., Smit, N. W., and Dikhoff, J., *Physica* **15**, 990 (1949); **16**, 297, 317 (1950).

178. Potter, R. F., *Phys. and Chem. Solids* **3**, 223 (1957); Keffer, F., *J. Chem. Phys.* **33**, 1267 (1960); Mooser, E., and Pearson, W. B., *Nature* **190**, 406 (1961); Cochran, W., *ibid.* **191**, 61 (1961).

179. Prener, J. S., and Williams, F. E., *Phys. Rev.* **101**, 1427 (1956); *J. Electrochem. Soc.* **103**, 342 (1956); *J. phys. radium* **17**, 667 (1956).

180. Apple, E. F., and Williams, F. E., *J. Electrochem. Soc.* **106**, 224 (1959).

181. Bube, R. H., "Photoconductivity in Solids." Wiley, New York, 1960.

182. Aven, M. H., and Potter, R. M., *J. Electrochem. Soc.* **105**, 134 (1958).

183. van Gool, W., and Klasens, H. A., *J. phys. radium* **17**, 664 (1956).

184. Melamed, N. T., *Phys. Rev.* **107**, 1727 (1957).

185. Kröger, F. A., and Vink, H. J., *Solid State Phys.* **3**, 307 (1956).

186. Froelich, H. C., *J. Electrochem. Soc.* **100**, 280 (1953).

187. van Gool, W., and Cleiren, A. P., *J. Electrochem. Soc.* **106**, 672 (1959).

188. Waymouth, J. F., *J. Electrochem. Soc.* **100**, 81 (1953).

189. Garlick, G. F. J., and Dumbleton, M. J., *Proc. Phys. Soc. (London)* **B67**, 442 (1954).

190. Browne, P. F., *J. Electronics* **2**, 1, 154 (1956).

191. Meijer, G., *Phys. and Chem. Solids* **7**, 153 (1958).

191a. Halsted, R. E., Apple, E. F., and Prener, J. S., *Phys. Rev. Letters* **1**, 134 (1958).

192. Apple, E. F., *Phys. and Chem. Solids* **13**, 81 (1960).

193. van Gool, W., and Cleiren, A. P., *Philips Research Repts.* **15**, 238 (1960).

194. Klasens, H. A., *J. Electrochem. Soc.* **100**, 72 (1953).

195. Kröger, F. A., *Brit. J. Appl. Phys. Suppl. No.* **4**, 58 (1955).

196. Lambe, J., and Klick, C. C., *Phys. Rev.* **98**, 909 (1955); *J. phys. radium* **17**, 663 (1956).

197. Bowers, R., and Melamed, N. T., *Phys. Rev.* **99**, 1781 (1955).

198. Broser, I., and Broser-Warminsky, R., *J. phys. radium* **17**, 791 (1956); *Z. Elektrochem.* **61**, 209 (1957); Broser, I., and Schulz, H. J., *J. Electrochem. Soc.* **108**, 545 (1961).

199. Tomlinson, T. B., *J. Electronics* **2**, 166, 293 (1956).

200. Melamed, N. T., *Phys. and Chem. Solids* **7**, 146 (1958).

201. Curie, G., and Curie, D., *J. phys. radium* **21**, 127 (1960).

202. Arbell, H., and Halperin, A., *Phys. Rev.* **117**, 45 (1960); *J. Chem. Phys.* **34**, 879 (1961).

203. Botden, P. J., *Philips Research Repts.* **6**, 425 (1951); **7**, 197 (1952).

204. Dexter, D. L., *J. Chem. Phys.* **21**, 836 (1953).

205. Diemer, G., van Gurp, G. J., and Hoogenstraaten, W., *Philips Research Repts.* **13**, 458 (1958).

206. Destriau, G., and Saddy, J., *J. phys. radium* **6**, 12 (1945).

207. Homer, H. H., Rulon, R. M., and Butler, K. H., *J. Electrochem. Soc.* **100**, 566 (1953).

208. Fritzsche, C., *in* "Solid-State Physics in Electronics and Telecommunications" (M. Désirant and J. L. Michiels, eds.), Vol. 4, p. 647. Academic Press, New York, 1960.

209. Wachtel, A., *J. Electrochem. Soc.* **107**, 602 (1960).

210. Schwager, E. A., *Z. Physik* **163**, 44 (1961).

210a. Butler, K. H., and Homer, H. H., U.S. Patent 2,745,811 (1956); Wachtel, A., Canadian Patent 629,747 (1961).

211. Thorington, L., Meeting Electrochem. Soc., Philadelphia, May 4–8, 1952 (Abstr. No. 52).

212. Zalm, P., Diemer, G., and Klasens, H. A., *Philips Research Repts.* **9**, 81 (1954).

213. Diemer, G., *Philips Research Repts.* **10**, 194 (1955).

214. Froelich, H. C., *J. Electrochem. Soc.* **100**, 496 (1953).

215. Burns, L., *J. Electrochem. Soc.* **100**, 572 (1953).

216. Waymouth, J. F., and Bitter, F., *Phys. Rev.* **95**, 941 (1954).

217. Lehmann, W., *J. Electrochem. Soc.* **104**, 45 (1957).

218. Morosin, B., and Haak, F. A., *J. Electrochem. Soc.* **108**, 477 (1961).

219. Solomon, A. L., and Goldberg, P., Meeting Electrochem. Soc., Chicago, May 1–5, 1960 (Abstr. No. 69).

220. Orlov, I. N., *Izvest. Akad. Nauk S.S.S.R. Ser. Fiz.* **21**, 731 (1957).

221. Miyashita, K., Takahashi, T., and Wada, M., *Rept. Research Inst. Elec. Comm. Tôhoku Univ.* **10**, 125 (1958).

222. Wendel, G., *Z. physik Chem. (Leipzig)* **206**, 169 (1956); Wendel, G., and Richter, G., *ibid.* **214**, 253; **215**, 80 (1960).

223. Kazankin, O. N., Pekerman, F. M., and Petoshina, L. N., *Izvest. Akad. Nauk S.S.S.R. Ser. Fiz.* **21**, 721 (1957); *Optics and Spectroscopy (U.S.S.R.)* **6**, 435 (1959).

224. Umberger, J. Q., U.S. Patent 2,965,580 (1960).

225. Dreeben, A., Meeting Electrochem. Soc., Chicago, May 1–5, 1960 (Abstr. No. 70).

226. Lehmann, W., *J. Electrochem. Soc.* **108**, 607 (1961).

227. Ballentyne, D. W. G., and Ray, B., *Physica* **27**, 337 (1961).

228. Wachtel, A., *J. Electrochem. Soc.* **107**, 682 (1960).

229. Jaffe, P. M., Meeting Electrochem. Soc., Chicago, May 1–5, 1960 (Abstr. No. 73).

230. Froelich, H. C., *J. Opt. Soc. Am.* **43**, 320 (1953).

231. Destriau, G., *J. phys. radium* **15**, 13 (1954).

232. Nakajima, S., Yasuoka, S., and Ichise, W., *Toshiba Rev. (Japan)* **15**, 622 (1960) (in Japanese).

233. Naraoka, K., and Kotera, Y., *Oyo Butsuri* **29**, 116, 863 (1960) (in English).

234. Kazankin, O. N., Pekerman, F. M., and Petoshina, L. M., *Optics and Spectroscopy (U.S.S.R.)* **7**, 458 (1959).

235. Favorin, V. N., and Poskacheyeva, L. P., *Optics and Spectroscopy (U.S.S.R.)* **7**, 422 (1959).

236. Damaskova, S., and Patek, K., *Czechoslov. J. Phys.* **B11**, 336 (1961).

237. Cusano, D. A., and Williams, F. E., *J. phys. radium* **17**, 742 (1956).

238. Lehmann, W., U.S. Patent 2,937,150 (1960).

239. Mattler, J., and Ceva, T., *in* "Luminescence of Organic and Inorganic Materials" (H. P. Kallmann and G. M. Spruch, eds.), p. 537. Wiley, New York, 1962.

239a. Levshin, V. L., and Tunitskaya, V. F., *Optics and Spectroscopy (U.S.S.R.)* **9**, 118 (1960).

239b. Thornton, W. A., Meeting Electrochem. Soc., Los Angeles, May 6–10, 1962 (Abstr. No. 41).

239c. Kröger, F. A., Luminescence in Solids Containing Manganese. Thesis, Univ. of Amsterdam, Amsterdam, Holland, 1940.

240. Henderson, S. T., Ranby, P. W., and Halstead, M. B., *J. Electrochem. Soc.* **106**, 27 (1959), and article *in* "Solid-State Physics in Electronics and Telecommunications" (M. Désirant and J. Michiels, eds.), Vol. 4, p. 714. Academic Press, New York, 1960.

241. Avinor, M., *J. Electrochem. Soc.* **107**, 608 (1960).

242. Ballentyne, D. W. G., *Phys. and Chem. Solids* **10**, 242 (1959).

243. Ballentyne, D. W. G., *J. Electrochem. Soc.* **107**, 807 (1960).

244. Gobrecht, H., Hahn, D., and Gumlich, H. E., *Z. Physik* **136**, 623 (1954).

245. Kellerud, G., and Yund, R., Meeting Geology Society of America (abstract on p. 143 of bulletin), Denver, Colorado, 1960.

246. Oranovskii, V. E., and Trapeznikova, Z. A., *Optika i Spektroskopiya* **5**, 303 (1958).

247. Antonov-Romanovskii, V. V., *Czechoslov. J. Phys.* **9**, 146 (1959).

248. Antonov-Romanovskii, V. V., *in* "Solid-State Physics in Electronics and Telecommunications" (M. Désirant and J. Michiels, eds.), Vol. 4, p. 653. Academic Press, New York, 1960.

249. Goldberg, P., *J. Electrochem. Soc.* **106**, 948 (1959).

250. Gergely, G., *J. phys. radium* **17**, 679 (1956).

251. Jaffe, P. M., U.S.A.F. ASD Tech. Rept. 61-167 (ASTIA AD-272,786); Ph.D. Thesis, Polytechnic Institute of Brooklyn, 1962.

252. Smith, R. W., *Phys. Rev.* **100**, 760 (1955).

253. Narita, S., *J. Phys. Soc. Japan* **15**, 128 (1960).

254. Hoogenstraaten, W., *J. Electrochem. Soc.* **100**, 356 (1953); Klasens, H. A., and Hoogenstraaten, W., *ibid.* p. 366.

255. Burns, L., U.S. Patent 2,774,902 (1956).

256. Arpiarian, N., *J. phys. radium* **17**, 674 (1956).

257. Lehmann, W., *Phys. Rev.* **101**, 489 (1956).

258. Lehmann, W., Canadian Patent 579,564 (1956).

259. Roux, J., *J. phys. radium* **15**, 176 (1954); **17**, 813 (1956); *Ann. phys.* [13], **1**, 493 1956).

260. Levy, L., and West, D. W., *Trans. Faraday Soc.* **35**, 128 (1939).

261. Destriau, G., Meeting Electrochem. Soc., Philadelphia, May 3–7, 1959 (Abstr. No. 52).

262. Alfrey, G. F., and Taylor, J. B., *Proc. Phys. Soc. (London)* **B68**, 775 (1955); *Brit. J. Appl. Phys. Suppl. No.* **4**, 44 (1955).

263. Neumark, G. F., *Phys. Rev.* **103**, 41 (1956).

264. Frankl, D. R., *Phys. Rev.* **100**, 1105 (1955).

265. Frankl, D. R., *Phys. Rev.* **111**, 1540 (1958).

266. Oranovskii, V. E., and Khmelinin, B. A., *Optics and Spectroscopy (U.S.S.R.)* **7**, 336 (1959).

267. Luyckx, A., Vandewauwer, J., and Ries, S., *in* "Solid-State Physics in Electronics and Telecommunications" (M. Désirant and J. Michiels, eds.), Vol. 4, p. 671. Academic Press, New York, 1960.

268. Steinberger, I. T., Bar, V., and Alexander, E., *Phys. Rev.* **121**, 118 (1961).

268a. Gillson, J. L., and Darnell, F. J., *Phys. Rev.* **125**, 149 (1962).

269. Halsted, R. E., and Koller, L. R., *Phys. Rev.* **93**, 349 (1954).

270. Thornton, W. A., *J. Appl. Phys.* **30**, 123 (1959); U.S. Patent 3,044,902 (1952).

271. Vlasenko, N. A., and Popkov, I. A., *Optics and Spectroscopy (U.S.S.R.)* **8**, 39 (1960).

272. Koller, L. R., and Coghill, H. D., *J. Electrochem. Soc.* **107**, 973 (1960).

273. Studer, F. J., Cusano, D. A., and Young, A. H., *J. Opt. Soc. Am.* **41**, 559 (1951); Studer, F. J., and Cusano, D. A., *ibid.* **45**, 493 (1955).

274. Feldman, C., and O'Hara, M., *J. Opt. Soc. Am.* **47**, 300 (1957).

275. Roberts, S., *J. Opt. Soc. Am.* **43**, 590 (1953).

276. Loebner, E. E., and Freund, H., *Phys. Rev.* **98**, 1545 (1955) (abstr.).

277. Bodo, Z., and Weiszburg, J., *Acta Phys. Acad. Sci. Hung.* **10**, 341 (1959).

278. Kremheller, A., *J. Electrochem. Soc.* **107**, 8 (1960).

279. Lehmann, W., *J. Electrochem. Soc.* **107**, 657 (1960).

280. Zalm, P., Diemer, G., and Klasens, H. A., *Philips Research Repts.* **10**, 205 (1955).

281. Halpin, A. T., and Goldberg, P., *J. Electrochem. Soc.* **108**, 1028 (1961).

282. Strock, L. W., *Acta Cryst.* **10**, 840 (1957).

283. Lempicki, A., Frankl, D. R., and Brophy, V. A., *Phys. Rev.* **107**, 1238 (1957).

284. Destriau, G., *Compt. rend. acad. sci.* **241**, 869 (1955); U.S. Patent 2,901,651 (1959).

285. Lehmann, W., *J. Electrochem. Soc.* **103**, 24 (1956).

286. Gungle, W. C., and Cleary, R. E., U.S. Patent 2,728,870 (1955); Lehmann, W., U.S. Patent 2,840,741 (1958); Bain, G. W., U.S. Patent 2,887,601 (1959).

287. Rabotkin, V. L., and Sokolov, V. A., *Optics and Spectroscopy (U.S.S.R.)* **8**, 144 (1960).

288. Schneer, C. J., *Acta Cryst.* **8**, 279 (1955).

289. Short, M. A., Steward, E. G., and Tomlinson, T. B., *Nature* **177**, 240 (1956).

290. Strock, L. W., *Illum. Eng.* **55**, 24 (1960).

290a. Baum, F. J., and Darnell, F. J., *J. Electrochem. Soc.* **109**, 165 (1962).

291. McKeag, A. H., and Steward, E. G., *J. Electrochem. Soc.* **104**, 41 (1957).

292. Pashinkin, A. S., Tishchenko, G. B., Korneeva, I. V., and Ryzhenko, B. N., *Kristallografiya* **5**, 261 (1960); Krucheanu, E., and Christyakov, Y. D., *ibid.* p. 364.

293. Aven, M., and Parodi, J. A., *Phys. and Chem. Solids* **13**, 56 (1960).

294. Nickerson, J. W., Goldberg, P., and Baird, D. H., Meeting Electrochem. Soc., Indianapolis, May 1–2, 1961 (Abstr. No. 30).

295. Skinner, B. J., and Barton, P. B., *Am. Mineralogist* **45**, 612 (1960).

296. Leverenz, H. W., "An Introduction to Luminescence of Solids," pp. 178, 296. Wiley, New York, 1950.

296a. Ballentyne, D. W. G., *Proc. Phys. Soc. (London)* **78**, 348 (1961).

297. Goldberg, P., *J. Appl. Phys.* **32**, 1520 (1961).

298. Bontinck, W., and Dekeyser, W., *Physica* **22**, 607 (1956).

299. Ellis, S. G., Herman, F., Loebner, E. E., Merz, W. J., Struck, C. W., and White, J. G., *Phys. Rev.* **109**, 1860 (1958).

300. Merz, W. J., *Helv. Phys. Acta* **31**, 625 (1958), and article *in* "Solid-State Physics in Electronics and Telecommunications" (M. Désirant and J. Michiels, eds.), Vol. 2, p. 811. Academic Press, New York, 1960.

301. Cheroff, G., and Keller, S. P., *Phys. Rev.* **111**, 98 (1958); see also Cheroff, G., Enck, R. C., and Keller, S. P., *ibid.* **116**, 1091 (1959).

302. Lempicki, A., *Phys. Rev.* **113**, 1204 (1959); J. Tauc, *Phys. Chem. Solids* **11**, 345 (1959); G. F. Neumark, *Phys. Rev.* **125**, 838 (1962).

303. Goldstein, B., and Pensak, L., *Phys. Rev.* **109**, 601 (1958); *J. Appl. Phys.* **30**, 155 (1959).

304. Watson, W. R., Dropkin, J. J., and Halpin, A. T., Meeting Electrochem. Soc., Chicago, May 2–6, 1954 (Abstr. No. 38); *Phys. Rev.* **94**, 777 (1954) (abstr.).

305. Hahn, D., and Seemann, F. W., *Z. Physik* **149**, 486 (1957); **150**, 122 (1958).

306. Lempicki, A., *J. Opt. Soc. Am.* **46**, 611 (1956).

307. Destriau, G., *Illum. Eng.* **51**, 197 (1956).

308. Hahn, D., and Seemann, F. W., *Z. Physik* **146**, 644 (1956).

309. Fujisaki, H., Matsumura, T., and Tanabe, Y., *Tôhoku Daigaku Kagakukeisoku Kenkyusho Hôkoku* **7** No. 2 (1958); Translation SLA 59-17899, John Crerar Library.

310. Alfrey, G. F., and Cooke, I., *Proc. Phys. Soc. (London)* **B70**, 1096 (1957).

311. Alfrey, G. F., Cooke, I., and Taylor, K. N. R., *in* "Solid-State Physics in Electronics and Telecommunications" (M. Désirant and J. L. Michiels, eds.), Vol. 2, p. 816. Academic Press, New York, 1960.

312. Harper, W. J., *J. Electronics. Soc.* **109**, 103 (1962).

313. Alfrey, G. F., and Taylor, K. N. R., *Helv. Phys. Acta* **30**, 206 (1957).

313a. Alfrey, G. F., and Taylor, K. N. R., *J. Electronics Control* **4**, 417 (1958).

314. Bube, R. H., "Photoconductivity in Solids," pp. 174, 364. Wiley, New York, 1960.

315. Woods, J., *J. Electronics Control* **5**, 417 (1958).

316. Goldberg, P., *J. Electrochem. Soc.* **106**, 34 (1959).

317. Hirahara, E., *J. Phys. Soc. Japan* **6**, 422, 428 (1951); Wagner, J. B., and Wagner, C., *J. Chem. Phys.* **26**, 1602 (1957).

318. Woods, J., and Champion, J. A., *J. Electronics Control* **7**, 243 (1959).

319. Maeda, K., *J. Phys. Soc. Japan* **13**, 1352 (1958).

320. Maeda, K., *Physica* **25**, 721 (1959); *J. Phys. Soc. Japan* **15**, 2051 (1960).

321. Larach, S., and Shrader, R. E., *Phys. and Chem. Solids* **3**, 159 (1957).

322. Coogan, C. K., *Proc. Phys. Soc. (London)* **B70**, 845 (1957).

323. Fuchshuber, R., Guillien, R., and Roizen, S., *Compt. rend. acad. sci.* **251**, 51 (1960).

324. Leverenz, H. W., "An Introduction to Luminescence of Solids," pp. 319, 388, 427. Wiley, New York, 1950.

325. Lehmann, W., *J. Electrochem. Soc.* **105,** 585 (1958).
326. Goldberg, P., and Faria, S., *J. Electrochem. Soc.* **107,** 521 (1960).
327. Ince, A. N., and Oatley, C. W., *Phil. Mag.* **46,** 1081 (1955).
328. Ince, A. N., *Proc. Phys. Soc. (London)* **B67,** 870 (1954).
329. Garlick, G. F. J., *Advances in Electronics* **2,** 163, 177 (1950).
330. Bukke, E. E., Vinokurov, L. A., and Fok, M. V., *Optika i Spektroskopiya* **5,** 172 (1958).
331. Thornton, W. A., *in* "Solid-State Physics in Electronics and Telecommunications" (M. Désirant and J. L. Michiels, eds.), Vol. 4, p. 658. Academic Press, New York, 1960.
332. Haake, C. H., *J. Appl. Phys.* **28,** 245 (1957).
333. Thornton, W. A., *J. Electrochem. Soc.* **108,** 636 (1961).
334. Thornton, W. A., *Phys. Rev.* **102,** 38 (1956); **103,** 1585 (1956).
335. Trofimov, V. S., *Optika i Spektroskopiya* **4,** 113 (1958).
336. Lehmann, W., *J. Electrochem. Soc.* **107,** 20 (1960).
337. Thornton, W. A., *J. Electrochem. Soc.* **107,** 895 (1960).
338. Thornton, W. A., *in* "Solid-State Physics in Electronics and Telecommunications" (M. Désirant and J. L. Michiels, eds.), Vol. 4, p. 602. Academic Press, New York, 1960.
339. Halperin, A., and Arbell, H., *Phys. Rev.* **113,** 1216 (1959).
340. Roberts, S., *J. Opt. Soc. Am.* **42,** 850 (1952).
341. Jerome, C. W., and Gungle, W. C., *J. Electrochem. Soc.* **100,** 34 (1953).
342. Ballentyne, P. W. G., *J. phys. radium* **17,** 759 (1956).
343. Lochinger, R., *Scientia Electrica* **4,** (4) (1958).
344. Luyckx, A., Vandewauwer, J., and Ries, S., *Ann. soc. sci. Bruxelles* **72,** 58 (1958).
345. Morehead, F. F., *J. Electrochem. Soc.* **105,** 461 (1958).
346. Morehead, F. F., *J. Electrochem. Soc.* **107,** 281 (1960).
346a. Thomsen, S. M., *RCA Rev.* **22,** 685 (1961).
347. Ratner, M., *Bull. Am. Phys. Soc.* [2] **4,** 370 (1959); [2] **5,** 70 (1960).
348. Wagner, K. W., *Arch. Elektrotech.* **2,** 371 (1914).
349. Ivey. H. F., Internal Westinghouse Report, May 19, 1952.
350. Brown, W. F., Jr., *J. Chem. Phys.* **23,** 1514 (1955).
351. Smith, R. S., *J. Appl. Phys.* **27,** 824 (1956).
352. Reynolds, J. A., and Hough, J. M., *Proc. Phys. Soc. (London)* **B70,** 769 (1957).
353. Higuchi, W. I., *J. Phys. Chem.* **62,** 649 (1958).
354. Meredith, R. E., and Tobias, C. W., *J. Appl. Phys.* **31,** 1270 (1960); *J. Electrochem. Soc.* **108,** 286 (1961).
355. Katona, G. P., *J. Electrochem. Soc.* **109,** 695 (1962).
356. Neumark, G. F., *Phys. Rev.* **116,** 1425 (1959).
357. Lehmann, W., *J. Electrochem. Soc.* **103,** 667 (1956).
358. Fritzsche, C., *Jenaer Jahrbuch* Part I, p. 309 (1960).
359. Thornton, W. A., *J. Appl. Phys.* **32,** 2379 (1961).
360. Ivey, H. F., and Thornton, W. A., *IRE Trans. Electron Devices* **ED8,** 265 (1961).
361. Harrick, N. J., *Phys. Rev.* **115,** 876 (1959); **118,** 986 (1960).
362. Destriau, G., and Domergue, L., *in* "Semiconductors and Phosphors" (M. Schön and H. Welker, eds.), p. 544. Wiley (Interscience), New York, 1958.
363. Thornton, W. A., *Phys. Rev.* **116,** 893 (1959).
364. Thornton, W. A., *Phys. Rev.* **122,** 58 (1961).
365. Thornton, W. A., *Bull. Am. Phys. Soc.* **3,** 233 (1958).
366. Favorin, V. N., and Kozina, G. S., *Optics and Spectroscopy (U.S.S.R.)* **10,** 43 (1961).
367. Thornton, W. A., Mass. Inst. Technol. Physical Electronics Conference, Cambridge, Massachusetts, 1961; *J. Appl. Phys.* **33,** 3045 (1962).

368. Thornton, W. A., *Phys. Rev.* **113**, 1187 (1959); U.S. Patent 2,972,692 (1961).

369. Favorin, V. N., Kozina, G. S., and Tikhonova, L. K., *Optics and Spectroscopy* (*U.S.S.R.*) **7**, 420 (1959).

370. Kozina, G. S., Favorin, V. N., and Anisimova, I. D., *Optics and Spectroscopy* (*U.S.S.R.*) **8**, 112 (1960); Kozina, G. S., and Poskacheyeva, L. P., *ibid.* p. 110.

370a. Fok, M. V., *Optics and Spectroscopy* (*U.S.S.R.*) **11**, 50 (1961).

371. Waymouth, J. F., and Bitter, F., *Phys. Rev.* **102**, 686 (1956).

372. Gisolf, J. H., and Kröger, F. A., *Physica* **6**, 1101 (1939).

373. Alfrey, G. F., and Taylor, J. B., *Brit. J. Appl. Phys. Suppl. No.* **4**, 44 (1955).

374. Haake, C. H., *Phys. Rev.* **101**, 490 (1956).

375. Haake, C. H., *J. Electrochem. Soc.* **104**, 291 (1957).

376. Haake, C. H., *J. Opt. Soc. Am.* **47**, 881 (1957).

377. Johnson, P. D., Piper, W. W., and Williams, F. E., *J. Electrochem. Soc.* **103**, 221 (1956).

378. Harman, G. G., and Raybold, R. L., *Phys. Rev.* **104**, 1498 (1956).

379. Fredericks, W. J., *Bull. Am. Phys. Soc.* **5**, 187 (1960).

380. Ivey, H. F., *IRE Trans. on Component Parts* **CP4**, 114 (1957).

381. Nail, N. R., Urbach, F., and Pearlman, D., *J. Opt. Soc. Am.* **39**, 690 (1949).

382. Waymouth, J. F., Jerome, C. W., and Gungle, W. C., *Sylvania Technologist* **5**, 53 (1952).

383. Mattler, J., *Compt. rend. acad. sci.* **239**, 1116 (1954); *J. phys. radium* **17**, 42 (1956).

384. Alfrey, G. F., *J. phys. radium* **17**, 719 (1956).

385. Patek, K., *Czechoslov. J. Phys.* **7**, 584 (1957).

386. Kazankin, O. N., and Petoshina, L. N., *Optika i Spektroskopiya* **4**, 76 (1958).

387. Matsumura, T., and Tanabe, Y., *Tôhoku Daigaku Kagakukeisoku Kenkyusho Hôhoku* **7**, 175 (1958); Translation 59–1700, John Crerar Library.

388. Vlasenko, N. A., *Optics and Spectroscopy* (*U.S.S.R.*) **8**, 215 (1960).

389. Kimata, M., and Nomura, T., *J. Phys. Soc. Japan* **11**, 466 (1956).

390. Hahn, D., *J. phys. radium* **17**, 748 (1956).

391. Gobrecht, H., Hahn, D., and Scheffler, K., *Z. Elektrochem.* **61**, 202 (1957).

392. Bril, A., Klasens, H. A., and Westerhof, T. J., *Physica* **24**, 821 (1958); Hahn, D., and Lertes, K., *Z. Physik* **156**, 425 (1959); Gobrecht, H., Nelkowski, H., and Hofmann, D., *ibid.* p. 657.

393. Lehmann, W., *Illum. Eng.* **51**, 684 (1956).

394. Lehmann, W., *J. Opt. Soc. Am.* **48**, 647 (1958).

395. Johnson, P. D., and Williams, F. E., *J. Chem. Phys.* **18**, 1477 (1950).

396. Bowtell, J. N., and Bate, H. C., *Trans. Illum. Eng. Soc.* (*London*) **20**, 223 (1955).

397. Tanaka, S., *J. Phys. Soc. Japan* **14**, 1123 (1959).

398. Kilburn, T., Hoffman, G. R., and Hayes, R. E., *Proc. Inst. Elect. Eng.* (*London*) **105B**, 136 (1958).

399. Vigean, F., *Compt. rend. acad. sci.* **236**, 1151 (1953).

400. Johnson, J. E., *J. Electrochem. Soc.* **108**, 852 (1961).

401. Hoffman, G. R., and Smith, D. H., *J. Electronics Control* **9**, 161 (1960).

402. Destriau, G., *J. phys. radium* **16**, 798 (1955).

403. Bonch-Bruevich, A. M., and Marenkov, O. S., *Optics and Spectroscopy* (*U.S.S.R.*) **8**, 449 (1960).

404. Roberts, S., *J. Appl. Phys.* **28**, 262 (1957).

405. Thornton, W. A., *J. Appl. Phys.* **28**, 313 (1957).

405a. Grigor'ev, N. N., and Kulyupin, Y. A., *Optics and Spectroscopy* (*U.S.S.R.*) **10**, 412 (1961).

406. Nudelman, S., and Mudar, J., *Bull. Am. Phys. Soc.* [2] **5**, 70 (1960).

407. Ivey, H. F., *Illum. Eng.* **55,** 13 (1960).

408. Frankl, D. R., Meeting Electrochem. Soc., Chicago, May 1–5, 1955 (Abstr. No. 32).

409. Mager, E. L., U.S. Patent 2,566,349 (1951).

410. Jaffe, P. M., *J. Electrochem. Soc.* **108,** 711 (1961).

411. Smith, I. L., Potter, R. M., and Aven, M. H., Meeting Electrochem. Soc., Chicago, May 1–5, 1960 (Abstr. No. 65).

412. Gordon, N. T., Seitz, F., and Quinlan, F., *J. Chem. Phys.* **7,** 4 (1939).

413. Gobrecht, H., and Kunz, W., *Z. Physik* **136,** 21 (1953).

414. Rajchman, J. A., Briggs, G. R., and Lo, A. W., *Proc. IRE* **46,** 1808 (1958).

415. Nudelman, S., and Matossi, F., *J. Electrochem. Soc.* **103,** 34 (1956).

416. Nudelman, S., and Matossi, F., *J. Electrochem. Soc.* **101,** 546 (1954).

417. Matossi, F., and Nudelman, S., *Phys. Rev.* **99,** 1100 (1955).

418. Matossi, F., *Phys. Rev.* **98,** 434 (1955); **101,** 1835 (1956).

419. Haake, C. H., *J. Appl. Phys.* **28,** 117 (1957).

420. Zallen, R., Eriksen, W. T., and Ahlburg, H., *J. Electrochem. Soc.* **107,** 288 (1960).

421. Liamichev, I. I., and Orlov, I. N., *Optics and Spectroscopy (U.S.S.R.)* **7,** 258 (1959).

422. Patek, K., *Czechoslov. J. Phys.* **B10,** 452 (1960).

423. Thornton, W. A., *Phys. Rev.* **123,** 1583 (1961).

423a. Kallmann, H., Kramer, B., and Weissmann, E., in "Luminescence of Organic and Inorganic Materials" (H. P. Kallmann and G. M. Spruch, eds.), p. 549. Wiley, New York, 1962.

424. Frankl, D. R., Birman, J. L., Neumark, G. F., and Lempicki, A., *J. phys. radium* **17,** 731 (1956).

425. Destriau, G., and Mattler, J., *J. phys. radium* **6,** 227 (1945).

426. Destriau, G., *Brit. J. Appl. Phys. Suppl. No.* **4,** 49 (1955).

427. Gobrecht, H., Hahn, D., and Seemann, F. W., *Z. Physik* **140,** 432 (1955).

428. Hahn, D., and Seemann, F. W., *Z. Naturforsch* **10a,** 586 (1955).

429. Hahn, D., and Seemann, F. W., *Z. Naturforsch* **13a,** 349 (1958).

430. Hahn, D., and Seemann, F. W., *in* "Solid-State Physics in Electronics and Telecommunications" (M. Désirant and J. L. Michiels, eds.), Vol. 4, p. 636. Academic Press, New York, 1960.

431. Mattler, J., *J. phys. radium* **17,** 725 (1956).

432. Kröger, F. A., *Physica* **22,** 637 (1956).

432a. Georgobiani, A. N., and Fok, M. V., *Optics and Spectroscopy (U.S.S.R.)* **11,** 48 (1961).

433. Georgobiani, A. N., and Fok, M. V., *Optics and Spectroscopy (U.S.S.R.)* **9,** 775 (1960).

434. Mattler, J., and Curie, D., *Compt. rend. acad. sci.* **230,** 1086 (1950).

435. Kuchar, K., *Czechoslov. J. Phys.* **9,** 679 (1959).

435a. Thornton, W. A., Meeting Electrochem. Soc., Los Angeles, May 6–10, 1962 (Abstr. No. 45).

436. Patek, K., *Czechoslov. J. Phys.* **9,** 460 (1959).

437. Patek, K., *Czechoslov. J. Phys.* **9,** 161 (1959).

438. Destriau, G., *J. Appl. Phys.* **25,** 67 (1954).

439. Matossi, F., *Phys. Rev.* **94,** 1151 (1954); *J. Electrochem. Soc.* **103,** 122, 662 (1956).

439a. Matossi, F., and Nudelman, S., *J. Electrochem. Soc.* **103,** 122 (1956).

440. Destriau, G., Mattler, J., Destriau, M., and Gumlich, H. E., *J. Electrochem. Soc.* **102,** 682 (1955).

441. Destriau, G., *Z. Physik* **150,** 447 (1958).

442. Curie, G., and Curie, D., *J. phys. radium* **15,** 61 (1954).

443. Heckscher, H., *J. Opt. Soc. Am.* **47,** 765 (1957).

444. Patek, K., *Czechoslov. J. Phys.* **B10,** 679 (1960).

445. Cusano, D. A., *Phys. Rev.* **98,** 546 (1955).

446. Williams, F. E., *Phys. Rev.* **98,** 547 (1955).

447. Loebner, E. E., and Hegyi, I. J., Meeting Electrochem. Soc., Philadelphia, May 3–7, 1959 (Abstr. No. 54).

448. Weiszburg, J., Schanda, J., and Bodo, Z., *Phil. Mag.* [8], **4,** 830 (1959).

449. Georgobiani, A. N., and Fok, M. V., *Optika i Spektroskopiya* **5,** 167 (1958).

449a. Georgobiani, A. N., and Fok, M. V., *Optics and Spectroscopy (U.S.S.R.)* **10,** 95 (1961); Georgobiani, A. N., *ibid.* **11,** 231 (1961).

450. Lehmann, W., *Bull. Am. Phys. Soc.* **3,** 45 (1958).

451. Steinberger, I. T., *in* "Solid-State Physics in Electronics and Telecommunications" (M. Désirant and J. L. Michiels, eds.), Vol. 4, p. 646. Academic Press, New York, 1960.

452. Patek, K., *Czechoslov. J. Phys.* **B11,** 18 (1961).

453. Weiszburg, J., *Acta Phys. Acad. Sci. Hung.* **10,** 337 (1959); **13,** 61 (1961).

454. Loebner, E. E., Symposium on Electroluminescence and Photoconduction in Inorganic Phosphors, Polytechnic Institute of Brooklyn, Brooklyn, New York, 1955. (Unpublished.)

455. Halsted, R. E., *Phys. Rev.* **99,** 1897 (1955); *J. Appl. Phys.* **29,** 1706 (1958).

456. Kallmann, H., Kramer, B., Spagnolo, F., and Spruch, G. M., *Phys. Rev.* **123,** 1661 (1961).

457. Aven, M. H., and Cook, D. M., *J. Appl. Phys.* **32,** 960 (1961).

458. Chynoweth, A. G., and Pearson, G. L., *J. Appl. Phys.* **29,** 1103 (1958).

459. Destriau, G., *J. phys. radium* **4,** 249 (1943); **7,** 43 (1946).

460. Ivey, H. F., *IRE Trans. Electron Devices* **ED6,** 335 (1959).

461. Coerdt, R. J., Meeting Electrochem. Soc., Philadelphia, May 3–7, 1959 (Abstr. No. 67).

462. Hamaker, H. C., *Philips Research Repts.* **2,** 55 (1947).

463. Longini, R. L., *J. Opt. Soc. Am.* **39,** 551 (1949).

464. Antonov-Roamovskii, V. V., *Zhur. Eksptl. i Teoret. Fiz.* **26,** 459 (1954).

465. Kröger, F. A., Vink, H. J., and van den Boomgaard, J., *Z. physik. Chem. (Leipzig),* **203,** 1 (1954); Kröger, F. A., Vink, H. J., and Volger, J., *Philips Research Repts.* **10,** 39 (1955).

466. Williams, R., *Phys. Rev.* **123,** 1645 (1961).

467. Kikuchi, M., and Iizima, S., *J. Phys. Soc. Japan* **14,** 852 (1959); **15,** 1345 (1960).

468. Yamashita, H., Ibuki, S., Yoshizawa, M., and Komiya, H., *J. Phys. Soc. Japan* **15,** 2366 (1960); Komiya, H., Ibuki, S., and Yamashita, H., *in* "Luminescence of Organic and Inorganic Materials" (H. P. Kallmann and G. M. Spruch, eds.), p. 523. Wiley, New York, 1962.

469. Woods, J., *J. Electronics Control* **3,** 225 (1957).

470. Steinberger, I. T., *Phys. and Chem. Solids* **15,** 354 (1960).

471. Lossew, O. W., *Physik. Z.* **32,** 692 (1931); *Vestnik Elektrotekh.* p. 247 (1931).

472. Claus, B., *Ann. der Phys.* **11,** 331 (1931); **14,** 644 (1932).

473. O'Connor, J. R., and Smiltens, J., eds., "Silicon Carbide." Pergamon, New York, 1960.

473a. Lely, J. A., and Kröger, F. A., *in* "Semiconductors and Phosphors" (M. Schön and H. Welker, eds.), p. 514. Wiley (Interscience), New York, 1958.

474. Hall, R. N., *J. Appl. Phys.* **29**, 914 (1958).

475. Greebe, C. A. A. J., and Knippenberg, W. F., *Philips Research Repts.* **15**, 120 (1960).

476. Tetzner, H., *Z. angew. Phys.* **1**, 153 (1948).

477. Szigeti, G., Bauer, G. T., and Weiszburg, J., *Acta Phys. Acad. Sci. Hung.* **4**, 57 (1954); Szigeti, G., *ibid.* p. 65.

478. Tiede, E., and Tomaschek, R., *Z. anorg. u. allgem. Chem.* **147**, 111 (1925).

479. Schön, M., *Z. Naturforsch.* **8a**, 442 (1953).

480. Rücker, D., *Z. angew. Phys.* **10**, 254 (1958).

480a. Gol'dman, A. G., *Doklady Akad. Nauk S.S.S.R.* **135**, 1108 (1960).

481. Weiszburg, J., *Acta Phys. Acad. Sci. Hung.* **1**, 95 (1960).

482. Eriksen, W. T., *in* "Silicon Carbide" (J. R. O'Connor and J. Smiltens, eds.), p. 376. Pergamon, New York, 1960.

483. Harman, G. G., and Raybold, R. L., *J. Appl. Phys.* **32**, 1168 (1961).

484. Philips, H. R., and Taft, E. A., *in* "Silicon Carbide" (J. R. O'Connor and J. Smiltens, eds.), p. 366. Pergamon, New York, 1960.

484a. van Daal, H. J., Greebe, C. A. A. J., Knippenberg, W. F., and Vink, H. J., *J. Appl. Phys.* **32**, 2225 (1961).

485. Pearson, G. L., *in* "Photochemistry of the Liquid and Solid State" (F. Daniels, ed.), p. 157. Wiley, New York, 1960.

486. Moss, T. S., "Optical Properties of Semi-Conductors." Academic Press, New York, 1959.

487. Conwell, E. M., *Proc. IRE* **40**, 1327 (1952); **46**, 1281 (1958).

488. Gunn, J. B., *Proc. Phys. Soc. (London)* **B66**, 330 (1953).

489. Brill, P. H., and Schwarz, R. F., *Phys. Rev.* **112**, 330 (1958); *Phys. and Chem. Solids* **8**, 75 (1959).

490. Haynes, J. R., Lax, M., and Flood, W. F., *Phys. and Chem. Solids* **8**, 392 (1959).

490a. Proc. Intern. Conf. on Semiconductor Physics, Prague, 1960, pp. 398, 423, 426. Academic Press, New York, 1961.

491. Gosnet, A., Parodi, O., and Benoit à la Guillaume, C., *Compt. rend. acad. sci.* **248**, 1628 (1959).

492. Benoit à la Guillaume, C., and Parodi, O., *J. Electronics Control* **6**, 356 (1959).

493. Pankove, J. I., *Phys. and Chem. Solids* **6**, 100 (1958).

494. Pankove, J. I., Thesis, Univ. of Paris, 1961.

495. Kessler, F. R., *Z. Naturforsch.* **13a**, 295 (1958).

496. Vavilov, V. S., Gippius, A. A., Gorshkov, M. M., and Kopylovskii, B. D., *Zhur. Eksptl. i Teoret. Fiz.* **37**, 23 (1959).

496a. Schmidt, P. F., and Church, C. H., *J. Electrochem. Soc.* **108**, 296 (1961).

497. Newman, R., *Phys. Rev.* **105**, 1715 (1957).

498. Benoit à la Guillaume, C., *Compt. rend. acad. sci.* **243**, 704 (1956).

499. Benoit, à la Guillaume, C., *Phys. and Chem. Solids* **8**, 150 (1959); *Ann. phys.* [13] **4**, 1187 (1959).

500. Sah, C. T., and Shockley, W., *Phys. Rev.* **109**, 1103 (1958); Bernard, M., *J. Electronics Control* **5**, 15 (1958).

500a. Benoit à la Guillaume, C., Report Contract AF61(052)-370, May 15, 1961 (ASTIA AD-262,073).

501. Pankove, J. I., *Phys. Rev. Letters* **4**, 20 (1960); *J. Electrochem. Soc.* **108**, 998 (1961).

502. Sclar, N., and Burstein, E., *Phys. Rev.* **98**, 1757 (1955).

503. Koenig, S. H., and Brown, R. D., *Phys. Rev. Letters* **4**, 170 (1960).

504. Ascarelli, G., and Brown, S. C., *Phys. Rev.* **120,** 1615 (1960).

505. Bernard, M., and Loudette, J., *Compt. rend. acad. sci.* **246,** 1177 (1958); Bernard, M., *Phys. and Chem. Solids* **8,** 332 (1959).

506. Nelson, J. T., and Irvin, J. C., *J. Appl. Phys.* **30,** 1847 (1959).

507. Kikuchi, M., and Tachikawa, T., *J. Phys. Soc. Japan* **14,** 1830 (1959).

508. Miller, S. L., *Phys. Rev.* **99,** 1234 (1955); Tauc, J., *Phys. and Chem. Solids* **8,** 219 (1959).

509. Davies, L. W., *Phys. Rev. Letters* **4,** 11 (1960); Davies, L. W., and Storm, A. R., Jr., *Phys. Rev.* **121,** 381 (1961).

510. Haynes, J. R., *Phys. Rev. Letters* **4,** 361 (1960).

511. Lampert, M. A., *Phys. Rev. Letters* **1,** 450 (1958).

512. Benoit à la Guillaume, C., and Parodi, O., *in* "Solid-State Physics in Electronics and Telecommunications" (M. Désirant and J. L. Michiels, eds.), Vol. 1, p. 294. Academic Press, New York, 1960.

513. Chynoweth, A. G., and McKay, K. G., *Phys. Rev.* **108,** 29 (1957); Vavilov, V. S., *Phys. and Chem. Solids* **8,** 223 (1959).

514. Champlin, K. S., *J. Appl. Phys.* **30,** 1039 (1959).

515. Chynoweth, A. G., and McKay, K. G., *J. Appl. Phys.* **30,** 1811 (1959); McKay, K. G., *Phys. Rev.* **94,** 877 (1954).

516. Kikuchi, M., *J. Phys. Soc. Japan* **14,** 682 (1959).

517. Chynoweth, A. G., and McKay, K. G., *Phys. Rev.* **106,** 418 (1957).

518. Batdorf, R. L., Chynoweth, A. G., Dacey, G. C., and Foy, P. W., *J. Appl. Phys.* **31,** 1153 (1960).

519. Goetzberger, A., *J. Appl. Phys.* **31,** 2260 (1960).

520. Kikuchi, M., and Tachikawa, ιK., *J. Phys. Soc. Japan* **15,** 835, 1822 (1960).

520a. Shockley, W., *Czechoslov. J. Phys.* **B11,** 81 (1961); Goetzberger, A., Proc. Intern. Conf. on Semiconductor Physics, Prague, 1960, p. 808. Academic Press, New York, 1961.

521. Gee, A., *J. Electrochem. Soc.* **107,** 787 (1960).

522. Loebner, E. E., and Poor, E. W., Jr., *Bull. Am. Phys. Soc.* [2] **4,** 45 (1959).

523. Mandelkorn, J., *Proc. IRE* **47,** 2012 (1959).

524. Kikuchi, M., and Iizuka, T., *J. Phys. Soc. Japan* **15,** 935 (1960).

525. Allen, J. W., and Gibbons, P. E., *J. Electronics Control* **7,** 518 (1959).

526. Gorton, H. C., Swartz, J. M., and Peet, C. S., *Nature* **188,** 303 (1960).

527. Grimmeiss, H. G., and Koelmans, H., *Phys. Rev.* **123,** 1939 (1961); see also Grimmeiss, H. G., Rabenau, A., and Koelmans, H., *J. Appl. Phys.* **32,** 2123 (1961).

528. Ullman, F. G., *Nature* **190,** 161 (1961).

529. Tommasina, T., *Compt. rend. acad. sci.* **129,** 957 (1899); Eichberg, F., and Kallir, L., *Sitzber. Akad. Wien.* **108,** 212 (1899); Berti, S. A., *Elettricista* **11,** 1 (1902); Güntherschulze, A., *Ann. Phys.* **21,** 929 (1906); Schluederberg, H., *J. Phys. Chem.* **12,** 623 (1908).

530. Dufford, R. T., Nightingale, D., and Gaddum, L. W., *J. Am. Chem. Soc.* **49,** 1858 (1927); Harvey, N., *J. Phys. Chem.* **33,** 1456 (1929).

531. Forrest, J. S., *Phil. Mag.* [7] **10,** 1007 (1930).

532. Dufford, R. T., *J. Opt. Soc. Am.* **18,** 17 (1929); Sullivan, R. R., and Dufford, R. T., *ibid.* **21,** 513 (1931).

533. Raoult, G., *Compt. rend. acad. sci.* **219,** 24 (1944).

534. Güntherschulze, A., and Betz, H., *Z. Physik* **74,** 681 (1932).

535. Betz, H., *Z. Physik* **95,** 189 (1935).

536. Audubert, R., and Viktorin, O., *J. chim. phys.* **34,** 18 (1937).

537. Gumminski, K., *Bull. acad. polon. sci. No.* **3-4A,** 145; *No.* **8-9A,** 457 (1939).

538. Anderson, S., *J. Appl. Phys.* **14,** 601 (1943).

539. Rummel, T., *Z. Physik.* **101,** 276 (1936).

540. van Geel, W. C., and Schelen, B. J. J., *Philips Research Repts.* **12,** 240 (1957).

541. van Geel, W. C., and Bouma, B. C., *Philips Research Repts.* **5,** 461 (1950), **6,** 401 (1951); van Geel, W. C., and Scholte, J. W. A., *ibid.* p. 54; **8,** 47 (1953).

542. Sasaki, Y., *Phys. and Chem. Solids* **13,** 177 (1960).

543. Adams, I., AuCoin, T. R., and Mellichamp, J. W., *J. Appl. Phys.* **33,** 244 (1962); Adams, I., and Mellichamp, J. W., *J. Chem. Phys.* **36,** 2456 (1962); Adams, I., AuCoin, T. R., and Wolff, G. A., Meeting Electrochem. Soc., Los Angeles, May 6–10, 1962 (Abstrs. Nos. 50 and 115).

544. Krieg, M., and Lange, E., *Naturwissenschaften* **30,** 208 (1952).

545. Woods, J., and Wright, D. A., *Proc. Phys. Soc. (London)* **B68,** 566 (1955).

546. Malter, L., *Phys. Rev.* **50,** 48 (1936); Koller, L. R., and Johnson, R. P., *ibid.* **52,** 519 (1937).

547. Jacobs, H., *Phys. Rev.* **84,** 877 (1951); Jacobs, H., Freely, J., and Brand, F. A., *ibid.* **88,** 492 (1952); Dobischek, D., Jacobs, H., and Freely, J., *ibid.* **91,** 804 (1953).

548. Welker, H., *in* "Solid-State Physics in Electronics and Telecommunications" (M. Désirant and J. L. Michiels, eds.), Vol. 2, p. 645. Academic Press, New York, 1960.

548a. Pankove, J. I., and Massoulié, M. J., *Bull. Am. Phys. Soc.* **7,** 88 (1962); Meeting Electrochem. Soc., Los Angeles, May 6–10, 1962 (Abstr. No. 48).

548b. Lorenz, M. R., and Binkowski, B. B., *J. Electrochem. Soc.* **109,** 24 (1962).

549. Landsberg, P. T., and Moss, T. S., *Proc. Phys. Soc. (London)* **B69,** 661 (1956).

550. Goodwin, D . W., and McLean, T. P., *Proc. Phys. Soc. (London)* **B69,** 689 (1956).

551. Adams, I., and Wolff, G. A., U.S. Patent 2,997,446 (1961).

552. Lehmann, W., Meeting Electrochem. Soc., Indianapolis, May 1–4, 1961 (Abstr. No. 29).

553. Fischer, A., *in* "Semiconductors and Phosphors" (M. Schön and H. Welker, eds.), p. 551. Wiley (Interscience), New York, 1958; also U.S. Patent 2,938,136 (1960), *J. Solid-State Electronics* **2,** 232 (1961).

554. Austin, I. G., and Wolfe, R., *Proc. Phys. Soc. (London)* **B69,** 329 (1956); Clark, C. D., Ditchburn, R. W., and Dyer, H. B., *Proc. Roy. Soc.* **A234,** 363 (1956); **A237,** 75 (1957); Wedepohl, P. T., *Proc. Phys. Soc. (London)* **B70,** 177 (1957); Mitchell, E. W. J., *Phys. and Chem. Solids* **8,** 444 (1959); Clark, C. D., *ibid.* p. 481.

555. Dyer, H. B., and Matthews, I. G., *Proc. Roy. Soc.* **A243,** 320 (1957); Elliott, R. J., Matthews, I. G., and Mitchell, E. W. J., *Phil. Mag.* **3,** 360 (1958); Dean, P. J., Kennedy, P. J., and Ralph, J. E., *Proc. Phys. Soc. (London)* **76,** 670 688 (1960); Champion, F. C., Dean, P. J., and Lightowlers, E., International Conference on Color Centers and Crystal Luminescence, Turin, 1960 (unpublished).

556. Bell, M. D., and Leivo, W. J., *Phys. Rev.* **111,** 1227 (1958).

557. Bloem, J., *Philips Research Repts.* **13,** 167 (1958); Frerichs, R., and Weichmann, J., *J. Appl. Phys.* **29,** 710 (1958).

558. Mackintosh, I. M., *Proc. Phys. Soc. (London)* **B69,** 115 (1956).

558a. Baryshev, N. S., *Fiz. Tverdogo Tela* **3,** 1428 (1961).

559. Rulon, R. M., and Butler, K. H., U.S. Patent 2,844,540 (1958).

560. Bowtell, J. N., and Bate, H. C., *Proc. IRE* **44,** 697 (1956).

561. Alburger, J. R., *Electronic Inds. Tele-Tech.* **16,** 50 (February, 1957).

562. Rosenberg, B., U.S. Patent 3,015,747 (1962).

563. Schmidt, F., *Ann. Physik* [4] **70**, 16 (1923).

564. Krautz, E., *Z. Naturforsch.* **4a**, 284 (1949).

565. Hinderer, H., *Ann. Physik* [5] **10**, 265 (1931).

566. Olson, K. W., and Danielson, G. C., *U.S. Atomic Energy Comm. Document* **ISC-492** (Iowa State College), 1954; also brief account in *Phys. Rev.* **92**, 1323 (1953).

567. Destriau, G., and Mattler, J., *J. phys. radium* **13**, 205 (1952).

568. Destriau, G., and Mattler, J., *J. phys. radium* **7**, 259 (1946).

569. Destriau, G., and Mattler, J., *J. phys. radium* **11**, 529 (1950).

570. Kotera, Y., and Naraoka, K., *Bull. Chem. Soc. Japan* **33**, 721 (1960); also brief account in *J. Electrochem. Soc.* **106**, 1066 (1959).

571. Vigean, F., *Compt. rend. acad. sci.* **232**, 819 (1951); Vigean, F., and Curie, D., *ibid.* p. 955.

572. Alexander, E., Low, W., Steinberger, I. T., and Wiesz, S. Z., *J. phys. radium* **17**, 737 (1956).

573. Nakamura, K., *Repts. Liberal Arts Fac. Shizuoka Univ. Nat. Sci.* **2**, 13 (1957).

574. Steinberger, I. T., and Bar, V., *Proc. Conf. Color Centers and Crystal Luminescence, Turin, 1960*, p. 222. (Unpublished.)

575. Low, W., Steinberger, I. T., and Braun, E. A., *J. Opt. Soc. Am.* **44**, 504 (1954).

576. Steinberger, I. T., Braun, E. A., and Alexander, E., *Phys. and Chem. Solids* **3**, 133 (1957).

577. Coustal, R., *Compt. rend. acad. sci.* **198**, 1403, 1596 (1934).

578. Déchêne, G., *Compt. rend. acad. sci.* **201**, 139 (1935); **205**, 850 (1937); *J. phys. radium* **9**, 109 (1938).

579. Destriau, G., *J. phys. radium* **4**, 32 (1943).

580. Destriau, G., and Mattler, J., *J. phys. radium* **9**, 258 (1948).

581. Destriau, G., *Compt. rend. acad. sci.* **230**, 1061 (1950).

582. Miller, T., *J. Appl. Phys.* **23**, 1289 (1952).

583. Daniel, P. J., Schwarz, R. F., Lasser, M. E., and Hershinger, L. W., *Phys. Rev.* **111**, 1240 (1958); Harshinger, L. W., and Lasser, M. E., Meeting Electrochem. Soc., Philadelphia, May 3–7, 1959 (Abstr. No. 82).

584. Bleil, C. E., and Snyder, D. D., *J. Appl. Phys.* **30**, 1699 (1959).

585. Destriau, G., *Compt. rend. acad. sci.* **218**, 791 (1944).

586. Jaffe, P. M., *J. Electrochem. Soc.* **106**, 667 (1959).

587. Halsted, R. E. *in* "The Role of Solid State Phenomena in Electric Circuits" Polytechnic Institute of Brooklyn Symposium Proceedings, (J. Fox, ed.), Vol. 7, p. 275. Wiley (Interscience), New York, 1957.

588. Vorob'ev, Y. V., and Karkhanin, Y. I., *Fiz. Tverdogo Tela* **3**, 206 (1961); Peka, G. P., and Karkhanin, Y. I., *Doklady Akad. Nauk S.S.S.R.* **141**, 63 (1961).

589. Destriau, G., *Compt. rend. acad. sci.* **245**, 1797 (1957).

590. Steinberger, I. T., Low, W., and Alexander, E., *Phys. Rev.* **99**, 1217 (1955).

591. Gumlich, H. E., *J. phys. radium* **17**, 117 (1956).

592. Gutjahr, H., and Matossi, F., *Z. Physik* **162**, 105 (1961).

593. Nakamura, K., and Kobayashi, A., *Repts. Liberal Arts Facul. Shizuoka Univ. Nat. Sci.* **2**, 43 (1958).

594. Kallmann, H., and Rosenberg, B., *Phys. Rev.* **97**, 1596 (1955).

595. Gobrecht, H., and Gumlich, H. E., *J. phys. radium* **17**, 754 (1956); *Z. Physik* **156**, 436 (1959).

596. Destriau, G., *J. chem. phys.* **34**, 327 (1937); *J. phys. radium* **4**, 77 (1943).

597. Destriau, M., *Compt. rend. acad. sci.* **238**, 2298 (1954).

598. Destriau, G., *J. phys. radium* **17**, 745 (1956).

599. Destriau, G., *in* "Solid State Physics in Electronics and Telecommunications" (M. Désirant and J. L. Michiels, eds.), Vol. 4, p. 598. Academic Press, New York, York, 1960.

600. Destriau, G., *J. phys. radium* **17**, 734 (1956).

601. Mattler, J., *Compt. rend. acad. sci.* **249**, 2051 (1959).

602. Mattler, J., Meeting Electrochem. Soc., Washington, D.C., May 12–16, 1957 (Abstr. No. 28).

603. Pingault, F., *in* "Solid State Physics in Electronics and Telecommunications" (M. Désirant and J. L. Michiels, eds.), Vol. 4, p. 594. Academic Press, New York, 1960.

604. Destriau, G., *Compt. rend. acad. sci.* **249**, 245 (1959).

605. Gobrecht, H., and Gumlich, H. E., *Z. Physik* **158**, 226 (1960).

606. Wendel, G., *Z. Naturforsch.* **15a**, 1011 (1960); *Monatsber. deut. Akad. Wiss. Berlin* **2**, 490 (1960).

607. Winkler, H., Röppischer, H., and Wendel, G., *Z. Physik* **161**, 330 (1961).

608. Wendel, G., *Monatsber. deut. Akad. Wiss. Berlin* **3**, 266 (1961).

609. Destriau, G., Consultant's reports to Westinghouse, Feb. 3, July 25, and Nov. 15, 1958.

610. Destriau, G., *Compt. rend. acad. sci.* **245**, 1913 (1957).

611. Destriau, G., Meeting Electrochem. Soc., Washington, D.C., May 12–16, 1957 (Abstr. No. 24).

612. Mattler, J., and Destriau, G., Consultant's reports to Westinghouse, June 3 and Oct. 30, 1959; March 4, 1960.

613. Mattler, J., Meeting Electrochem. Soc., Philadelphia, May 3–7, 1959 (Abstr. No. 53).

614. Mattler, J., Consultant's report to Westinghouse, July 27, 1960.

615. Andrianov, A. S., and Kats, M. L., *Optics and Spectroscopy (U.S.S.R.)* **11**, 228 (1961).

616. Low, W., *Phys. Rev.* **98**, 556 (1955).

617. Mattler, J., *J. phys. radium* **17**, 758 (1956).

618. Messier, J., and Mattler, J., *Compt. rend. acad. sci.* **250**, 3822 (1960).

619. Coche, A., and Henck, R., *J. phys. radium* **20**, 827 (1959).

620. Henck, R., and Coche, A., *J. phys. radium* **22**, 59 (1961).

621. Henck, A., and Coche, A., *J. phys. radium* **22**, 98 (1961).

622. Henck, R., Thesis, Univ. of Strasbourg, 1960.

623. Gobrecht, H., Gumlich, H. E., Nelkowski, H., and Langer, D., *Z. Physik* **149**, 504 (1957).

624. Gobrecht, H., Gumlich, H. E., and zum Bruch, J., *Z. Physik* **162**, 169 (1961).

625. Pingault, F., and Destriau, G., Meeting Electrochem. Soc., Philadelphia, May 3–7, 1959 (Abstr. No. 51).

626. Pingault, F., *Compt. rend. acad. sci.* **249**, 248 (1959).

627. Mattler, J., Consultant's report to Westinghouse, March 4, 1960.

628. Gumlich, H. E., Meeting Electrochem. Soc., Los Angeles, May 6–10, 1962 (Abstr. No. 49); Gobrecht, H., Gumlich, H. E., Nelkowski, H., and Lacmann, K., *Z. Physik* **168**, 237 (1962).

629. Kallmann, H., and Spruch, G. M., *Phys. Rev.* **103**, 94 (1956); Kallmann, H., and Dresner, J., *ibid.* **114**, 71 (1959).

630. Bube, R. H., Larach, S., and Shrader, R. E., *Phys. Rev.* **92**, 1135 (1953).

631. Fridkin, V. M., *Doklady Akad. Nauk S.S.S.R.* **131**, 290 (1960).

632. Cusano, D. A., Thesis, Rensselaer Polytechnic Institute, Troy, New York, 1959; Image Intensifier Symposium, Fort Belvoir, Virginia, 1958; also, *in* "Luminescence of Organic and Inorganic Materials" (H. P. Kallmann and G. M. Spruch, eds.), p. 494. Wiley, New York, 1962.

633. Cusano, D. A., *Phys. Rev.* **106,** 604 (1957).

634. Woods, J., *J. Electronics Control* **3,** 531 (1957).

635. Vinokurov, L. A., and Fok, M. V., *Optics and Spectroscopy (U.S.S.R.)* **7,** 152 (1959).

636. Ballentyne, D. W. G., *Phys. and Chem. Solids* **21,** 131 (1961).

637. Lehmann, W., unpublished Westinghouse report, Nov. 13, 1957.

638. Matossi, F., *Phys. Rev.* **99,** 1332 (1955).

639. Orthuber, R. K., and Ullrey, L. R., *J. Opt. Soc. Am.* **44,** 297 (1954).

640. Diemer, G., Klasens, H. A., and van Santen, J. G., *Philips Research Repts.* **10,** 401 (1955).

641. Rosenthal, J. E., *Proc. IRE* **43,** 1882 (1955).

642. Kazan, B., and Nicoll, F. H., *Proc. I.R.E.* **43,** 1888 (1955).

643. Fok, M. V., *Soviet Radio,* 1961.

644. Kitamura, S., Kubo, T., and Yamashita, T., *J. Phys. Soc. Japan* **16,** 351 (1961).

645. Diemer, G., *Physica* **27,** 979 (1961).

646. Vorob'ev, A. A., and Kuchin, V. D., *Izvest. Tomsk. Politekh. Inst.* **91,** 385 (1956).

647. Gelling, W. G., and Haanstra, J. H., *Philips Research Repts.* **16,** 371 (1961).

648. Basov, N. G., Osipov, B. D., and Khvoshchev, A. N., *Zhur. Eksptl. i Teoret. Fiz.* **40,** 1882 (1961).

649. Keyes, R. J., and Quist, T. M., *Proc. IRE* **50,** 1822 (1962).

650. Howard, B. T., *Phys. Rev.* **98,** 1544 (1955).

651. Hall, R. H., Fenner, G. E., Kingsley, J. D., Soltys, T. J., and Carlson, R. O., *Phys. Rev. Letters* **9,** 366 (1962); Nathan, M. I., Dumke, W. P., Burns, G., Dill, F. H., Jr., and Lasher, G., *Appl. Phys. Letters* **1,** 62 (1962).

652. Georgobiani, A. N., *Optics and Spectros.* (U.S.S.R.) **12,** 421 (1962).

653. Georgobiani, A. N., and Golubeva, N. P., *Optics and Spectros.* (U.S.S.R.) **12,** 455 (1962).

AUTHOR INDEX

Numbers in parentheses are reference numbers and are included to assist in locating references when the authors' names are not mentioned in the text. Numbers in italic refer to the page on which the reference is listed.

A

Accardo, C. A., 2(61), 6(61), 132(61), 133(61), 134(61), 138(61), *242*

Adams, E. N., 5(118), *244*

Adams, I., 2(47), 166, 170, *242, 256*

Ahlburg, H., 79(420), 81(420), 98(420), *252*

Aigrain, P., 2(52), 141, 142, *242*

Alburger, J. R., 182, *256*

Alexander, E., 28(268), 60(268), 77(268), 78(268), 82(268), 108(268), 185, 188(576), 190(575), 199(590), 200(590), *24, 257*

Alfrey, G. F., 2(38), 28(262), 34, 36(310, 311), 38, 42, 52, 55(262, 373), 56(384), 57, 59, 103, 105, 106, 108, 154(38), 156(38), 196, 230, *242, 248, 249, 251*

Allen, J. W., 2(44), 5(124), 156, 161(525), 170(44), *242, 244, 255*

Anderson, S., 163, 164, 165, *255*

Andrianov, A. S., 179, 208(615), 219, *258*

Anisimova, I. D., 49(370), *251*

Antonov-Romanovskii, V. V., 27(247), 30(247), 36(247), 37(247–248), 38(247), 44(247), 46(248), 67(247), 77(247), 81(247), 119(248), 125(464), *247, 253*

Apple, E. F., 17(180, 191a, 192), 52(180), *245, 246*

Arbell, H., 17(202), 52(202), *246, 250*

Arpiarian, N., 27, 28, *248*

Ascarelli, G., 144, *255*

Astafurov, A. V., 2(77), *243*

AuCoin, T. R., 166(543), 170, *256*

Audubert, R., 163, *256*

Austin, I. G., 172(554), 173, 175, *256*

Aven, M. H., 16(182), 17(182), 19(182), 32(293), 76(411), 118, *245, 249, 252, 253*

Avinor, M., 26(241), *247*

B

Bain, G. W., 30(286), *248*

Baird, D. H., 32(294), *249*

Ballentyne, D. W. G., 21(227), 26, 27, 32, 33(227), 39(342), 40(342), 109, 115, 236(636), *247, 249, 250, 259*

Bar, V., 28(268), 60(268), 77(268), 78(268), 82(268), 108(268), 185, 204, *248, 257*

Barton, P. B., 32(295), *249*

Baryshev, N. S., 176, *256*

Basov, N. G., 2(648), 170, *259*

Batdorf, R. L., 152, *255*

Bate, H. C., 64, 72(396), 178, *251, 256*

Bauer, G. T., 133(477), *254*

Baum, F. J., 31(290a), *248*

Bell, M. D., 173, *256*

Benoit à la Guillaume, C., 2(52), 141, 142, 143, 147, *242, 254, 255*

Bernanose, A., 2(78), 175(78), *243*

Bernard, M., 143, 144, *255*

Berti, S. A., 161, *255*

Bess, L., 7(138), *244*

Betz, H., 162, 163, *255*

Binkowski, B. B., 171, *256*

Birman, J. L., 82(424), *252*

Bitter, F., 29, 44, 46, 50, 68(371), 77, 78, 79, 102, *246, 251*

Bleil, C. E., 196, 204, *257*

Bloem, J., 175, *256*

Bodo, Z., 29, 84(277), 99(448), 115, *248, 253*

Böer, K. W., 2(21), 4, 5, 127, 129, *241, 244*

Bonch-Bruevich, A. M., 68, 77(403), 99, *251*

Bontinck, W., 33, *249*

Botden, P. J., 17(203), *246*

Botwell, J. N., 64, 72(396), 121(396), *251*

Bouma, B. C., 1(17), 2(17), 164(17), 165(17), 166(17), *241, 256*

261

17, 18(20), 24(20, 231), 25(231), 28,
30, 33(307), 35, 36, 37, 42, 46, 54(1),
56(20), 65(20), 67, 68, 73(284), 78
(20), 83, 84, 85, 89, 90(1), 92(307),
99, 102, 113(402), 120(20), 121(20),
123, 130, 167, 177, 181(1), 182(20),
183, 184, 185, 187, 192, 193, 194, 195,
196, 197, 198, 199(438), 204, 207 (596),
208(440), 209, 210, 211, 212, 213(599),
216, 218, 219, 220, 223, 224, 225(441),
226, *241, 243, 246, 247, 248, 249, 250,
251, 252, 253, 257, 258*
Destriau, M., 187(440), 208(440, 597),
210(440, 597), 211(440), 218(440), *257*
Dexter, D. L., 7(139), 4, 13(139), 17
(204), *243, 244, 246*
Diemer, G., 2(22), 17(205), 18(212, 213),
19(212, 213), 28, 29, 30(213), 31, 34
(213), 39(213), 40(212), 44(280), 46
(212), 50(212), 51(212), 63(212), 67
(212), 68(212), 84(212), 90(212), 92
(212), 99(212), 103(280), 104(280),
119(213), 127, 128, 208, 238(640), *241,
246, 248, 259*
Dikhoff, J., 17(177), *245*
Dill, F. H., Jr., 169(651), *259*
Ditchburn, R. W., 172(554), *256*
Dobischek, D., 168(547), *256*
Domergue, L., 46, *250*
Dreeben, A., 21(225), 33(225), *247*
Dresner, J., 226, *258*
Dropkin, J. J., 34(304), 82(304), 83, 97
(304), *249*
Duboc, C. A., 7(151), 120, *245*
Dufford, R. T., 161(530), 162, *255*
Dumbleton, M. J., 17(189), *245*
Dumke, W. P., 7(144), 141, 169(651),
244, 259
Dutton, D., 5(116), *244*
Dyer, H. B., 172(554), 173, *256*

E

Eagles, D. M., 7, *244*
Eichberg, F., 161(529), *255*
Elinson, M. I., 2(68), 166(68), *242*
Elliott, R. J., 173(555), *256*
Ellis, S. G., 33(299), 118(299), *249*
Enck, R. C., 33(301), 118(301), *249*
Eriksen, W. T., 79(420), 81(420), 98
(420), 138, *252, 254*
Esaki, L., 4, *243*

F

Faria, S., 36, *249*
Favorin, V. N., 24(235), 25(235), 46(366),
47(366), 49, *247, 250, 251*
Feldman, C., 28, 59(274), *248*
Fenner, G. E., 169(651), *259*
Firth, B. G., 2(33), 168(33), *241*
Fischer, A., 2(29, 58), 167, 172, 173, 177,
241, 242, 256
Flood, W. F., 141(490), *254*
Fok, M. V., 35(449a), 37(330), 50, 85,
86, 88, 94, 100, 104, 236(635), 238
(643), *250, 251, 252, 253, 259*
Forrest, J. S., 161, *255*
Foy, P. W., 152(518), *255*
Frankl, D. R., 28(264, 265), 30(283), 31
(283), 33, 66, 73, 78(264), 79(265),
80, 81(265), 82, 83, 92, 95, 96, 97, 98,
99(265), 101, 108, 119(283), *248, 252*
Franz, W., 3(86), 5(127), 10(86), *243, 244*
Fredericks, W. J., 55, *251*
Freely, J., 168(547), *256*
Frenkl, J., 3(88), 4(88), *243*
Frerichs, R., 2(69), 175, *242, 256*
Freund, H., 29(276), 30, *248*
Fridkin, V. M., 216, *258*
Fritzsche, C., 18, 44, 45, *246, 250*
Froehlich, H. C., 16(186), 17(186), 18
(214), 19(186, 214), 20(214), 21(186),
24(230), 25, *245, 246, 247*
Frölich, H., 3(84), 4, 9(84), *243*
Fuchshuber, R., 35(323), 39(323), 125
(323), *249*
Fujisaki, H., 34(309), 36(309), *249*

G

Gaddum, L. W., 161(530), *255*
Garlick, G. F. J., 1, 3(9), 17(189), 37
(329), 39(13), 102, 188(13), *241, 245,
250*
Gee, A., 153, *255*
Geller, M., 4(100), 107(100, 101), 236
(100, 101), *243*
Gelling, W. G., 2(647), 21, 22, 166(647),
259
Georgobiani, A. N., 35(449a), 85, 86, 88,
94, 100, 104, 179, *252, 253, 259*
Gergely, G., 27(250), 193(250), *247*

SUBJECT INDEX

A

Acceleration-collision mechanism for EL, 8, 9, 163
 in ZnS, 52, 102–112, 114
Accumulation of carriers as mechanism for EL, 11
Activators
 Cu concentration, effect of in ZnS, 23, 24, 45, 67, 70, 71, 186
 Mn concentration, effect of in ZnS, 25, 213–216, 218, 220, 223
 saturation of, 64
 in Zns (see also ZnS), 13–16
Alkali halides
 alpha particle scintillations in, 197
 electroluminescence in, 179
 enhancement of photoluminescence in, 219
 tunneling of electrons in, 4, 108
Alpha particle scintillations
 enhancement of, 219–221, 223
 non-uniform excitation, effects of, 221, 226
 quenching of, 38, 196, 197
Aluminum nitride, 170
Aluminum oxide, 161–166, 168
 Cr in, 166
 Malter effect in, 168
 Mn in, 163, 166
Aluminum phosphide, 171
Avalanches, electron, 4, 129, 168

B

Barium sulfide, 167
Barium titanate, 176
Beryllium oxide, 168
Boron nitride, 171, 172
Bremsstrahlung, 11, 132
"Bridge" formation in liquid dielectrics, 31, 50, 73
"Build-up" of EL emission, 65–67, 79, 83, 93, 100, 107, 113, 116

C

Cadmium selenide, 166, 194
Cadmium sulfide
 electroluminescence in, 127–130
 optical absorption, effect of field on, 5, 196
 oxygen in, 75
 quenching of luminescence of, 194–196
Cadmium telluride, 31, 33, 167
Calcium sulfide, 167
Calcium tungstate, 177, 179
Cathodoluminescence
 correlation with EL, 63, 64
 enhancement by fields, 168, 221–223, 226, 230, 232
 quenching by fields, 197
Cathodothermoluminescence, 60
Coactivators
 Cl concentration in ZnS, effect of, 23, 24, 45, 67, 70, 71
 in ZnS, 13–16, 20, 22, 74–76
Coherent emission, 169
Color of emission in ZnS
 changes during life, 68
 changes for pulse excitation, 79
 changes during sinusoidal cycle, 83, 99
 composition, effect of, 16, 21–26
 difference for ac and dc excitation, 50, 101
 frequency, effect of, 25, 50–52
 temperature, effect of, 25, 51–52
"Contact electroluminescence," 19, 32, 107, 178, 179
Contacts, particle-to-particle, in ZnS, 18, 19, 31, 89, 123
Copper oxide
 electroluminescence in, 175, 176
 quenching of luminescence in, 197
Crystallographic effects
 disorder in ZnS and effects on EL, 31–35, 117–119, 152
 lattice vacancies in ZnS, 13, 16, 75
 orientation of crystals, effects of, 29–31, 73, 185
 structure of ZnS and effects on EL, 13, 21, 22, 29–33, 118, 119, 186

D

Déchêne effect, 192
Diamond, 172–175
Dielectric breakdown, 3

Dislocations, *see* Crystallographic effects

E

Efficiency of electroluminescence, 1, 7,
60–65, 169
in ZnS, 60–65, 71, 94, 110–112
Electric fields, effects of on solids, 3–5
on excited phosphors, 181–240
field-induced non-radiative transitions,
63, 99, 187, 204–207
on infrared quenching, 207–208
on infrared stimulation, 188–191
on luminescence centers, 10
quenching of electroluminescence, 98,
99
on trapped electrons (*see also* Gudden-
Pohl effect), 4
Electrical properties of ZnS, 36, 39–42,
48, 49, 71, 72, 116, 150
Electroflors, 182
Electroluminescence, 1
distinction from photoluminescence, 2
materials in which observed, 2
types of, 11
Electrocathodoluminescence, 181
Electrodes, effect of metal on ZnS, 34, 89
Electromagnetophotonic effect, 144
Electrophotoluminescence, 181
Electrothermoluminescence, 60
Emission of light
delayed, in ZnS, 78–83, 85–109, 116
"edge," in ZnS, 13, 27, 116, 120
mechanisms of, 7, 11
Energy band gap
in II–VI compounds, 13
in III–V compounds, 169
Energy transfer in phosphors, 17
Enhancement of luminescence in EL ZnS,
230–240
Cu emission, 234–236
mechanism of, 236–240
Mn emission, 230–232
P, As, Sb emission, 231–232
photoconductivity, connection with,
234, 236, 240
self-activated emission, 233
Enhancement of luminescence in non-EL
phosphors, 208–230
additives, effect of, 218, 221, 225
infrared, effect on, 223–225

mechanism of, 225–230
Mn concentration, effect of, 213–216,
218, 220, 223
Mn, importance of, 208, 212, 219, 223,
225
Enhancement ratio, definition, 192
Excitons, 5, 142, 143, 146, 147
Extraction of carriers, 195

F

Fermi level, 28, 135, 143
Ferroelectric materials, EL in, 176, 177
Field emission, *see* Tunneling
Frequency, effects of on ZnS
on color of EL emission, 25, 50–52
on efficiency of EL, 61, 110–112
in enhancement of luminescence, 209,
210, 213, 216–218, 220, 221, 223,
225, 232
in Gudden-Pohl effect, 183
on intensity of EL emission, 53–56, 83,
104, 105, 112
on maintenance of EL output, 70, 77
in quenching of luminescence, 194, 195,
197, 199
and temperature, interrelation, 52, 53
on waveform of EL emission, 85–101,
203

G

Gallium antimonide, 168
Gallium arsenide, 168, 169
Gallium nitride, 98, 155, 169–171
Gallium phosphide, 98, 154–161
relationship to ZnS, 154
Galvanoluminescence, 1
in Al₂O₃ and other oxides, 161–168
of Ge, 142
of Si, 153
of SiC, 132
Gas discharge, analogy to EL, 127–128
Germanium, 139–145
alloys with Si, 168
forward-biased junctions, 139–144
magnetic field, effect of, 140, 141, 144
oxygen in, 144
reverse-biased junctions, 144–145
Gudden-Pohl effect, 5, 182–193, 205–207